AD/ITD/TEC/11

G000055315

UNITED NATIONS C⌐⌐⌐ ⌐⌐⌐⌐ ⌐ ⌐VELOPMENT

DEUTSCHES ZENTRUM FÜR ENTWICKLUNGSTECHNOLOGIEN

TECHNOLOGICAL DYNAMISM IN INDUSTRIAL DISTRICTS: AN ALTERNATIVE APPROACH TO INDUSTRIALIZATION IN DEVELOPING COUNTRIES?

Papers and synthesis of discussions of a symposium on industrial districts and technology

held at the Palais des Nations, Geneva on 16 and 17 November 1992

UNITED NATIONS
New York and Geneva, 1994

NOTE

- Symbols of United Nations documents are composed of capital letters combined with figures. Mention of such a symbol indicates a reference to a United Nations document.

- The views expressed in this volume are those of the authors and do not necessarily reflect the views of the United Nations secretariat. The designations employed and the presentation of the material do not imply the expression of any opinion whatsoever on the part of the United Nations secretariat concerning the legal status of any country, territory, city or area, or of its authorities, or concerning the delimitation of its frontiers or boundaries.

- Material in this publication may be freely quoted or reprinted, but acknowledgement is requested, together with a reference to the document number. A copy of the publication containing the quotation or reprint should be sent to the UNCTAD secretariat.

UNCTAD/ITD/TEC/11

UNITED NATIONS PUBLICATION
Sales No. E.94.II.D.3
ISBN 92-1-112337-2

CONTENTS

P A R T   O N E

PART TWO

PART THREE

INDUSTRIAL DISTRICTS AND TECHNOLOGICAL CHANGE: A STUDY OF THE GARMENT INDUSTRY IN DELHI

Case study by Ghayur Alam 257

INDUSTRIAL DISTRICTS IN DEVELOPING COUNTRIES

Case study of Singapore by Liew Mun Leong 267

PART FOUR

Abbreviations

APEMEFAC	Peruvian Association of Footwear Industry
APIC	Peruvian Association of Apparel Industry
CAD	Computer Aided Design
CAM	Computerized Aided Manufacturing
CBK	Consortium for Capital Goods Industry Development
CESMA	Centre for Mechanized Services to Agriculture
CIM	Computer Integrated Manufacturing
CIS	Cyprus Industrial Strategy
CITER	Textile Information Centre for Emilia-Romagna
CITERA	Agriculture Information Center for Emilia-Romagna
CJEPD	Central Java Enterprise Development Project
NC	Controlled Numerically
CNC	Computerized Numerically Controlled
CNA-FNALA	National Confederation of Artisans-National Federation of Artisans in Wood and Furnishings
CSIL	Centre of Light Industry Studies
DESD	Department for Social and Economic
EC	European Community
ECLAC	Economic Commission for Latin America and the Caribbean
ERVET	Regional Development Agency of Emilia-Romagna
GATE	German Appropriate Technology Exchange
GDP	Gross Domestic Product
GINTIC	Grumman International/Nanyang Technological University Institute of CIM
IDs	Industrial Districts
ILO	International Labour Organization
IMCB	Institute of Molecular and Cell Biology
IME	Institute of Microelectronics
IMT	Institute of Manufacturing Technology
INTECH	Institute for New Technologies
ISS	Institute of Systems Science

IT	Information Technology
ITC	International Trade Centre
ITI	Information Technology Institute
KIET	Korean Institute of Economics and Technology
LDCs	Least Developed Countries
LOS	Little Owner System
MDF	Medium-Density Fibreboard
MID	Marshallian Industrial District
MIDC	Metal Industries Development Centre
MTC	Magnetics Technology Centre
NCB	National Computer Board
NGOs	Non-Governmental Organizations
NICs	Newly Industrializing Countries
NSTB	National Science and Technology Board
NTU	Nanyang Technological University
NUS	National University of Singapore
OECD	Organization for Economic Cooperation and Development
ISS	Institute of Systems Science
ISTAT	Central Institute of Statistics
PDAS	Product Development Assistance Scheme
PEMTEC	Pequeña Empresa Tecnología y Sociedad
R&D	Research and Development
RDAS	Research and Development Assistance Scheme
RSEs	Research Scientists and Engineers
RTD	Research and Technological Development
SBAC	Small Business Advisory Centre
SCX	Subcontractor Exchange Programme
SDRs	Regional Development Companies
SISI	Small Industries Service Institutes
SISIR	Singapore Institute of Standards and Industrial Research
SMEs	Small- and Medium-Size Enterprises
TCMD	Transnational Corporations and Management Division
TESA	Technical Cooperation
TNCs	Transnational Corporations

TNO	Netherlands Organization for Applied Scientific Research
TTD	Technology Transfer Division
TUI	Technological University Institute
UNCTAD	United Nations Conference on Trade and Development
UNDP	United Nations Development Programme
UNIDO	United Nations Industrial Development Organization
USAID	United States Agency for International Development

FOREWORD

Small and medium enterprises (SMEs) and their role in, and contribution to, the process of economic growth and development have become the subject of revived and growing analysis, perhaps because of the dynamism of this sector in developed countries over the past decade. Contrary to earlier analyses, the focus is now on the internal configuration of enterprises, the economic and social context in which they function and their linkages with other enterprises, including large ones, as factors explaining this dynamism. This approach, encompassed by the concept of "industrial districts", offers new insights into the potential role of SMEs in the development of developing countries. It is this role which needs to be further explored. This is the context in which UNCTAD, in cooperation with, and with the financial support of, the Deutsches Zentrum für Entwicklungstechnologien of the Federal Republic of Germany decided to organize a symposium on "The role of industrial districts in the application, adaptation and diffusion of technology". The symposium was held in Geneva on 16 and 17 November 1992.

A better understanding of the development of linkages within industrial districts and their role in inducing efficient technological development - that is technological development associated with the creation of competitive industries - was regarded as vital to the identification of viable technology-related policies for SME development in developing countries. A clearer understanding of the implications of the work carried out in developed countries, on the one hand, and specific characteristics of the SME configuration in the developing countries, on the other, was perceived as providing a useful basis for advancing the work in this area. The contribution made by the Deutsches Zentrum für Entwicklungstechnologien towards the success of the symposium is gratefully acknowledged. It is hoped that the publication of the papers and the synthesis of the discussions that took place during the symposium will be of value not only to research workers and academics but also to policy-makers seeking a better understanding of the interlinkages between technology and SME development.

INTRODUCTION

The contribution of technology to the process of economic growth and development has been subject to growing analysis in recent years. As a result, increasing recognition is being given to the role of technology as a determinant of growth in output and international competitiveness. There is also a focus on the complex relation between technology transfer and development of technological capabilities. Since the 1980s, the rapid expansion in world trade in goods has been almost entirely due to manufactures, particularly in those industries where, directly or indirectly, investment in research and development and design forms a high percentage of the valued added. Even in more traditional sectors, such as textiles and machine tools, the faster growing product groups are those where knowledge-content is relatively high. Several developing countries have experienced spectacular growth in the export of manufactures, having succeeded in capturing ever-increasing shares in both industrialized and developing country markets. These countries have also been experiencing high rates of overall economic growth. They had also, *inter alia,* taken prior action to strengthen their domestic technological base in terms of an economic environment conducive to innovation, development of human capital and supportive institutions.

Even in the trade of raw materials and basic foodstuffs, which has grown slowly or not at all, country performance may be shown to be linked to technological capacities in terms of both production and organizational techniques. Yet another development, which is of particular relevance to those developing countries which had faced financial constraints during the 1980s, is that foreign direct investment - one of the main forms of technology transfer - has been concentrating on a small number of countries. By the end of the

1980s, foreign direct investment to the least developed countries was only US$ 200 million, down from US$ 300 million in 1980.

A growing amount of research points to the complementarity between foreign investment, technology transfer and domestic technological capabilities. Experience has shown that an appropriate blending of national technological capability-building in combination with measures ensuring the endogenization of imported technology has led to what has been called "technological dynamism".*

The recognition of the importance of technology as factor in production has imparted new urgency to the need for upgrading technological capabilities in developing countries but this has gone hand-in-hand with the disappointing experience of the large majority of them in their efforts to build up technological capabilities and to industrialize. The policies of the 1970s, very often involving the transplant of turnkey projects operating at sub-optimal levels of efficiency and capacity utilization, have scarcely contributed to increasing the capacities of these countries to absorb, adapt or generate the technologies they need for development. Following the debt crisis and the ensuing financial constraints, many developing countries have been obliged to undertake very strict adjustment programmes to stabilize their economies. Furthermore, the changing global environment has been leading them, along with aid agencies, to a broader re-examination of development strategies, putting more emphasis on the role of markets, in the allocation of resources, as well as on the firm, for the generation of technology. In this re-examination, several issues have been identified. What should be the extent and type of government intervention? What are, respectively, the roles of, and relations among, the different economic agents? How do policies for technological and human resource development relate to trade or to industrial or regional policies? What is the role of institutions? What does the definition of technology and,

---

* "Analytical report to the eighth session of UNCTAD", UNCTAD secretariat (TD/358), 1992.

therefore, technology transfer comprise? The present volume, which is the outcome of an UNCTAD/GATE symposium on the role of industrial districts in the application, adaptation and diffusion of technology, attempts to analyze some of these issues. In doing so, it takes a new look at industrialization through small-firm development within the configuration of closely-knit networks of firms.

Although dating back to Alfred Marshall's work at the turn of the century, the concept of "industrial districts" has been revitalized in connection with attempts to explain the successful performance of a variety of small regional economies in terms of economic growth, ability for endogenous development and resilience in the face of economic crises or international competition. The debate in the developed countries, where most of the literature has originated, focuses on the robustness of this performance over time and on how far and under what conditions it is reproducible in other developed regions. The debate as regards developing countries is similar but there are two additional dimensions. The first has to do with the fact that, whatever the conditions, they may not necessarily be present in developing countries. The second concerns the policy lessons, if any, that could be derived for the benefit of developing countries, even if they do not have districts resembling those found in the developed countries. In Part IV, Späth, in her synthesis of the symposium, has focused on those two dimensions which were at the centre of the discussions.

Before entering the debate on the policy implications of "industrial districts" as a new form of industrial organization, the various concepts should be recalled. As opposed to some theorists, Van Dijk, in his paper, "The interrelations between industrial districts and technological capabilities development: concepts and issues", has opted for a very broad definition of "industrial districts". He points out that the concept remains evasive and can only be partially defined by a set of common key characteristics. In focusing on the successful cases, he uses their common characteristics to explain their performance, then links some of these elements to policy issues of relevance to developing countries. At the macro-level, "flexible specialization" and "new competition" have been presented as development in the thinking on industrialization policies. At the micro-level, flexibility, inter-firm linkages and local support systems form the elements for the development of entrepreneurship.

Amin (who was unable to attend the symposium), commenting on Van Dijk's paper, has offered another perspective. He supported Van Dijk's approach whereby forcing of different, and perhaps even incompatible, realities into the same conceptual basket was viewed as problematic, since the experience of each type of agglomeration, despite its characteristics in common with other types, would yield a different policy message. He has developed his view through a stylized account of the achievements and failures of two districts in Italy, one corresponding to the Marshallian type of industrial district, the other being closer to the "informal" agglomerations of developing countries. According to Amin, the two districts studied, which had in common many of the characteristics defining industrial districts, were diametrically different from one another in their capabilities to grow or respond collectively and swiftly to new market pressures and to steer their evolution along a particular development trajectory.

Turning to the mechanisms of technology-creation and diffusion within districts, the note by Bellandi, on "Decentralized industrial creativity in dynamic industrial districts", distinguishes between two approaches to industrial creativity. The first has originated in formal R&D centres while the second was formed on the production floor; he has called the latter: decentralized industrial creativity (DIC). While he sees "industrial districts" as idealized forms of certain types of small-firm systems, having properties which permit the systematic manifestation of DIC, he also sees the need for their coexistence and interaction with creativity resulting from formal R&D.

Asheim, in his paper on "Industrial districts, inter-firm cooperation and endogenous technological development: the experience of developed countries", like Amin and Bellandi, opts for a narrow definition of industrial districts, but identifies different models of industrial districts with varying potential for technological capacity-building. Differences in inter-firm linkages, in the internal resources and competence of small and medium-sized firms with respect to technology as well as differences in the level of government intervention imply different potentials for capacity-building with regard to the application, adaptation and diffusion of technologies. Thus, districts characterized by a low cooperative environment, and a low level of internal competence not offset by government support, show the lowest potential. One of the districts discussed by Amin belongs to this category. In most examples of successful "industrial districts" which start with low levels of internal competence, local government intervention and/or professional institutions, by providing real services, have been able to raise the potential of firms in the district for technological capacity-building in the application, as well as adaptation and diffusion of technology. Two interesting observations from Asheim's paper, as regards the lessons that could be derived from developed countries' experience, are: first, all things being equal, government intervention or the existence of appropriate institutions raises the collective potential of the district for diffusion of technology; secondly, the districts of high potential not only have firms with high internal competence but also tend to have access to formal R&D. Moreover, they also tend to interact with institutions outside the district itself.

Villarán explores the first link with the experience of developing countries. After providing a brief critique of Asheim 's paper, he discusses some of the clusters of small firms in Peru. His conclusion is that, while such clusters do not meet the criteria used in discussing "industrial districts" in developed countries, a number of policy measures can still be inferred. Taking into consideration that: (a) small-scale industry is an extended phenomenon in developing countries; (b) important segments of small-scale industry have demonstrated dynamism, flexibility and the capacity to adapt to external changes and to react to policy measures; and (c) the large-scale, formal and overprotected sector in many developing countries is in crisis, much can be gained from examining "industrial districts" in the developed countries in terms of policy measures and promotion of tasks and institutions for technological up-grading.

Kozul-Wright, in her paper "Technological diffusion in the Italian Marshallian industrial district of Brianza", starting from an essentially evolutionary perspective and employing empirical data from a survey of 20 firms, analyses the experience of a successful Italian district active in the furniture industry. The paper provides information on the types of innovations introduced by the firms, and the factors that have influenced their creation, as well as the diffusion of technology within the district. As regards the factors of the district's success, her evidence supports the important role of innovation. She concludes that the establishment of linkages and an appropriate pattern of interaction between activities constituting the broad process of furniture-making within a supportive public policy are central to the success of Brianza.

Nadvi also examines the overall relevance of the concept of "industrial districts" to nascent industrialization in developing countries. In his paper, "Industrial district experiences in developing countries", he reviews the scanty literature on developing countries, but instead of attempting to fit the diverse developing country experiences with small firm clusters into the supposed ideal type framework, he emphasizes that there are likely to be different types of industrial districts which undergo different stages of development. The critical factor is to be aware of the contextual and historical specificity that has shaped such districts and influenced the way they function. Cases of developing-country small-firm clusters are then analyzed in terms of the implications of four factors for technological development, namely, inter-firm relations, the role of the "social milieu ", the role of institutions, and finally the fact that, in the majority of developing countries, such clusters operate under surplus labour conditions.

Concerning policy implications, a major question raised is whether an "industrial district", which encompasses both social and economic space, can be replicated by planned intervention from above or whether it is essentially an endogenous development which had best be fostered from below. Using the notion of stages of development of industrial districts, Nadvi points out that, while in a number of cases potential "industrial districts"-type formations have evolved, their further progress requires external intervention and support. This raises the question of the modalities by which such support can be articulated. While the review suggests that the industrial district framework, and especially the inter-firm interactions associated with it, are helpful in encouraging capabilities for achieving incremental technological changes, there is limited evidence of the presence of substantial technological dynamism. There is also very limited evidence concerning the role played by technology transfer from foreign sources. Nadvi observes that what has been missing in both developed and developing country case studies is an analysis of actual mechanisms through which inter-firm collaboration has been leading to the upgrading of technological capabilities and diffusion of technology.

Two papers on case studies drawn from India and Singapore illustrate some of the points raised by Nadvi. Alam, in his paper "Industrial districts and technological change: a study of the garment industry in Delhi", has focused on the small-firm cluster of Okhla which has recently emerged as a major centre of export garment production. According to his research the clustering effect has entailed a number of advantages for the firms inside, although some of the features of the cluster do not conform to characteristics commonly attributed to industrial districts in developed countries. There was an absence of horizontal linkages combined with slow technological uptake. As the firms operated under labour surplus conditions they relied on low wages for their competitive advantage. Moreover, he found in-built conditions in the cluster which prevented the adoption and diffusion of more advanced technologies. In conclusion, he points out that a better understanding of the role of industrial districts in developing countries requires further and more-focused research in relatively technology-intensive areas.

The Singapore case, presented by Liew, is an example of a more advanced developing country where foreign sources have provided the original impetus to technological capability-building and where the creation of clustering is being stimulated through intervention from above. The particular conditions of Singapore with its small territory and population, however, are not considered representative of developing countries. In fact, the whole country can be assimilated into one industrial district.

Vijay Kelkar

Director
International Trade Division

UNCTAD

PART ONE

THE INTERRELATIONS BETWEEN INDUSTRIAL DISTRICTS AND TECHNOLOGICAL CAPABILITIES DEVELOPMENT: CONCEPTS AND ISSUES

Meine Pieter Van Dijk *

INTRODUCTION

What is an industrial district? When Marshall used the term at the beginning of this century, he referred to what he had seen in the United Kingdom.[1] He noticed that a number of industries which had been grouped together benefited from economies of scale usually associated with large firms.[2] The discussion now going on about the usefulness of the industrial district concept for developing countries adds a number of characteristics, some of which may be wishful thinking.[3] A distinction should be made between industrial districts as a positive (analytical) category and industrial districts as a normative concept. A positive analysis would help to explain how the successful industrial districts did it. The normative question deals with something we would like to create. The question is: can the success of certain industrial districts be replicated?

The intuitive definition of an industrial district would be: a group of interdependent industrial firms which have developed strong relations among themselves, which have fostered innovation and contributed to higher (collective) efficiency. The question of the definition of an industrial district will be taken up in more detail in section I below. The role of industrial districts in industrialization has been getting increasing attention, but its importance for innovation and technology diffusion has not been sufficiently studied. Thus an attempt will be made also to shed some light on that issue.

* Regional Economics and Urban Research Department, Economic Faculty, Erasmus University, Rotterdam (Netherlands).

Section II discusses a change in the thinking about industrialization strategies to be pursued by third world countries. Import substitution was the strategy of the 1950s and 1960s, then export-led industrialization became popular in the 1970s, particularly after the success of the four "tigers" (Hongkong, Singapore, Republic of Korea and Taiwan Province of China). Presently the flexible specialization and new competition concepts suggest a different strategy.[4] These concepts will be examined and, in particular, the role of technology and innovation, industrial clusters, networks and inter-firm cooperation as key variables of these new strategies will be discussed under the heading: the macro level.

Section III goes deeper into the factors at the macro level, explaining the dynamics of industrial districts. Entrepreneurship, the enterprise-support system, the importance of a well-functioning labour market and the continuously ongoing spatial reorganization process will be discussed. It will be argued that the question of optimal scale of operation, of choice of sectors to be developed and the pursuit of regional development policies are no longer as important for industrial development.

Finally, in section IV, the key issues concerning the interaction between industrial districts and the development of local technological capabilities will be discussed individually:

(a) What makes an industrial district a centre of innovation and industrial development?

(b) Does an industrial district need to be a geographical cluster, or are interlinked networks of industries enough?

(c) Why is an industrial estate or an industrial free-trade zone not necessarily an industrial district?

(d) How can we identify the potential of a region (or network) to become an industrial district?

(e) What can the government (at the national, state and city level) do to develop industrial districts?

(f) How can we enhance the technological innovation and diffusion capacity of an industrial district?

(g) Do we need similar/related economic activities (sectoral specialization), or can different subsectors be promoted at the same time?

(h) What would be the role of small and micro enterprises in an industrial district and how could they become really integrated?

(i) From an industrial district to urban or regional development?

I. KEY CHARACTERISTICS OF INDUSTRIAL DISTRICTS

Industrial districts defined

Industrial districts are geographically defined as: "productive systems characterized by a large number of firms that are involved at various stages and in various ways in the production of a homogeneous product. A significant feature is that a very high proportion of these firms is small or very small" (Pyke *et al.*, 1990). Characteristics which will be discussed separately in this section are the importance of inter-firm relations in industrial districts, the presence of competition and cooperation which usually characterizes industrial districts and the role of innovations and technological developments.

The literature discusses industrial districts in relation to small-scale production, flexible specialization and the production of technologically advanced products. The question is whether the advantages of the classical industrial district, described already by Marshall (1920), can be positively encouraged by local interest groups and systematically supported by governments.

Storper (1989) mentions well-known nineteenth century industrial districts: Lyon for the silk industry; the cutlery and tool sectors of Solingen and Sheffield; and the textile industries in Philadelphia and Pawtucket. More recent examples in four major industrialized countries are: the Baden-Württemburg region in southern Germany (Schmitz, 1991); the "Third Italy" in northern Italy (Pyke, *et al.* eds., 1990); new high technology industrial districts such as Silicon Valley and Orange County in the United States of America (Storper, 1990) and Toyota City in Japan.

Some authors refer to industrial districts as a particular industrial organization. Industrial organization is primarily a sub-discipline of economic science which studies the functioning of markets, starting with their structure and the behaviour of the firms active in these markets. In calling an industrial district an industrial organization, we make reference to a particular collection of firms operating in similar markets and related through all kinds of inter-firm relations. Becattini (1992) stresses that the industrial district represents a point in the range between completely vertically integrated and completely independent firms. The particular collection of firms found in a certain place and the existing interrelations between them may be deduced by empirical investigation. We should distinguish such an empirical result from the insights which can be gained from the literature concerning the sub-discipline: industrial organization. The results can be used both in a positive way to analyze what is taking place and in a normative way to recommend what should happen in order to turn a location into an industrial district by applying the insights of industrial organization.[5]

Differentiation or dualism

The industrial sector is not homogeneous. Not all industrial subsectors have the same problems nor are the problems of enterprises of different sizes similar. There are many ways to classify industrial enterprises. Dualistic concepts like small *versus* large, informal *versus* formal, organized *versus* unorganized and lower *versus* upper circuit are well known (for a review, see Van Dijk, 1986).[6]

Galbraith (1979) distinguished between large oligopolistic or monopolistic firms preoccupied with growth and market share and small firms. The latter were seen as so tightly constrained by the markets that this factor determined their decisions on price, quantity produced and capital investments. They are basically survivors, not interested in growth and powerless to affect their market share. Berger and Piore (1980) suggest dualism has a technological basis. They distinguish between large firms catering for stable segments of demand and small firms catering for the unpredictable, fluctuating part of demand. Another technological dualism is found in industries experiencing decreasing costs (or increasing returns to scale; the so-called natural monopolies) and those where average costs increase again after a certain scale has been reached.

Although more distinctions may be suggested, what really matters are the definition used to make the distinction, the purpose of separating two or more segments and the validity of the theory underlying any distinction. This paper will be particularly concerned with dynamic firms *versus* non-dynamic ones, arguing that small enterprises (defined in terms of a certain number of employees) in an industrial district can be more dynamic than larger ones and those outside the district. This is the case if the small firms can redress their structural weakness by integrating themselves into a larger network of inter-firm cooperation. They can then gain economies of scale and scope similar to those of large firms.

The stress on the potential of small enterprises is one of the eye-openers of the flexible specialization concept, which rightly puts emphasis on the importance of horizontal and vertical links among independent firms. They may be enterprises of different sizes, but they have backward linkages with suppliers and forward linkages with their clients and cooperate and/or compete with each other. In the case of flexible specialization, two modes of organization are distinguished: the so-called large-scale and small-scale variant of flexible specialization. In the first case, flexible specialization results from the clustering of small firms and strong inter-firm division of labour. The large-firm variant exists when large firms decentralize and specialize internally or use specialized suppliers (the Japanese subcontracting system).

Technology and innovation

Schumpeter pointed to the innovative entrepreneur who creates and resolves various kinds of technological and organizational disequilibria. The neo-classical theory assumes, however, that entrepreneurs will choose the most appropriate technology only on the basis of their relative efficiency. According to the (neo-classical) theory, once the choice of a technology has been made, entrepreneurs will change the technology only in case of a major shock. Technologies are described in terms of fixed technical coefficients. However, as Hicks (1979: 47) remarked, the techniques of production were not changing rapidly in the days of Adam Smith, hence the technical coefficients could be regarded as rather firm. In practice, technological choices are dictated by more than relative efficiencies. Moreover, technical coefficients are not sufficient to determine relative costs. The relative prices of other production factors also play a role. If they change, the optimal technology may be a different one.[7]

The neo-classical theory uses, in fact, a very narrow definition of technology and does not take continuous innovation into account. In the broad sense, technology is not just a question of machines or tools. Technology and innovation are also related to the design and quality of the product, the type and quality of raw materials used, the organization of production and the packaging of the final product. Given the broader definition, technology is not something fixed, but rather it is changing constantly, resulting in different production costs and gains in productivity. An industrial district contributes to the process of innovation and technological development.

Innovation at the level of the firm is, essentially the outcome of a cumulative process. It is cumulative in the sense that technologies of production used today influence learning processes and the nature of accumulated experience in the individual firm or the collectivity of firms in an industrial district (Cooper, 1992). Moreover, technological change is often localized. According to Atkinson and Stiglitz (1969: 315), technological change may be better represented by a localized "bulge" in the neo-classical industry production function, rather than by a uniform shift of the whole frontier.[8] Finally, Cooper (1992 points to the factors determining the appropriability of new technologies. Knowledge incorporated into new technologies can be appropriated, to different degrees, by the innovating enterprise. There exist large differences in this respect, but an industrial district may help to get the maximum out of a new technology because other enterprises using the same technology differently may be observed.

Inter-firm relations: different methods of organization

The flexible specialization and the new competition concepts both stress the importance of inter-firm relations. Industries operating under flexible specialization function in a sophisticated network of inter-firm relations. Firms generally subcontract to each other and often share knowledge. Jointly they develop new production methods and new products.

The new competition stresses the existence of a whole gamut of arrangements, ranging from subcontracting to consultative cooperation. Licensing, strategic alliances and consultative cooperation are alternative modes of organization that are gaining importance in the new competition. Best (1990:2) considers the managerial hierarchy to be an expensive means of coordination, which more often could take place via the market or through consultative cooperation among mutually interdependent firms. This suggests that vertical disintegration of large firms would make more sense, instead of further integration of suppliers or sales outlets. Van Dijk, *et al.* (1992) has found the same process taking place in the automobile industry in Western Europe.[9]

These different formal arrangements may be of use in the modern formal sector. In the smaller enterprises, different forms of collaboration occur. Entrepreneurs may borrow equipment from each other or share important orders. What counts is the blend of competition and cooperation which promotes innovative capabilities and competitive efficiency. Inter-firm cooperation enables firms to choose how they want to become or remain competitive. Often the low and high roads to industrialization are distinguished, the low road being based on cheap labour while the high road stresses innovation (Sengenberger *et al.*, 1992: 11).

Competition and cooperation

It is well known that competition encourages innovation. The structure of capitalist competition is determined by market conditions (number of competitors, their size and the openness of the markets), price structures, factor supplies and factor prices. Competition has increased since 1970 because of improved transport and communication, the economic crisis at the beginning of the 1980s, further economic integration in Europe and North America and higher rates of international cross-penetration of markets.

Likewise, cooperation has also increased, although in many different forms. The number of licensing agreements and strategic alliances, strategic networks (Jarillo, 1988), long-term contracts to supply, reciprocal sales arrangements, cooperation on technology and other forms of cooperative competition have increased. However, the cost of developing new technologies and models has increased tremendously in, for example, the automobile, lorry and airplane industries. Many large firms have become aware that smaller ones may be better in certain fields. Cooperation can be the result of a common background, mutual interest or the development of a local business community. It is important because it helps to socialize knowledge and to control opportunistic behaviour (Storper, 1989:274).

The importance of the particular combination of competition and cooperation is seized by the flexible specialization and new competition concepts. The first stresses the importance of clusters and networks to develop these relations, while the second points to the importance of different modes of organization, which may range from subcontracting to consultative cooperation.

The policy context

The national policy context is very important for a dynamic industrial sector. The government must create a positive policy environment. Often structural adjustment programmes try to do so. Examples from Europe show how important industrial policies and industry support institutions have been for the development of a dynamic industrial sector. In Ireland, for example, a wide range of agencies, usually supported wholly or in part by public funds, assists industry in a variety of ways (O'Farrell, 1986). These agencies help with job creation, training, research and development, exporting, financial assistance and industrial relations.

Flanders, in northern Belgium, is often considered as an example of an industrial district. It had the largest share of new firms created in Belgium in 1984 (Donckels and Bert, 1986). The corresponding public policy is considered a response to the economic recession of the 1970s, which led to the closure of big companies and to steeply rising unemployment. The national, regional and local governments in Belgium took a number of initiatives, such as:

(a) Creating specific zones for small- and medium-sized enterprises;

(b) Establishing business centres (since 1983), each supporting about 20 new firms offering premises, supply of common services (secretaries, telephones, conference space, etc.) and of management assistance;

(c) Providing larger premises for entrepreneurs needing more space;

(d) Stimulating Regional Development Companies (SDRs) to encourage technological innovation in small- and medium-sized firms;

(e) Organizing local-level information sessions and seminars in collaboration with professional bodies, such as the Chambers of Commerce;

(f) Sending experts from the SDRs to the small- and medium-sized enterprises to assist them with the introduction of new technologies;

(g) Setting up in 1983 a technological innovation and renewal cell for Flanders to promote technology transfer, and finally,

(h) Inviting the Institute for Permanent Education at the secondary level to establish 21 training centres in the region.

The establishment of an appropriate policy environment and these specific policy measures created the technological climate within which new technology-based firms could emerge. Given their geographical proximity and the interrelations between firms, it can be called an industrial district.

Industrial districts, a conclusion

Schmitz (1992: 65) concludes that there is no clear definition of flexible specialization and, hence, much of the debate on that subject suffers from definitional confusion. Is the same true for industrial districts? The author's conclusion is that some characteristics can be mentioned on which everybody seems to agree, while others have been attached to the concept without much empirical evidence.

Conditions for a successful industrial district mentioned by Pyke *et al.* (1990) and Pyke and Sengenberger (eds.,1992) are summarized in table 1. They have been distinguished by the present author as those on which most authors agree and those which seem less supported by empirical evidence.

Characteristics which are often mentioned are inter-firm cooperation, cooperation blended with competition, the importance of local value systems, flexibility, an innovative capacity, geographical proximity, sectoral specialization, the provision of a local pool of skilled labour and the presence of a large number of small firms. Willingness to work together to resolve potential clashes of interest, the widespread entrepreneurial spirit and ability, active municipal and local governments, a local consensus, common values and the promotion of a social compromise have not really been empirically supported. More research will be necessary to determine what are necessary and what are sufficient conditions for a successful industrial district.

Industrial districts are often considered as an alternative form of industrial organization. They are certainly an alternative to vertical integration and the atomized system of dispersed capitalist firms seeking profit maximization through tough competition, the pursuit of monopolies and in-house research and development activities.

II. THE MACRO-LEVEL: STRATEGIES TO ACHIEVE INDUSTRIALIZATION

Policies for achieving an optimal production system

Industrial production may be organized in alternative technological, institutional and spatial configurations. If something like an optimal production system were to exist, technological, institutional and spatial alternatives would need to be chosen very carefully. Individual entrepreneurs and different levels of government may not have the same preferences. In the end, the market will decide, but government policies at the national, regional and local levels influence the decisions of individual entrepreneurs, which determine the outcome of the market process.

An optimal industrial production system

The optimal industrial production system in a country will be market, location, culture and technology-specific. It would be an optimal solution at a certain moment of time; it should be realized that the dynamic optimal system may be quite different from the optimal static one. Over time, consumers' tastes and income change, locations gain or lose interest because of infrastructural, transport and environmental considerations, the culture may change and technology advances constantly, just like the policy and competitive context.[10] Much will depend on the starting point. Is one talking about a least developed country or about a newly industrializing country? Are large enterprises dominant, or do small enterprises play an important role? Does a country have an industrial tradition or must it start its industrial development from scratch? The latter type of country would be affected differently by the crisis of Fordist mass production discussed below, as well as by the new international division of labour which has emerged since the 1980s and in which East Asia is playing a quite important role. It would be more difficult for the least developed countries to become competitive in the world market.

To determine the importance of these developments and to assess their weight is one of the challenges of an appropriate industrialization strategy. Originally, import substitution strategies were recommended to the third world, suggesting that industrialization could just be copied from the more developed countries and a certain degree of capital and protection would be all that was required. Later, export-led industrialization stressed the importance of competition on the world market as a means of becoming competitive and earning foreign exchange. Recently, the flexible specialization concept has put emphasis on innovation and flexibility as key elements for industrial competitiveness. The new competition strategy may be considered as an integration of the export-led and flexible specialization strategy. This will be discussed briefly in the following section.

Table 1

Characteristics of industrial districts

Agreed upon in the literature:
1. Inter-firm relations
2. Cooperation blended with competition
3. The importance of a local value system
4. Flexibility in production methods, labour input and product
5. Innovative capacity
6. A large number of small firms
7. Geographical proximity
8. Sectoral specialization
9. The provision of a local pool of skill

Characteristics of which the importance is not really empirically supported:

10. Willingness to work together to resolve clashes of interest
11. Widespread entrepreneurial spirit and ability
12. Active municipal and local governments
13. A local consensus and common values
14. The promotion of a social compromise

Source: Pyke *et al.* (eds. 1990) and Pyke and Sengenberger (eds. 1992). Selection Meine Pieter Van Dijk.

From import substitution to flexible specialization strategies

Mass production became the characteristic of the industrial sector after the first world war. The assembly line introduced by Henry Ford quickly dominated automobile manufacture, electrical appliances and machinery industries. Continuous- flow processes were the equivalent adopted by the steel and chemical industries. At that stage of industrialization, scale became important; final products were more and more standardized; their prices declined and productivity of labour increased because of higher investments per employee and a marked division of labour.

Developing countries tried, between 1950 and 1970, to transfer the Fordist mass production model to their own economies and some of the larger countries were particularly successful in this respect (Brazil, for example, Storper, 1990). In the 1970s, the mass production system started to fall apart. Fordism was criticized because it became increasingly difficult to balance assembly-line supply with effective consumer demand. The Fordist organization of production has usually been coupled with Taylorism in management (Taylorist-organized production), whereby a clear line of command is established with executives on one side and workers on the other - - a fundamental weakness of many Western economies (Best, 1990: 1). Storper (1990: 423) adds that "the structure of international competition which evolved over the 1970s and 1980s no longer permits its reimplantation". Even in the developed countries, after the two oil crises and the structural adjustment process that they triggered, the Fordist mass production was no longer the dominant model in a number of industrial sectors.

Similarly, a number of factors have contributed to the re-emergence of small and micro enterprises in developing countries. Often the closure of many modern factories has led to offsprings in the small-scale sector. Lay-offs in the public sector have also led people to start small enterprises to support their families. Micro and small enterprises are thus becoming increasingly important again in most developing countries and so a strategy needs to be devised to maximize the contribution of this sector to the development process.

Post- or Neo-Fordism is a new principle that appeared after the global crisis at the beginning of the 1980s. It aims at flexibilization; in developed countries, it has meant automation, informatization and robotization. There has been a corresponding trend away from vertical integration in one branch, towards subcontracting to specialized independent (often small) firms. Basically, neo-Fordism takes as a principle of organization the use of semi-autonomous groups of producers, depending on a centralized information system. In this way, producers are able to respond efficiently to fluctuating and differentiated demand (Mendez, 1991). Correspondingly, new management techniques are tried out, sometimes copied from Japan. An operationalization of the concept for research in developing countries has been given by Van Dijk (1992a) and is summarized in table 2.

Storper (1990) points to the importance of market saturation and a pervasive spatial decentralization process as an explanation of the decline of mass production. Competition from Japan and between North America and Western Europe has been cutting into domestic markets in North America and Europe. The necessary rationalization and restructuring has led to plant closures, more unemployment and geographical decentralization, according to Storper.[11]

Industrialization does not need to follow the mass production model. The alternative of flexible specialization stresses decentralization of big factory chains and redeployment of productive forces in small units, to take advantage of flexible technologies. Piore and Sabel (1984) suggest that flexibly specialized industries have three defining characteristics: (a) They produce a wide range of products for highly differentiated markets and they constantly change these goods in response to changing tastes and in order to expand their markets; (b) Individual firms use widely applicable technologies. They prefer to invest in general-purpose machines than in large dedicated machine systems; and (c) Flexibly specialized industries balance competition and cooperation among firms.

Flexible specialization points to the importance of craftsmanship and small enterprises. Standardized products and the lowest production costs are not the most important variables. The concept could provide an alternative industrial policy for developing countries if it could be turned into an industrialization strategy. At present, such a strategy would be particularly relevant for the somewhat more

Table 2

Operationalization of the flexible specialization concept

Definition of key terms for research in Burkina Faso
- Multi-purpose equipment and innovation, skilled labour, with an innovative mentality use general purpose equipment to produce whatever is in demand.
- Clusters of enterprises of small-firm communities, the seedbed for an exchange of ideas. Moreover, physical proximity facilitates the exchange of ideas; it also makes the development of institutions and their interventions easier and more effective.
- Interaction/networking, the whole set of subcontracting and collaboration efforts between small enterprises and between smaller and larger ones.
- Collective efficiency, the result of the physical presence nearby of other innovative producers.
Enterprise-level variables and indicators:
Technology: Multi-purpose equipment and skills required Innovation: Indications of product and process innovations Inter-firm cooperation: Subcontracting or other arrangements Clustering: Industrial zones in Ouagadougou and Bobo Dioulasso Networking: Formal (Chambers of Commerce) and informal (Lebanese) organizations of businessmen

developed and second-tier newly industrializing countries. The challenge will be to go from the analytical concept of flexible specialization to a prescriptive one which would also work in the least developed countries. Evidence from Burkina Faso suggests that a country needs at least a certain level of development of its industrial sector before flexible specialization can be expected.

"New competition": flexibility and export-orientation

The term "new competition" was introduced by Best (1990). New competition is contrasted with old competition based on mass production and lowest cost. The old competition comprised "market-coordinated, vertically-specialized industrial enterprises" (Best, 1990: 7). The concept is more general than the flexible specialization concept. At the centre of the new competition is the entrepreneurial firm, "an enterprise that is organized from top to bottom to pursue continuous improvement in methods, products and processes" (Best, 1990: 2).[12] Such a firm seeks the competitive edge by superior product design (which may or may not lead to lower costs) and organizational flexibility which manifests itself in a variety of inter-firm complexes. These range from the groups of small Italian firms linked by cooperative associations for joint marketing, technological advance and financial underwriting to the giant Japanese organizational structures incorporating trading companies, banks and manufacturing enterprises.[13] Entrepreneurial firms try to capture export markets where possible. The emergence of the new competition has taken the United Kingdom and the United States by surprise, according to Best.

The new competition is distinguished from the old by four dimensions. The new competition is about strategic action within each dimension, strategic referring to market-shaping activities in contrast to market-reacting responses. The dimensions are:

(a) The organization of the entrepreneurial firm; it has a strategic orientation to choose the terrain on which to compete;

(b) Coordination across phases of production in the production chain; the choice is not restricted to plan, market or hierarchy, but consultative-cooperative inter-firm relations may exist among mutually interdependent firms;[14]

(c) The organization of the sector;[15] this refers to a variety of inter-firm practices and extra-firm agencies such as trade associations, apprenticeship programmes, labour education facilities, joint marketing arrangements and regulatory commissions, each facilitating inter-firm cooperation;[16]

(d) Patterns of industrial policy; according to Best, a healthy industrial sector depends upon combining competition with cooperation and this needs to be achieved by policies. Successful industrial policies should help to shape markets, have a production instead of a distributional focus and be strategically focused.

The new competition does not necessarily affect all sectors of the economy. The traditional non-exporting sectors, in particular, may be less affected. A second critical remark could be that Best does not explain why, all of a sudden, the new competition arose.[17] Finally it is not a theory which is easy to operationalize so as to find out whether it applies only in a given situation (see Van Dijk, 1992b).

Table 3 summarizes the differences between flexible specialization and the new competition.

Flexible specialization focuses more on the firm within the industry and the way it uses its technology, while the new competition looks at world-wide markets and puts more stress on the different modes of organization that are possible in branches where vertical disintegration is the rule (for example, the automobile and electronics

Table 3

Flexible specialization and new competition compared

Indicator	Flexible specialization	New competition
Objective of firm	Profit and survival in a dynamic market	Profit and a growing share of the market
Strategy	A strategy of continuous innovation, responding quickly to market requirements	Pursue continuous improvements in methods, products and processes; shape industrial sectors and markets: choose the terrain on which to compete
Market forms	Medium concentration, segmented markets	Global competition approaches full competition
Modes of organization	Large or small-scale variant of flexible specialization with subcontracting relations	Range of arrangements from subcontracting to consultative cooperation
Explanatory variables	Innovative mentality; multi-purpose technology; clusters and networks; skilled manpower; collective efficiency	Organizational flexibility: - different forms of internal organization - different modes of organization - superior product design
Corresponding government policies	Start innovation centres; promote sub-contracting; promote clusters of production activities; create an industrial community (networks); combine inter-firm cooperation with competition	Encourage firms to seek strategic alliances; help to shape markets by targeting strategic sectors; give a production focus to industrial policies

industries).[18]   The key variable in flexible specialization is technology, while the new competition stresses improvements in methods, products and processes, including organizational forms, financing arrangements or marketing strategies.   Both stress the importance of continuous alertness, the combination of some competition with some collaboration and the advantages of subcontracting relations. Policies, in the case of flexible specialization, concentrate on creating clusters and networks and an environment prone to innovation, while the new competition theory stresses the importance of shaping markets and of targeting strategic sectors. government policies should have a production focus and encourage firms to seek strategic alliances.

III. THE MICRO-LEVEL: FACTORS DETERMINING THE DYNAMICS OF THE INDUSTRIAL DISTRICTS

Entrepreneurship and flexibility

Schumpeter identified the entrepreneur as the dynamic force in development. The entrepreneur makes the innovation or implements the idea.   It turns out to be very difficult to say who is an entrepreneur and especially who is a good one.   However, it was often thought that there was a shortage of good entrepreneurs in the third world. Certainly the percentage of independent entrepreneurs is small in most societies. However, theories stressing the seedbed function of small enterprises and evidence concerning the number of people starting up on their own account every day in the third world and Eastern Europe go against this assertion. Entrepreneurship is often considered as a sixth sense and something that is very difficult to learn.   Nevertheless, a few entrepreneurship development programmes do exist and it is certain that entrepreneurship develops best in a conducive environment.

The problem with entrepreneurship development programmes is that they have always aimed at the individual entrepreneur. They have assumed that the enterprise has to encompass and master all related business functions. Cooperative attitudes and inter-firm linkages have normally been neglected (Späth, 1992).

Entrepreneurship also requires flexibility. In an industrial context, this can be defined as the ability to shift promptly from one process and/or product configuration to another and to adjust quantities of output rapidly up or down over the short run. Flexible specialization stresses this quality and Storper (1990: 431) observed an increasing production flexibility in four major groups of industries: (i) Selected high-technology manufacturing and related services: (ii) Craft-based production in batches; (iii) Producer and financial services; and (iv) Restructured consumer durables and heavy capital goods production.

The enterprise support system

The challenge for governments is to support entrepreneurship development by creating the right policy environment. An enabling environment helps an entrepreneur to develop his/her business. This is not only a question of policy environment, as has been brought out in the example of Flanders. Institutions which play an important role are technical schools and vocational training and management centres, financial institutions and technical assistance projects. In some countries, entrepreneurship development programmes have been launched. Given the central role of technology and innovation in the industrialization process, innovation centres and technology diffusion projects also need to be mentioned.[19]

The red tape which a new entrepreneur has to face is an argument for a single window agency for ensuring coordinated provision of licenses and permits for enterprises of different sizes. The authorities running an industrial estate often fulfil this function (c.f. Hub Chowdi in the Baluchistan province of Pakistan; Van Dijk, 1992d). A proper infrastructure and services such as water supply, electricity and communication facilities, are also important. Finally, sometimes extension services exist to help the entrepreneurs.

The United Nations Industrial Development Organization (UNIDO) has carried out a number of programmes for subcontracting and enterprise-to-enterprise cooperation. Recently an international subcontracting exchange was set up in India with the support of UNIDO. It is part of a new international network of industrial subcontracting exchanges for the Central Asian region, including India, Bangladesh, Sri Lanka, Mauritius, Indonesia and the Philippines (*Indian Express*, 10-7-1992). Training, transfer and development of technology and marketing of industrial products could also be improved through international and regional cooperation.

A dynamic labour market

Rapid industrial development requires a good functioning labour market. A comparison between some African countries and the newly industrializing countries in Asia showed that the latter generally had a well-trained labour force, while wages were relatively low (Van Dijk, 1992e). In Africa, urban-based trade unions have often managed to negotiate for somewhat higher wages, while the level of education and training of the workers is often lower.[20] Wages and the corresponding labour and employment regulations are relevant only for workers in the modern formal and large-scale sector. Workers in small firms are usually more flexible and often do not get the legal minimum wage.

Education and wage levels are two important variables, but the availability of specialists, the willingness of workers to change jobs and location within a country, are also important for industrialization. A person going from one industrial firm to another may often bring a lot of experience with him or her, which may contribute to the learning process in that particular industry. Flexibility is difficult to enforce, however. Given the importance of skills, it is recommended to plan training programmes in (potential) industrial districts, particularly those linking theoretical knowledge with practical experience.

In the framework of structural adjustment, an improvement of the functioning of labour markets is often an objective. Resistance to this kind of policy change is high, however, particularly if labour is well-organized and has much to lose. With training programmes and manpower planning, the government can try to work on the supply side. Well-functioning labour exchanges or advertising in local newspapers, on radio or television may help to match supply with demand.

A continuous spatial reorganization process

The above-mentioned factors lead to a continuous spatial reorganization of industries. The larger firms, in particular, tended to decentralize in the 1970s and 1980s.[21] Automobile industries world-wide brought their research and design facilities closer to their customers abroad. Certain high-tech textile industries came back from the third world to Europe. Top-of-the-range products, in particular (yachts in the shipping industry), or products that were very sensitive to change in consumer tastes (for example, computer-designed woollen sweaters) returned.

The spatial reorganization process is influenced by improved infrastructure and communication. Economic integration, increasing congestion and pollution in certain places -- all contribute. However, there are sometimes conflicting tendencies. The "just-in-time" supply system introduced by the Japanese car producers requires, for example, suppliers to be located in a range of 500 kilometres from the factory, to avoid risks of delivery delay. Conversely, this is not necessarily true for all automobile parts. The controlling variable in this case may be the kind of part. Sensitive or strategic parts, those containing, for example, a large degree of high-tech or crucial for the image and quality of the car will be bought nearby. Tyres, batteries and other standard products will be bought wherever they are cheap.

Less important factors: the region, sector and scale

Previously, a lot of importance was given to regional development policies. Development should, however, be spread country-wide;

governments, like the socialist Government of Sekou Toure in Guinea Conakry or the Congress party in India, have tried to spread industries equitably throughout the country. The instruments used ranged from incentives to direct participation in the company. Looking back, it is doubtful whether these regional development policies have really contributed much to the development of these regions. It is certain that an isolated industry in a remote region cannot develop linkages with other industries and will tend to do everything itself. In such a case, the chances of developing a dynamic region are slim.

We found it hard to identify, for example, a real industrial district in India. The city of Bangalore, with its dynamic electronics industries, is one of the few clear cases. Sekhar (1983) has argued that the Government of India utilized a wide-ranging set of policy measures to influence the location of industries. The objective was to disperse industries away from large metropolitan areas and to promote the development of less developed regions. He concludes that the policy should be based more on incentives and less on control measures. The present policy has led to a wastage of resources, to distortions and a lack of spread-effects of large, often public-sector units, in the local economy. More seriously, from the point of view of flexible specialization or new competition, no diffusion of innovations takes place in these remote areas if there are only one or two big industries.

The performance of certain sectors can vary widely. Most successful industrial districts have operated in very specific sectors (e.g. textiles, furniture, ceramics). Still, the large number of different examples would suggest that industrial districts could operate in almost any sector. The major conditions for success are demand, innovation and firm interrelations.

Finally, much has been written about the importance of scale. But Marshall (1920) had noted that "the advantages of production at a large scale can be as well attained by the aggregation of a large number of small masters into the district as by the erection of a few large works". Technological innovations have reinforced this development. It is claimed, for example, that mini- steel industries, mini-cement factories and mini-sugar factories can be as profitable as their larger counterparts.[22] In the meantime, they benefit from lower transport costs.

It can also be argued that smaller industries are more flexible than larger firms. However, one has to be careful with such statements, because very small firms often lack the means to invest in flexibility. Some of the larger industries have discovered how bureaucratic they have become and are presently making departments more independent, by turning them, for example, into profit centres.

The objective of many studies has been to understand the mechanisms of generation of synergies among components of an industrial district. Some call it 'collective efficiency' while others call it external economies of scale or agglomeration economies.[23]

IV. ISSUES CONCERNING INDUSTRIAL DISTRICTS AND INNOVATION

What makes an industrial district a centre of innovation and industrial development?

Pyke *et al.* (1990) argue that industrial districts should be conceived as a social and economic whole. There are intensive interrelations between the social, political and economic spheres: "the functioning of one, say economic, is shaped by the functioning and organization of the others". The advantage of this interpretation is that the success of an industrial district is not just considered the result of economic and technological factors. Subsequently, they mention adaptability and innovativeness as hallmarks of the industrial district and stress the communal capacity to cater for rapidly changing product demands, depending on a flexible labour force and flexible productive networks.

The motor of success has not been the large vertically integrated (multinational) corporation with all its scale advantages and market power. In the Third Italy, organization and leadership came "from small, often family-owned, businesses linked together by an articulated division of specialization". However, Pyke *et al.* (1990) also warn that there are big differences between industrial districts. They mention differences in respect of variations in local culture, political allegiances, skill levels, levels of technology, relations between firms and between the latter and institutions. Their conclusion is that these differences appear to be much more variations in degree, or around common themes, rather than differences in essence.

Best (1990: 235) mentions the institutional capacity of industrial districts continuously to learn, adjust and improve their economic performance. The enterprises in the districts are often more innovative in the development of products, production processes and marketing channels. Coordination in a dynamic industrial district is not planned but quasi-spontaneous. However, the innovative atmosphere and entrepreneurial dynamism are certainly part of the secret of success of these districts. Innovativeness and adaptability are hallmarks of industrial districts; flexible productive networks mean that the enterprise can satisfy rapidly increasing demand. Leadership often comes from small family-owned businesses in the Third Italy; businesses are linked together by an articulated division of specialization.

Does it need to be a geographical cluster, or are interlinked networks of industries enough ?

Geographers tend to take a geographical interpretation of the industrial district concept. They think in terms of proximity. Distances, the quality of the infrastructure and transportation play an important role in their considerations. Sociologists stress the family background of entrepreneurs, entrepreneurial spirit and networks of ethnic or otherwise related entrepreneurs. Economists consider the costs of communication and distribution the most important element and devise rules such as 500 kilometres being the limit for suppliers of strategic car parts.

Knorringa (1992) makes the point that flexible specialization, as in the case of the footwear industry in Agra (India), may not become the export industry it could because of the caste differences between the high caste international traders knowing the market and the lower caste small artisans actually making the shoes. The major reason would be the lack of communication and understanding between the two groups, which hinders effective communication on matters like required models, desired quality and other relevant marketing information.

The Indian and Italian cases (Pyke *et al.*, 1990) stress the importance of cultural ties and networks. The successful examples of industrial districts mentioned earlier are all limited to a certain physical area, however. Much depends on the nature of the inputs and outputs. A service will be bought nearby and strategic parts will bought in the area, particularly if frequent contact is necessary to develop a part satisfying specific requirements. Standard products can come from anywhere, depending on their price and transportation cost.

Why is an industrial estate or an industrial free-trade zone not necessarily an industrial district?

In a recent paper, the author tried to establish the importance of being located on an industrial estate in Burkina Faso, to determine the importance of clustering for modern industries (Van Dijk, 1992f). Industries located on the three industrial estates were generally bigger in terms of investment, employment and turnover. They are also somewhat older, had more government participation in their capital (albeit not statistically significant) and, significantly more often, foreign participation in their capital.

An important variable was the lower percentage of turnover exported, which indicates that these are often import-substitution industries. It is also striking that the percentage of value added in the turnover was lower, suggesting simple processing units. The capital-intensity was significantly higher, such as the productivity of labour, which probably reflects the higher investment and the more capital-intensive nature of production. However, the firms were less often profitable. Remarkably, only one-quarter of the new competition firms were located on the industrial estates, while this was the case for 50 per cent of the firms classified as fitting into the flexible specialization concept.

The notion of industrial districts will still have to be developed in Burkina Faso. The present industrial estates certainly do not serve that purpose. No small and micro enterprises prevail; there is little subcontracting, technological innovation or innovation diffusion taking place. Neither do government policies stimulate these developments.

Many developing countries, just as in municipalities in the Netherlands, create industrial estates. They hope these will turn into centres of economic growth. In reality, industrial estates are often monuments to unachieved dreams. Even if all the proper infrastructure were provided, entrepreneurs might still not be attracted to them, since they may consider the estate to be badly located, fear being obliged to pay higher taxes and all kinds of rates, or find no advantage in being located there. Industrial estates in West Africa are often built for the larger import-substitution industries. These industries are not flexible, have very low value-added and are certainly not export-oriented. There is usually no place reserved for small and micro enterprises on these estates and many people have procured land for speculative purposes only!

How can we identify the potential of a region to become an industrial district?

Porter (1990) presents a method for analyzing clusters of related and supporting industries. While he seeks the determinants of the success of countries, his methods could also be used for identifying regions with potential. For certain countries, the four major determinants for success are (production) factor conditions, demand conditions, the presence of related and supporting industries and the structure and culture of domestic competition. Porter mentions two additional factors: chance events (such as important technological break-throughs) and the role of the government.

His method may be useful in identifying factors which have played a role in the development of countries. Historians have the knowledge of hindsight. Predicting these developments and steering them in a certain direction may, however, be much more difficult, as will be argued in the next section. Table 2 above provided a checklist of factors which may contribute to the success of industrial districts. The list can be also be used to formulate the preconditions for success. It still remains a problem to create those conditions, even with a willing and capable government at the national, provincial (or state) and local levels.

What can the government (at the national, state and city levels) do to develop industrial districts?

The key question is whether the development of industrial districts in the past has been a spontaneous process or whether it was triggered by certain policy measures. Of the examples mentioned, some probably developed without special government support, but we would still stress that the government can help to create the right conditions for the development of industrial districts.

However, Storper (1990) stresses rightly that there is no standardized policy formula for state intervention. We are certainly not talking about direct government participation in industrial production, about complicated procedures to obtain permissions or about an extensive regulatory framework. Policies to create an enabling environment are required. National, provincial and local government can usually each make a distinctive contribution to the positive policy environment required for a successful industrial district.

If the government creates the conditions, the private sector should take up the challenge. A very clear division of labour is needed, however, and while the government should not act as an industrialist, the entrepreneurs should not try to achieve individually what the government could do successfully for the business community as a whole. Can the government, at the national, state (or provincial) or local level do much to develop industrial districts? Most examples mentioned had developed without much government support. Unfortunately, there is no standardized policy formula of government intervention to create an industrial district, but different levels of government can help to create the enabling environment. Examples of policies recommended in the case of a World Bank study in Burkina Faso are summarized in table 3. A clear division of labour between the government and the private sector is necessary. The government should create the conditions and stimulate the private sector to take up the challenge.

How can we enhance the technological innovation and diffusion capacity of an industrial district?

It is particularly important to assess the role of technological innovation and diffusion in the development of industrial districts. In cases like Silicon Valley, Baden-Württemburg and Bangalore, it is very clear that innovations played a role and that technology was very important. This, however, does not answer the question as to what the mechanisms are for indigenous technological learning in industrial districts. More research in this respect is necessary and is at present being undertaken by some of the specialized institutes of the United Nations University.

The second question is how the local technology level and innovative capacity can be improved. Technology centres, vocational training and better education could all contribute to the development of an innovative mentality. Universities and technical schools could contribute as well, but often need to be encouraged to play such a role.

Finally, the development of a technology policy and the promotion of innovation diffusion is important. Cooper (1992) argues that, if one is interested in technology policies in the context of developing countries, one should look at innovation studies in developed countries -- which is what his paper does. As far as technology diffusion is concerned, specialized organizations like TNO in the Netherlands may play an important role.[24]

There may be a need for technical assistance activities, for example, to help formulate technology policies or to set up technology development organizations in developing countries. United Nations organizations, such as the United Nations Conference on Trade and Development and the United Nations Industrial Development Organization, play an important role in this respect. To sum up, technology centres, good education and training and the stimulation of practice-oriented research could all contribute to the development of an innovative mentality on the part of management and workers. The government should formulate technology policies and support the relevant research organizations.

Do we need similar/related economic activities (sectoral specialization) or can different subsectors be promoted at the same time?

What works better? A multiplication of producers making similar products or specialization, along with a high division of labour resulting in a marked inter-firm division of labour? Pyke *et al.* (1990) stress that, in the Third Italy, where a group of establishments "specializing in a particular stage of production or service complements those of others in "the district", there is a kind of organic interdependency". Because of this and the resulting advanced division of labour, the collectivity of small firms is able to achieve economies of scale which were generally thought to be the advantage of a very large corporation.

Specialization in an industrial district, and the resulting division of labour among firms in related backward and forward activities, is an impetus to technological innovation and the further improvement of products and the production processes. Some of the examples mentioned concern clusters around certain processes and products. These require products with wide possibilities for suppliers and subcontractors. The advantage in this respect is more rapid innovation and adaptation, although Schmitz (1991) argues that even when firms cluster around certain processes and products, innovation and fast adaptation do not necessarily follow.

Besides the examples of vertical cooperation, there are also examples of horizontal cooperation,.as in the field of marketing. In the case of shoe and textile-based industrial districts in the Third Italy, joint marketing by a number of small enterprises has definitely contributed to their success. This certainly requires related economic activities.

On the one hand, the examples given so far usually represent the former case. The car and airplane industry in Baden-Württemburg and the computer industry in Silicon valley were the engines of growth. On the other hand, we know that the agglomeration economies of big cities are often related to the large number of different sectors in these cities. Scale may be the determining factor in the case of cities. In the case of an industrial district, one should start with the development of one sector. Eventually add-on effects can be expected.

What would be the role of small and micro enterprises in an industrial district and how can they become really involved?

What is the contribution of small enterprises to the success of industrial districts? In the case of the Third Italy, the contribution of small firms to the success story has been noted (Goodman and Bamford, 1989). In practice, there are often biases in government policies against small enterprises. Examples have been found in Ireland by O'Farrell (1986: 172-179) and in the case of Senegal by Van Dijk (1987). Pyke et al. (1990: 4) formulate the issue very briefly: "the key problem for small firms appears not to be that of being small, but of being isolated".

Schmitz (1992) argues that, in Baden-Württemburg, large firms have dominated the scene. He rightly distinguishes the large and small-scale variant of flexible specialization. Toyota, as a major car assembling company, may be considered as an example of the large-scale variant of the flexible specialization strategy and an example of intensive vertical cooperation.

In the literature, it is quite clear that small enterprises have played a major role in the success of many industrial districts in northern Italy and in Silicon Valley (United States). In fact, many consider the entry of the big multinationals to be a serious risk for such industrial districts. The big firms may be less innovative, less inclined to subcontract and to work jointly with smaller firms on technology and product development.

<u>From an industrial district to urban or regional development</u> ?

The tenth issue has to do with the link between an industrial district and urban or regional development and will be discussed separately. Different geographical terms are found in the literature on industrial districts, such as clusters, agglomerations, zones and regions and they are used without always being properly defined. Clusters can be defined as geographical agglomerations with a sectoral specialization (Schmitz, 1992). An agglomeration can be another word for a cluster, but may also refer to a city. In the latter case, it makes sense to distinguish between primate cities, big cities and secondary towns. Zones are defined in Pyke *et al.* (1990: 22) as a limited geographical area which is specifically characterized by a certain dominant production and the zone is a mixture of family, political and social life. Finally, regions are larger, often natural geographical and/or administrative units.

Pyke and Sengenberger (1992) discuss industrial districts as a powerful model of endogenous economic development. The challenge of regional development would be to try to make an industrial district the engine of growth for the region, or a blueprint for the regeneration of local and regional economies. Regional development planning used to be very much concerned with blueprints and development from above. Nowadays, regional governments try to create an enabling environment for economic activities and have to take into account all the conditions to make something an industrial district, as mentioned in table 1 above.

Industrial districts are often associated with urban industrial subsystems. Primate and big cities usually have a certain policy and budgetary autonomy to define industrial policies. They may have a better financial basis than regional governments, if the urban tax base is well developed. Their concern is usually just the city, while regional authorities have to worry about the spread of development.

Cities are usually considered as incubators of new economic activities. The external economics are considered very important, particularly for existing small firms and the development of new activities and new firms. According to Storper (1990), flexible production might make it possible to break with patterns of extreme metropolitan primacy, because these industries are relatively "independent of the agglomeration economies available in old centres of Fordist industry".

The original incubator hypothesis states that new firms, because of agglomeration effects, start in the centres of big cities and leave their starting location because of expansion, and therefore a lack of space, after a gestation period (De Jong and Lambooy, 1986). These authors also conclude, however, that the traditional incubation theory is far too simplistic. Techno-economic changes and spatial transformations have led to different patterns. First, the external economies can be found in the much wider area of the urbanized territory. Secondly, improved infrastructure and communication possibilities have made the factor of distance less important. The conclusion is that industrial districts will certainly contribute to regional or urban development. It is more difficult, however, to turn it around and to make an industrial district development part of an urban or regional development plan.

Much of the literature on developing countries deals with urban and regional development problems. It would be positive for a particular city or region if it would develop an industrial district as the engine of growth. It is very difficult to draw the boundary of an industrial district and its area may not be the same as a specific region or a big city. This problem will not be discussed in this section, but rather it will be assumed that there will be a positive interaction between the development of an industrial district and regional or urban development. The question is how the urban and regional development literature relates to the industrial district discussion.

The growth pole concept was introduced by Perroux in 1955 and stressed that growth is concentrated and that centrifugal forces emanate from the centre, while centripetal forces are attracted. The concept is somewhat similar to the industrial district jargon, except that the growth pole theory is less explicit about the important variables. Both concepts share the problems of being poorly defined, of working with some notion of a concerned area which is never uniformly defined and, finally, both tend to stress the pole or district and to neglect the adjoining region. More importantly, the industrial district literature stresses explicitly the importance of different modes of organization, of technology and innovation, of a certain entrepreneurial culture and of a leading sector.

The growth pole concept seems closely related to the discussion of the role of cities as centres having agglomeration economies. Unlike the industrial district approach, these agglomerations are multi-sector phenomena and benefit from specific factors, such as concentration of inhabitants, good location and short distances between enterprises. In its practical applications, the role of large industries has always been stressed in the case of the growth pole concept.

In regional economics, the equity aspect has played an important role. Regional development policies often focused on the weaker regions, where many of the attractive points for industrial development were missing. It is, therefore, not surprising that finding an industrial district in India, where the government has systematically tried to disperse economic activities, is not an easy task. Many of these industries have hardly no forward or backward linkages, but function as large inefficient protected producers and as such would be a refutation of the growth pole theory.

CONCLUSIONS

One may wonder whether the industrial district concept really helps us much. The term is poorly defined and we do not really know what makes an industrial district tick, there being no clear recipe for governments to turn a district into a dynamic one. However, the subject has focused attention on a key issue of industrial development: how can we develop the industrial sector more rapidly and make it a competitive sector? The previous analysis has at least shown the importance of certain factors, like innovation, networks and industrial policies, even if we cannot really determine their exact weight and even if we are not sure that all the relevant factors have been examined. Amin and Robins (1990) argue that many of the so-called districts are very different phenomena and they are doubtful about possibilities for replication. Storper, in the same book, points to the dynamics of industrial districts. Some have disappeared and others have come up, which proves, according to him, that the success of industrial districts is replicable.

"Once a dynamic industrial district" does not mean "always a dynamic industrial district". The nineteenth century examples mentioned earlier show how quickly an industrial district becomes less dynamic and even forgotten. Amin and Robbins (1990) warn that multinational corporations pose a threat to the independence of small-firm districts because they may swallow them up. Others point to the problem of maintaining efficiency, given the new international competition. The greatest danger is probably too much satisfaction with what has been achieved, leading to an unavoidable lack of dynamism. Pyke *et al.* (1990; 9) finish their introduction on a positive note, however, stressing that various types of intervention and reorganization could maintain the success story! Table 4 gives an impression of the kind of policy recommendations which could be formulated if governments wished to promote industrial districts and flexible specialization.

Table 4

Recommendations for industrial development in Burkina Faso

(a)	Support the creation of a centre for innovation and quality improvement, helping entrepreneurs with product design, improvement of production methods and the optimal use of multipurpose equipment
(b)	Recommend the use of multi-purpose equipment, particularly in the smaller production units and promote their introduction
(c)	Promote clusters of enterprises of different sizes active indifferent sectors. For example, reserve space for smaller units in the existing industrial zones, where co-operative competition between small and large enterprises would be possible
(d)	Stimulate the formation of networks of entrepreneurs
(e)	Support subcontracting arrangements as a way to reinforce the industrial tissue

Source: Van Dijk (1992b).

The industrial district concept could be a step forward, if a clear definition were to be agreed upon and if the positive and normative aspects were separated. A positive analysis would show their existence and shed light on the factors contributing to their dynamic development in the past. A positive analysis would also have to make a number of assumptions in order to recommend to governments how an existing area could be turned into an industrial district. In practice, not all of these assumptions would be necessarily realistic and the phenomenon may not be easily replicable.

REFERENCES

Adelman, I. (1984), "Beyond export-led growth", in: *World Development*, vol. 12, no. 9.

Amin, A. and K. Robbins (1990), "Industrial districts and regional development, limits and possibilities", in Pyke *et al.* (eds., 1990).

Atkinson A. and J. Stiglitz (1969), "A new view of technological change", in *Economic Journal*, vol. 79 (315), September.

Becattini, G. (1989), "The Marshallian industrial district as a socio-economic notion, in Pyke *et al.*(eds., 1990).

Berger, S. and M. J. Piore (1980), *Dualism and Discontinuity in Industrial Societies*, Cambridge: University Press.

Best, M. H. (1990), *The New Competition, Institutions of Industrial Restructuring*. Cambridge: Harvard University Press.

Chandler, A.D. (1977), *The Visible Hand*. Cambridge: Harvard University Press.

Clarke, R. (1985), *Industrial Economics*, Oxford: Blackwell.

Cohen, M.A. (1991), *Urban Policy and Economic Development, an Agenda for the 1990s*, Washington: IBRD.

Cooper, C.M. (1992), *Are innovation Studies on Industrialised Economies Relevant to Technology Policy in Developing Countries?* The Hague: ISS Development Economics Seminars.

David, P. (1975), *Technical Choice, Innovation and Economic Growth*, Cambridge: University Press.

Donckels R. and C. Bert (1986), "New firms in the local economy: the case of Belgium" in Keeble and Wever (eds., 1986).

Debresson, C. (1989), "Breeding innovation clusters: a source of dynamic development" in *World Development*.

Dijk, M.P. Van (1986), *Burkina Faso, Le Secteur informel de Ouagadougou*, Paris: L'Harmattan.

Dijk, M.P. Van (1987), *Senegal, Le secteur informel de Dakar*, Paris: L'Harmattan.

Dijk, M.P. Van (1992a), "How relevant is flexible specialization in Burkina Faso's informal sector and the formal manufacturing sector?" in Rasmussen *et al.* (eds., 1992).

Dijk, M.P. Van (1992b), "New competition/flexible specialization and industrialization in Indonesia and Burkina Faso", Stuttgart: EARIE Conference.

Dijk, M.P. Van (1992c): "Methodological problems of informal sector research, with results of a follow-up study in Ouagadougou, Burkina Faso", in C. Reichert (*et al.*, eds., 1992): *Empirische Sozialforschung über Entwicklungsländer*, Saarbrücken: Verlag Breitenbach.

Dijk, M.P. Van (1992d), "Planning industrial development in Balochistan", Quetta: Planning and Development Department.

Dijk, M.P. Van (1992e), "What relevance has the path of the NICs for Africa", in Bass (*et al.*, eds.,1992), *African Perspectives Yearbook 1990/91*, Hamburg: Lit.

Dijk, M.P. Van (1992f) "The importance of flexible specialization, new competition and industrial districts for the modern industrial sector in Burkina", Lund, Workshop EADI Working Group on Industrialization in the Third World.

Dijk, M.P. Van and H. Secher Marcussen (eds.,1990), *Industrialization in the Third World, the Need for Alternative Strategies*, London: F. Cass.

Dijk, M.P. Van, G. Asselbergs and L. Sleuwaegen (1992), *Vertical disintegration in the European Automobile Industry*, Rotterdam: Ecozoek.

Galbraith, J.K. (1979), *The New Industrial State*, New York: New American Library.

Goodman, E. and J. Bamford (eds., 1989), *Small Firms and Industrial Districts in Italy*, London: Routledge.

Hicks, J. (1979), *Causality in Economics*, Oxford: Basil Blackwell.

Jacobs, D. and M.W. de Jong (1992), "Industrial clusters and the competitiveness of the Netherlands" in *De Economist*, vol. 140, no. 2.

Jarillo, J.C. (1988), "On strategic networks", in *Strategic Management Journal*, vol. 9 December.

Jong, M. de and J.G. Lambooy (1986), "Urban dynamics and the new firm: the position of Amsterdam in the Northern Rimcity", in Keeble and Wever (eds., 1986).

Keeble, D. and E. Wever (eds.,1986), *New Firms and Regional Development in Europe*, London: Croom Helm.

Knorringa, P. (1992), "Adaptive capabilities in the Agra footwear cluster", Lund: Workshop EADI Working Group on Industrialization in the Third World.

Marshall, A. (1920), *Principles of Economics*, London: Macmillan.

Mendez-Rivero, D. (1991), *Informalization of the Venezuelan Labour Force*, The Hague: ISS.

O'Farrell, P. (1986), "The nature of new firms in Ireland: empirical evidence and policy implications", in Keeble and Wever (eds., 1986).

Piore, M. and C.F. Sabel (1984), *The Second Industrial Divide, Possibilities for Prosperity*, New York: Basic Books.

Porter, M.E. (1990), *The Competitive Advantage of Nations*, New York: The Free Press.

Pyke, F., G. Becattini and W. Sengenberger (eds., 1990), *Industrial Districts and Inter-firm Co-operation in Italy*, Geneva: International Institute for Labour Studies.

Pyke, F. and W. Sengenberger (eds., 1992), *Industrial Districts and Local Economic Regeneration*, Geneva: International Institute for Labour Studies.

Rasmussen, J., H. Schmitz and M.P. Van Dijk (eds., 1992), "Flexible specialization: a new view on small industry", *IDS Bulletin*, vol. 23, no. 3 July.

Reich, R. B. (1991), *The Work of Nations: Preparing Ourselves for 21st Century Capitalism*, New York: Vintage Books.

Schmitz, H. (1991), "Industrial districts, model and reality in Baden-Württemberg", in Pyke and Sengenberger (eds.,1992).

Schmitz, H. (1992), "On the clustering of small firms, in Rasmussen *et al.* (eds., 1992).

Sekhar, A. (1993), "Industrial location policy: the Indian experience", Washington: IBRD World Bank, *Staff Working Paper*, no. 620.

Sengenberger, W., G.W.Loveman and M.J. Piore (eds.,1992), *The Re-emergence of Small Enterprises*, Geneva: International Institute for Labour Studies.

Storper, M. and A. J. Scott (1988), "The geographical foundations and social regulation of flexible production complexes", in J. Wolch and M. Dear (eds.), *The Power of Geography*, London: Allen and Unwin.

Späth, B. (1992), "The institutional environment and communities of small enterprises", in Rasmussen *et al.* (eds., 1992).

Storper, M. (1989), "The transition to flexible specialization in the US film industry", in *Cambridge Journal of Economics*, vol. 13.

Storper, M. (1990) "Industrialization and the regional question in the Third World: lessons from post-imperialism; prospects of post-Fordism", in *International Journal of Urban and Regional Research*, vol. 14, no. 3.

Williamson, O. (1975), *Markets and Hierarchies, Analysis and Antitrust Implications: A Study of the Economics of Internal Organization*, New York: The Free Press.

NOTES

1. I wish to thank Brigitte Späth for her detailed and useful comments on a first draft of this paper.

2. Economies of scale occur when the percentage increase in production is higher than the percentage increase in the factors of production. According to Adam Smith, specialization would lead to economies of scale. Economies of scope are related to advantages of producing several products at the same time, while using the same facilities (the marketing, transport, etc.).

3. See Pyke *et al.* (eds.,1990 and 1992) and Sengenberger *et al.* (eds.,1992).

4. Not discussed in this paper are other less important industrialization strategies. Agricultural-led industrialization was advocated, for example, by Adelman (1984), while an alternative strategy stressing the importance of small enterprises, appropriate technology and regional markets has been elaborated in Van Dijk and Secher Marcussen (eds., 1990).

5. It is striking that the literature on industrial districts makes very little use of the results of the subdiscipline industrial organization, although many of the terms used to describe an industrial district find their origin in industrial organization theory.

6. The distinction can be based on size, legal or location criteria (Van Dijk, 1992c).

7. In developed countries, changes in factor prices stimulate a search for a new technique which economizes in that factor which has become relatively scarce.

8. This suggestion was used by David (1975) who proposed an explanation of localization based on learning processes in production.

9. The theory of imperfect markets, of transaction costs and technological developments (in particular, lean production and flexible manufacturing) are used to explain the vertical disintegration trend. The importance of economic integration in Europe is analysed separately.

10. The determination of an optimal production system taking all these developments into account would require a very complex dynamic model. Since not all of these changes can be predicted and properly quantified to allow their incorporation into a model that can be estimated, in practice the factors often need to be analysed one by one and subjective decisions taken.

11. The latter process of multinationals dispersing research, design development and engineering activities from single or dual locations to multiple ones may have reached its limits, because of coordination problems. This is illustrated by a recent decision of Ford of Europe to reallocate tasks between its British and German development facilities, because four centres to coordinate (United Kingdom, Germany, Detroit, U.S.A., and its Mazda affiliate in Japan) were too much (*Financial Times*, 27 February 1992).

12. He distinguishes the entrepreneurial firm from the hierarchical firm of Chandler (1977) and Williamson (1975). Administration in a managerial hierarchy is considered an expensive way of coordination, which more often could take place via the market, or through consultative-cooperation among mutually interdependent firms.

13. Best stresses institutional pluralism. The same positive result can be achieved through different institutional arrangements. He notably compares the different arrangements in Italy, Japan and Germany.

14. This is broader than Williamson (1975), who discusses coordination only via the market or via hierarchies.

15. Best (1990: 17) notes that conventional economics, which sharply divides micro-economics from macro-economic topics obscures a third level of organization crucial to explaining the

competitiveness of firms, namely the sector institutions or the extra-firm infrastructure.

16. Examples mentioned by Best (1990: 17).

17. The hypothesis that comes up immediately is the introduction of new technologies (more flexible and computer-controlled equipment), the segmentation of major producer markets and the increased globalization of the economy owing to increased trade and improved communications.

18. See Van Dijk *et al.* (1992) for the automobile industry. Similarly, the *Wall Street Journal*, European ed. (18 November 1991) notes that the process of vertical disintegration may have reached its limits in the electronics industry.

19. Späth (1992) also gives examples of the ineffectiveness of technology transfer centres in developing countries.

20. The number of dependents on one salaried worker is generally also higher in Africa.

21. The smaller enterprises in industrial districts may be less flexible as far as the choice of their locations is concerned.

22. Scale still plays a role in sectors such as mining, oil refinery, car assembly and airplane production.

23. Localization and urbanization economies are two kinds of agglomeration economies. Localization economies are external to the firm, but internal to an industry; urbanization economies are external to both the firm and the industry. The first results from the increased demand for goods and services from specific industries (Cohen, 1991: 34).

24. TNO is a government supported research organization specialized in the development of industrial technologies, product

design and quality improvement. It serves particularly small and medium enterprises in the Netherlands.

THE POTENTIAL FOR TURNING INFORMAL ECONOMIES INTO MARSHALLIAN INDUSTRIAL DISTRICTS

Ash Amin *

INTRODUCTION

Much of the interest today in industrial districts stems from the hope that lessons can be learnt from the experience of successful local economies in the advanced countries, in order to enable a similar pattern of self-sustaining growth in developing countries and regions. This hope has been given fresh impetus by a coalition of development economists and sociologists who seem to agree that the principle of "flexible specialization" which guides the successful industrial districts is appropriate in developing country contexts, owing to the presence of common elements such as craft traditions, informal and flexible work practices and structures of social cooperation (IDS, 1987 and 1991; Storper, 1990; Murray, 1990; Schmitz, 1989). Viewed from the perspective of policy-makers in developing areas such a growth strategy has immediate appeal, since it is an inexpensive, low-to-medium technology solution which draws upon local resources to unleash a process of self-sustaining and locally "embedded" development, free of the constraint of dependency on international financial institutions, transnational corporations and international regulatory agencies dominated by the North.

The paper by Van Dijk is in keeping with this tradition, even though it falls short of proposing normative solutions and of embracing the optimism of the above view. The paper reviews the

* Centre for Urban and Regional Development Studies, University of Newcastle-upon-Tyne.

literature on contemporary industrial districts, to abstract a set of defining characteristics which the author then uses to construct a profile of the "ideal type" industrial district. This achieved, the paper goes on to raise a number of policy questions relating to the technological status of industrial districts as well as their applicability to other spatial contexts - questions, which, in the main, receive only scant attention and remain unanswered.

Such an approach to the development potential of industrial districts, based as it is on conflating a variety of experiences into one ideal type, is problematic. Principally it runs the risk of forcing different, and perhaps even incompatible, realities into the same conceptual basket. I have argued elsewhere (Amin and Robins, 1990) that the dynamics of growth in craft-based industrial districts are quite different from those in other examples of local agglomerations such as high-tech complexes (e.g. Silicon Valley and other technopoleis) or large-firm-based centres of local industrial agglomeration (e.g. Baden Württemberg). To label them all "industrial districts" is particularly problematic from a policy perspective, since the experience of each type of agglomeration, despite common characteristics with other types, yields a different policy message. For example, the experience of craft areas in Italy illustrates the salience of small-firm cooperation, product specialization, artisan abilities and informal social and institutional arrangements. The experience of Silicon Valley, on the other hand, demonstrates the need for huge R&D budgets, proximity to centres of technological innovation, vast reserves of venture capital and excellence in technology-intensive products. Similarly, the experience of Baden-Württemberg shows up the centrality of large firms which are well embedded into the regional economy owing to the relatively high level of regionalization of institutional support for diffuse entrepreneurship, through the public provision of finance, high-quality training, education, R&D and communications infrastructure.

The more serious problem, with the ideal type approach, however, is that it abstracts away the historicity and interconnectedness of processes which exert a determining influence on the capability of an area to become an industrial district. The burgeoning volume of case study literature on industrial districts illustrates only too clearly the salience of at least three factors, whose importance escapes an approach which scans across different types of territorial configurations to build up an "identikit" composed of single, policy-capturable attributes. One factor is time, that is, the gradual historical sedimentation of socio-economic processes and institutions which shape the development trajectory taken by an economy. The second factor is the widely held opinion that the success of industrial districts lies less in individual attributes than in the interaction - often fortuitous - of a system-like structure underpinning individual entrepreneurship. The third factor is spatial specificity, that is, the role of socio-cultural and institutional characteristics which some local contexts possess, and which are almost impossible to reproduce elsewhere. To take these three factors seriously - time and the indeterminacy of its outcomes, the systemic nature of industrial districts, and spatial specificity - implies *a priori* recognition of the potential limitations of short-term and single-factor-based policy efforts to encourage the formation of industrial districts.

The intention of the paper is to flesh out this point by adopting a different approach to that taken by Van Dijk. The generalizations are based on an analysis of the real experiences of selected areas of agglomeration in the advanced economies. The paper offers a stylized account of the achievements and failures of two craft-based areas of product specialization in Italy. One, a leather tanning area called Santa Croce sull'Arno, is a mature industrial district in Tuscany. The other, Stella, in the old historic centre of Naples, specializes in footwear, but is a poor, "informal" economy which faces enormous difficulty in ever becoming a prosperous industrial district. The idea behind this choice is to contrast two extremes on a development path, using small firms specializing in a particular commodity and drawing upon strong artisan and "communal" traditions. This particular choice of examples has been selected to illustrate that while "informal" economies (of which there is an abundance in developing countries) might share some commonalities with advanced-country, small-firm industrial districts (e.g. artisan traditions, product specialization, family and kinship ties, flexible labour markets), they confront major obstacles impeding a transition to the status of "industrial district". The final section of the paper summarizes the key differences between a so-called Marshallian industrial district and an informal economy like Stella and then goes on to discuss the policy problems involved in enabling the latter to develop the structures of the former.

I. SANTA CROCE IN TUSCANY: AN ADVANCED INDUSTRIAL DISTRICT[1]

Santa Croce is a small town in the lower Arno Valley, 40 kilometres east of Pisa, which specializes in the production of medium to high quality cured bovine leather for predominantly the 'fashion' end of the shoe and bag industries. There are only two other major leather tanning areas in Italy: Arzignano in the Veneto, which is dominated by a small number of large, vertically integrated and highly mechanized tanneries, orientated towards the furnishing and upholstery industry; and Solofra in the South (Campania), which specializes in less refined, non—bovine, cured leather for the clothing industry. The lower Arno Valley accounts for about 25 per cent of the national employment in the leather and hide-tanning industry.

In Santa Croce, an area no larger than 10 square kilometres, are clustered 300 artisan firms employing 4,500 workers and 200 subcontractors employing 1,700 workers. The real figures are probably much higher as the latter capture only those firms officially registered, respectively, with the Santa Croce Association of Leather Tanners and the Association of Subcontractors. In 1986, the combined turnover of these 500 firms was £860 million (one—tenth of which was that of the subcontractors). On average, the area derives 15 per cent of its sales revenue from exports, almost 80 per cent of which are destined for the European Community. Although the share of exports has been growing, the industry is still heavily dependent on the Italian market, particularly upon buyers in Tuscany, who account for over 40 per cent of the domestic market.

Twenty years ago, Santa Croce was not a Marshallian industrial district (see the concluding section for a definition of this). There were many fewer firms, production was more vertically integrated, the product was more standardized (albeit artisanal) and the balance of power was very much in favour of the older and larger tanneries. Today, Santa Croce is a highly successful "flexibly specialized" small-firm industrial district. It derives its competitive strength from specializing in the seasonally based fashion—wear niche of the industry. Typically, market conditions in this sector — e.g. product volatility, a very short product life—cycle, design—intensity, flexibility of volume — demand innovative excellence and organizational flexibility which Santa Croce has been able to develop and consolidate over the past two decades by building upon its early artisan strengths.

The boom in demand for Italian leather fashion—wear in the 1970s and 1980s provided the occasion for area—wide specialization and growth in the output of cured leather. That such growth was to occur through a multiplication of independent small firms, supported by a myriad of task—specialist subcontractors, was perhaps more a result of specific local peculiarities than an outcome of the new market conditions. Opposed to the highly polluting effects of the tanning process — Santa Croce is one of those places in which you can recognize the Marshallian "industrial atmosphere" by its smell — the local Communist administration was unsympathetic to factory expansion applications and also refused, until very recently, to redraw the Structure Plan to allow for more and better factory space. This, together with the strong tradition of self—employment and small-scale entrepreneurship in rural Tuscany, effectively led to a proliferation of independently owned firms, scattered in small units all over Santa Croce. Two further encouragements to this process of fragmented entrepreneurship were, first, the preference of local rural savings banks to spread their portfolio of loans widely but thinly to a large number of applicants as a risk—minimization strategy and, secondly, the variety of fiscal and other incentives offered by the Italian State to firms with less than 15 employees.

This initial, and somewhat "accidental", response to a situation of rapidly expanding demand was gradually turned into an organizational strong point capable of responding with minimum effort and cost to new and rapidly changing market signals. The tanners — many of whom call themselves "artists" — became more and more specialized, combining their innate designer skills with the latest in chemical and organic treatment techniques, to turn out leathers of different thickness, composition, coloration and design for a wide variety of markets. The advantage for buyers, of course, was the knowledge that any manner of product could be made at the drop of a hat in Santa Croce.

The small firms were also able to keep costs down without any loss of productive efficiency through different mechanisms of cooperation. One example is the joint purchase of raw materials in order to minimize price. Another is the pooling of resources to employ export consultants. The main device for cost flexibility, however, has been the consolidation of an elaborate system of putting–out between tanners and independent subcontractors (often ex–workers). The production cycle in leather tanning is composed of 15 to 20 phases, of which at least half are subcontracted to task–specialist firms (for example, removal of hair and fat from uncured skins, splitting of skins, flattening and drying). Constantly at work, and specializing in operations which are most easily mechanized, the subcontractors have been able to reduce drastically the cost of individual tasks while providing tanners with the numerical flexibility demanded by their market. This articulate division of labour among locally based tanners and subcontractors — combining simultaneously the advantages of complementarity between specialists and competition between the numerous firms operating in identical market niches — is perhaps the key factor of success.

Other factors have also played a part. One is area specialization. Santa Croce, like other industrial districts, past and present, is a one- product town which offers the full range of agglomeration and external economies associated with local excellence along the entire chain of activities associated with leather tanning. In the area are warehouses of major international traders of raw and semi–finished leather as well as offices of independent import agents, brokers and customs specialists. There are the depots of the major multinational chemical giants as well as locally owned companies selling paints, dyes, chemicals and customer–specific treatment formulae to the tanners. There are at least three savings banks which, consistently, have provided easy and informal access to finance. There are several manufacturers of plant and machinery, tailor–made for the leather-tanning industry, and there is a ready supply base for second–hand equipment and maintenance services. There are several scores of independent sales representatives, export agents and buyers of finished leather in the area. The local Association of Leather Tanners, the Mayor's office, the bigger local entrepreneurs and the Pisa offices of the Ministry of Industry and Trade also act as collective agents to further local interests at national and international trade fairs. There are several international haulage companies and shipping agents capable of rapidly transporting goods to any part of the world. There is, at the end of the value–added chain, a company which makes glue from the fat extracted from the hides and skins. There is, finally, a water purification depot collectively funded by the leather tanners, the effluence of which is sold to a company which converts the non–toxic solids into fertilizer. No opportunity is missed in Santa Croce.

The entire community in Santa Croce, in one way or another, is associated with leather tanning. This provides new opportunities, through spin–off, along the value-added chain which, in deepening and refining the social division of labour, guarantees the local supply of virtually all of the ingredients necessary for entrepreneurial success in quality–dependent, volatile markets. To use the language of neoclassical economics, over and above firm–specific and asset–specific advantages, exists an area–wide asset which individual entrepreneurship draws upon. This "valorization" of the milieu is a product of the progressive deepening of the social division of labour (vertical disintegration) at the local level. The area not only produces specialized skills and artisan capability, but also powerful external economies of agglomeration and a constant supply of industry—specific information, ideas, inputs, machinery and services — Marshall's "industrial atmosphere".

Thus far, the success of Santa Croce as a Marshallian industrial district has been ascribed to two broad sets of factors. One is the fortuitous combination, since the early 1970s, of new market opportunities (the fashion-wear sector) and a minimum set of inherited local capabilities (leather tanning skills, a craft culture and so on). The second is the progressive vertical disintegration of the division of labour and its local containment.

There is also a third factor which has come to play a key role in safeguarding the success of the area. This is the institutionalization, at the local level, of individual sectoral interests (e.g. the Association of Tanners, the Association of Subcontractors, savings banks, the Mayor's office, trade union branches, etc.), as well as a sense of common purpose which draws upon Santa Croce's specialization in one industry and the intricate interdependencies of a vertically disintegrated production system. Not only has this prevented the growth of rogue forms of individual profiteering which could destabilize the system of mutual interdependence, but it has also created a mechanism for collectivizing opportunities and costs as well as ensuring the rapid transmission of information and knowledge across the industrial district.

The "collectivization of governance" has been of particular importance for the industrial district in recent years, as it has tried to cope with new pressures. By the mid—1980s, a honeymoon period of spectacular success for virtually all enterprises was coming to an end. This was the result of growing competition in international markets from fashion—wear oriented tanneries in South-East Asia, a decline in demand from the Italian footwear industry, big price increases coupled with shortages in the availability of uncured skins and hides, and new costs attached to the introduction of environmental controls on effluence discharge. These are problems which have affected the entire community: problems which different interest groups have not been able to resolve individually. Resulting collective responses have ranged from joint–funding by the tanners of an effluent treatment plant and multi–source funding (involving tanners, subcontractors, a local bank and the regional authorities) of an information service centre which offers advice on market trends, management skills and information technology, through to frequent and heated debates on new trends affecting the industry, held in the bar of the central square. How successful these efforts will be is uncertain. What matters, however, is that Santa Croce continues to possess a local institutional capability to respond collectively and swiftly to new market pressures and to steer the evolution of the industrial district in a particular direction.

This said, however, there is already some evidence to suggest that, into the 1990s, the organization of industry in Santa Croce will be "post–Marshallian", that is, less locally confined and less vertically disintegrated. Increasingly, the trend is for tanners to import semi–finished leather, owing to difficulties in obtaining uncured hides and skins. If this practice becomes the norm, more than half of the production cycle will be eliminated from the area, to the detriment of locally based hide importers, subcontractors and chemical treatment firms. There is also a threat of "forward" internationalization of the division of labour. A handful of companies – the oldest and the most powerful – have begun to open distribution outlets overseas along with tanneries, usually through joint ventures, in countries either producing hides and skins or promising growth in the leather goods industries. They have also gone into the business of selling turn–key tanneries for the East European countries, a development which stands to threaten Italian tanneries, including those in Santa Croce, if the finished leather is imported by the domestic leather goods industry.

The risk, then, is that Santa Croce will come to perform only specific tasks in an internationally integrated value–added chain, thus risking a shake out of firms dependent upon tasks no longer performed locally. Through a narrowing of functional competencies, the area's industrial system will become less vertically disintegrated. Such a narrowing runs the risk of undermining the institutional synergy and richness of activity which, hitherto, had secured the area's success as an industrial district. It is also possible that, with functional simplification and the offer of larger and better premises more recently by the local authority in its new Structure Plan, the larger tanners will seek to internalize individual production tasks more than before. Initial signals of such a development include the recommendation by the Associations of Tanners and Subcontractors that transfers to the new industrial zone involve horizontal mergers, stricter loan scrutiny by banks of applications for business start—ups and the grouping of firms into business consortia in order to maximize on firm—level economies of scale in such activities as purchasing and marketing.

If the twin processes of internationalization of the division of labour and vertical integration at the local level become the dominant trend, Santa Croce will lose its current integrity as a self—contained regional economy. But, and this is the point, it will continue to remain a central node within the leather tanning industry. Twenty years of Marshallian growth have made Santa Croce into a nerve centre of artisan ability, product and design innovation and commercial acumen within the international, fashion—oriented, leather goods *filière*. This unrivalled expertise will guarantee its survival as a centre of design and commercial excellence in the global market for tanned leather, even if the craft activities are reduced or internalized.

II. STELLA IN NAPLES: SPECIALIZATION WITHOUT GROWTH[2]

Stella, a closely-knit community in the heart of old Naples, is an unusual district where high levels of poverty and unemployment co-exist with a bustling, and often illegal, small-firm economy. What makes the area unusual, in the context of other urban areas in the

South, is its high level of artisanal specialization in a particular industry. Stella specializes in the footwear industry, especially at the middle and upper end of the market for quality shoes: a specialization which dates back to the area's reputation for hand-made leather gloves for the Neapolitan aristocracy during the eighteenth and nineteenth centuries. Today, the area boasts the presence of such a well-known brand name as Mario Valentino and its vast network of subcontractors who fashion high-quality shoes and bags from the leather which the company provides them. In more recent years, the area has also seen the growth of numerous sweatshops which employ cheap and deskilled youth and female labour to produce poor- quality shoes for low-income markets in the South as well as the Middle East and North Africa. In between the subcontractors and the sweatshops, however, there exists a large number of independent craft-based firms whose medium-to-high quality hand-finished shoes find their way to buyers in the national and European markets.

Many of the characteristics of these 5 to 25-person craft firms are similar to those which appear to have made the Third Italy industrial districts so successful. The owners are master craftsmen capable of turning, in no time, designs copied from magazines and trade fairs into good quality shoes. Through its polyvalent workers, multipurpose tools and rule-of-thumb management and organizational practices, the production process can respond rapidly to changing market signals. The use of family labour or other known members of the community permits both wage and deployment flexibilities, while the lack of job opportunities and the illegality of the firm allows further cash savings, respectively, on salaries and tax and social security contributions. Agglomeration and produce specialization attracts buyers, and to some extent, sellers of raw materials and machinery. This also makes Stella a training ground for learning appropriate skills, a seed-bed for innovation, and a source not only of skilled labour, but also, thanks to strong kinship ties, of a dependable and compliant workforce.

Stella is not, however, an industrial district. The most obvious difference is that the majority of the craft firms, despite their artisanal excellence, are constantly teetering on the edge of closure. For them, business is about survival rather than growth, and this is because of a number of problems which include: market access and expansion difficulties; erratic or poor-paying contracts from the principal clients; lack of financial and marketing expertise; inadequate funds and poor creditworthiness; and poor access to business services. These firms are not at the centre of a virtuous circle of self-sustaining local economic development, as are the clusters of specialist small firms in the Third Italy.

Stella's specialist shoe producers do not constitute a locally networked economic system, and it is this key difference (from the Marshallian industrial district) which prevents both the individual firms and the locality from developing. The firms, despite their agglomeration, are isolated from each other and are almost entirely dependent upon their own resources for their survival. With the exception of sole manufacture and a fairly extensive reliance upon homeworking, the production process is not vertically disintegrated. There is no division of tasks among firms, and consequently, no economies of scale through specialization, no exchange of ideas, information or goods, and no potential for spin-offs and new start-ups through further vertical disintegration. There is no local pool of appropriate intermediate goods and specialized services and so the small firms suffer from all the diseconomies and elevated transactional costs associated with vertical integration when it occurs in small-scale entrepreneurship. While the firms of the industrial district are in many ways like the departments of a corporation, the artisans of Stella are forced into carrying out the tasks of the whole corporation internally, but without any scale advantages or resources.

This problem of very high production and management costs resulting from vertical integration is compounded by the absence of any form of collective or institutional (private or public) provision of good quality subsidized premises, infrastructure and business services. The firms have none of the financial, technical, marketing, infrastructural and advisory support that has played a crucial role in helping small firms develop in the most successful Third Italy industrial districts (Brusco, 1989). This is not because of the illegality of the firms, but because of the pure and simple absence of a specialized business services sector and a competent or willing public sector in Naples. As in the Third Italy, the strength of the small firms lies in their craft ability, but not their financial, marketing or organizational skills. Consequently, the absence of local institutional support badly penalizes them.

The final difference of vital importance between Stella and the systemic character of contemporary industrial districts is the absence of a collective social and political subculture which binds together entrepreneurs, workers, families and institutions such as trade unions, the local authorities and the chamber of commerce, around a common set of local economic and social aspirations. This very rare populist subculture appears to have played a critical role in Tuscany, Emilia Romagna and the Veneto (Trigilia, 1986). Though Stella is not an atomized or socially fragmented area of the sort that is common in advanced capitalist economies, its lay-catholic traditions, strong family and kinship ties, and social solidarity (notably in the face of hardship) do not extend so far as to allow the development of a communitarian or cooperative business culture. Life is too difficult and opportunities too rare to enable a dismantling of the economic individualism, competitiveness and secrecy which is necessary for survival in a context of poverty. The penalty, however, is that the possibility of developing an open informational, cultural and institutional network, which seems to be central for generating a system of collectivized growth, is ruled out.

III. CONCLUSION: FROM INFORMAL ECONOMY TO INDUSTRIAL DISTRICT?

Like other examples of rural industrialization based on consolidated, product specialist small-firm networks (e.g. Carpi and

Prato in Italy, Oyonnax in France, Sakaki in Japan, the Canton Jura in Switzerland), Santa Croce is a typical Marshallian industrial district. Its success as a self-reliant local economy draws upon a certain "industrial atmosphere", first discussed by Alfred Marshall in the context of nineteenth century English industrial districts such as Sheffield (cutlery) and the Lancashire textile areas. According to the Marshallian definition, the distinctive feature of an industrial district is that it is an integrated system of local entrepreneurial, institutional and social interdependencies, that is, a collectivity of dense linkages between individual actors. An industrial district is much more than the simple agglomeration of small firms in a related industry which draw upon flexible work practices, informal market arrangements and kinship ties to earn a living.

Marshall's notion of a local "industrial atmosphere" has been rediscovered (Becattini, 1990; Bellandi, 1989) with regard to a number of area-wide or systemic features which guarantee economic rewards to individual firms and, more importantly, ensure a process of self-sustaining economic development. Four features, in particular, stand out. One is product specialization. This does not occur at the level of the individual firm, something which, in the case of the small firm, can often result in a costly degree of vertical integration owing to the difficulty in achieving adequate scale economies in the production of intermediate goods and services. The industrial district, in contrast, is like a large corporation with its walls broken down; it is an integrated system with a detailed division of tasks between specialist producers, each of whom reaps the cost benefits accruing from task-based, rather than product-based, specialization.

A second, and related, feature is the local containment of the division of labour, leading to, as already shown in the case of Santa Croce, local specialization along the entire length of a given value-added chain and related business services. Such local industrial embeddedness is not pre-given or automatic, but rather the outcome of progress towards building up a large enough final market to guarantee a respectable volume of demand to local firms for intermediate goods and services. In the absence of this, there are few incentives for local spin-off and task specialization involving new small firms.

"Industrial atmosphere", however, signifies much more than inter-firm dependence. It represents, above all, the consolidation of an area as a centre of knowledge creation, inventiveness, entrepreneurial capability and information dissemination within a given global industrial *filière* (Amin and Thrift, 1992a). This is the third central feature of industrial districts. To be sure, this high innovation capability rarely amounts to excellence, in the craft areas, in development and application of advanced technologies. Marshallian industrial districts, in the main, derive their competitive strengths from the use of flexible, multi-purpose, technologies (which could be "traditional" or electronic), craft ability and product adaptability (rather than generation of new products). Thus, beyond the attributes of individual entrepreneurs, industrial districts act like a collective brain; the product of years of experience and know-how pulsing through every channel of the local economic system (firms, institutions, households, etc), and thereby enabling the creation, and dissemination of new "stories" innovation and knowledge on a generalized basis. This capability is, as it were, in the "air" and in the "blood" of the inhabitants of an industrial district, transmitted on the basis of inter-generational continuity and face-to-face contact. In possessing such a diffuse innovation capability, Marshallian industrial districts are able to assimilate and transmit new industrial "stories" across the entire system.

It is the collective aspect of knowledge creation and diffusion, which is the hallmark of the Marshallian industrial district. What contributes to the consolidation of an industrial atmosphere of socialization, sociability, studied trust (Sabel, 1992; Lorenz, 1990) and cooperation is not at all clear. Some of the factors, however, might include the following: economic interdependence; a common industrial purpose; binding cultural norms and values which sanction against rogue behaviour and system-threatening inter-firm conflict or the excessive pursuit of self-interest; the experience of sharing certain common services and resources; a tradition of collective representation or institutionalization of sectional interests; and the presence of public institutions working on behalf of the greater collectivity (e.g. access to training colleges, trade fairs, industrial estates, infrastructure, etc.).

The fourth feature of Marshallian industrial districts is the presence of a certain "institutional thickness" (Amin and Thrift, 1992b), defined as an elaborate network of institutions whose task is to represent, mediate conflicts and collaborate with each other. At the simplest level, "institutional thickness" amounts to strong institutional presence, that is, a plethora of institutions of different kinds (e.g. chambers of commerce, innovation centres, financial institutions, training agencies, trade associations, unions, local authorities, government agencies, marketing boards, etc.) which are highly proactive and provide a basis for widespread trust in collective representation. Above this level, industrial districts exhibit a high degree of interaction among the institutions (contact, cooperation, information exchange), to yield a kind of system-wide, "corporatist" sense of common enterprise, which serves to mediate inter-institutional conflicts, forge a collective culture, and provide strong representation of local interests in the wider political economy.

The above four features - inter-firm dependence, structures of sociability, "local industrial atmosphere" and "institutional thickness" - are the essence of a Marshallian industrial district. They constitute the bedrock of economic success, in providing a rich tapestry of inputs, services and external economies of agglomeration in support of individual entrepreneurship.

The key question for policy-makers and policy analysts, then, is whether informal economies like Stella in Naples, of which there is an abundance in the developing and newly industrialized countries, can become Marshallian industrial districts. The presence of many common characteristics suggests that the possibility cannot be lightly dismissed. Both types of economy have clusters of small firms in the same industry, strong artisan traditions, similar technologies, an embedded knowledge-base and ability to invent and adapt, informal market arrangements, strong family and kinship ties, and a marked sense of local identification. But, as the case study of Stella has demonstrated, these informal economy characteristics on their own are not a guarantor for economic success, but often only a means of survival in a context of limited economic opportunity.

Research on the wealthier, Marshallian areas tends to suggest that it is the element of inter-firm cooperation, structures of sociability, local "industrial atmosphere" and "institutional thickness" which poorer informal economies need to develop so that individual entrepreneurship can draw upon an elaborate system of local support. The very recognition of this observation has two important policy implications. First, it helps to identify the broad areas in which policy action is desirable; the suggestion being that is not factors affecting individual entrepreneurial capability which require attention, but those which support the firm. Thus, for instance, it is efforts to provide real, industry-specific services to firms (Brusco, 1989; Cooke and Morgan, 1991), to foster task specialization and inter-firm cooperation, to advertise the products of an area (e.g. via trade missions or trade fairs), to secure long-term reproduction of sector-specific skills, which are likely to be of greater benefit than efforts to improve, for example, the technological expertise and awareness of entrepreneurs, their physical location and premises, their management skills and so on. In other words, what is required is not an upgrading of firm-specific attributes, but of the milieu underpinning entrepreneurship. Support should be provided to the extent that externalities can be maximized in order to reduce the cost burden on individual firms resulting from too high a level of vertical integration. Small firms in informal economy context are isolated and forced to rely on their own resources, and this is a major reason for their inability to prosper.

The second policy implication to emerge from a recognition of the four key Marshallian attributes is that coordinated action is required across a spectrum of factors, building up to the construction of systemic support for economic activity, along and across value-added chains. In Marshallian industrial districts, the firms draw upon the local milieu for finance, ideas, intermediate goods, services, markets, skills, information, and so on. It is the simultaneous availability of a composite number of factors which is most striking, the implication being that policy support in less-favoured areas needs to avoid single-factor based solutions.

Whether, however, in reality, it is possible for areas like Stella to achieve Marshallian status through public policy intervention is quite another matter. The earlier discussion on the salience of cooperation, inter-dependence "industrial atmosphere" and "institutional thickness" implies that this might not be easy to achieve. At best, it is possible to envisage policy solutions designed to promote task specialization among firms (e.g. via incentives to promote firm formation in missing areas of specialization). However, the effectiveness of policy-led action in the remaining three areas is questionable.

Turning to the question of "institutional thickness", a distinguishing weakness of informal economies is the absence of efficiently-run, pro-active public institutions working together to provide support for the wider economic collectivity. Such economies are notorious for the absence of efficiently-run institutions or other forms of professional representation. They may be narrowly sectarian and overtly antagonistic towards representative authorities. Often, they tend to work as a coalition of elites which fail to represent the wider collectivity. Institutional "thinness", sectarianism and elitism are typical of income-scarce and opportunity-scarce economic contexts. In such contexts, the construction of Marshallian "institutional thickness" is likely to be strongly resisted because it stands to challenge the power and authority of existing elite institutions which flourish in a context of limited opportunities. Even if such resistance can be overcome, the build-up of multiple institutions of representation and the development of a consensus cutting across them is a long and laborious process, likely to test the good intentions of the lengthiest of policy designs.

Even more acute is the difficulty of generating an "industrial atmosphere" which pervades a local economy and the web of sociability. Though some argue that cultures of cooperation are not innate to communities, but rather the product of material interdependencies between individuals or historically demonstrated benefits arising from cooperation (Sabel, 1992), the problem still remains: it is nearly impossible to construct common goals and sociability in contexts dominated by the pursuit of self-interest and individualism as a basic condition of survival. First, the enlargement of rules of "trust" and cooperation to include the wider collectivity is an objective which requires the replacement of embedded cultural norms and rules of behaviour, a process which takes an enormously long time to achieve and one also likely to be easily thwarted along the way. Secondly, sociability is an outcome which, if anything, tends to grow organically out of communities, and usually as a result of the emergence, for one reason or another, of mergers or new forms of collaboration between entrepreneurs and between different institutions of representation. To achieve this by policy dictate or overnight institution-building is an impossible dream.

In the final analysis, then, the transition from informal economy to Marshallian industrial district, despite the existence of similarities between the two types of economic system, may well prove to be an elusive policy goal.

REFERENCES

Amin, A. (1989), "Specialisation without growth: small footwear firms in Naples", Goodman, E., Bamford, J. and P. Saynor (eds.) *Small Firms and Industrial Districts in Italy*, Routledge, London.

Amin, A. and K. Robins (1990), "The re-emergence of regional economies? The mythical geography of flexible specialisation", *Society and Space*, 8, 7-34.

Amin, A. and N. Thrift (1992a), "Neo-Marshallian nodes in global networks", *International Journal of Urban and Regional Research*, 16, 4, forthcoming.

Amin, A. and N. Thrift (1992b), "Living in the global", *mimeo*, Centre for Urban and Regional Development Studies, University of Newcastle-upon-Tyne.

Becattini, G. (1990), "The Marshallian industrial district as a socio-economic notion", Pyke, F. and G. Becattini (eds.) *Industrial Districts and Inter-firm Cooperation in Italy*, ILO, Geneva.

Bellandi, M. (1989), "The industrial district in Marshall", Goodman, E., Bamford, J., and P. Saynor (eds.), *Small Firms and Industrial Districts in Italy*, Routledge, London.

Brusco, S. (1989), "A policy for industrial districts", Goodman, E., Bamford, J., and P. Saynor (eds.) *Small Firms and Industrial Districts in Italy*, Routledge, London.

Cooke, P. and K. Morgan (1991), "The network paradigm: new departures in corporate and regional development", Report Number 8, Regional Industrial Research, Cardiff University.

IDS (1987), Cyprus Industrial Strategy: Report for UNDP/UNIDO, Institute of Development Studies, Brighton.

IDS (1991), A Strategy for Industrial Restructuring in the Dominican Republic: Report for UNDP, Institute of Development Studies, Brighton.

Lorenz, E.H. (1990), "Trust, community and flexibility: toward a theory of industrial districts", *mimeo*, University of Notre Dame.

Murray, R. (1990), "Flexible specialisation in small island economies: the case of Cyprus", *mimeo*, Institute of Development Studies, Brighton.

Sabel, C.F. (1992), "Studied trust: building new forms of cooperation in a volatile economy", Discussion Paper, Science Center, Berlin.

Schmitz, H. (1989), "Flexible specialisation - a new paradigm for small scale industrialisation?", Discussion Paper 261, Institute of Development Studies, Brighton.

Storper, M. (1990), "Industrialisation and the regional question in the third world: lessons of post-imperialism; prospects of post-Fordism?", *International Journal of Urban and Regional Research*, 14, 3, 423-444.

Trigilia, C. (1986), "Small firm development and political subcultures in Italy", *European Sociological Review*, vol.2: 161-75.

NOTES

1.   This section is taken from Amin and Thrift (1992a), which draws upon evidence from Santa Croce and the City of London to theorize on the status of such areas as Marshallian nodes in global industrial networks.

2.   This section summarizes the results of a field survey conducted in Naples in the mid-1980s and reported more fully in Amin (1989).

DECENTRALIZED INDUSTRIAL CREATIVITY IN DYNAMIC INDUSTRIAL DISTRICTS

Marco Bellandi [*]

INTRODUCTION

Small firms are not a homogeneous phenomenon. In the Italian case, three models of small firms have been identified: first, the model of the traditional artisan firms; secondly, the model of the dependent firms, included within the subcontracting networks of large firms; thirdly, the model of the industrial district, characterized by a local system of specialized forms, rooted in a local network of social norms and institutions, not dependent on external hierarchies, but open to exchanges.[1]

In Italy and abroad, the third model has attracted growing interest. The model of the industrial district and the pertinent facts have allowed an opportunity to reflect at a microeconomic level, on the possibility of variety and development from below, as opposed to the dominance of the top-down model based on large internal and external hierarchies.[2] A key issue is the assessment of the endogenous innovation capacities of the industrial districts.[3] The present note offers some reflections on this issue, starting from the definition of the potentialities for innovation, which depend on the mobilization of the energies, ingenuity and creativity of the large groups of people involved in product processing and use.

[*] Department of Economics, University of Florence, Italy.

I. DECENTRALIZED INDUSTRIAL CREATIVITY: DEFINITION

Within the "top-down" model, specialized research and development (R&D) divisions are seen as the only places where industrial creativity is systematically practised and innovation is systematically produced; this is then consistent with the vision that, in modern industry, few people think while the majority only executes. Some observations on how innovation processes work within identified industrial districts suggest a not so marginal role for industrial creativity "from below". A similar role is also attached to the latter in other contexts, e.g., the Japanese paradigm of the big firm, as defined by Masahiko Aoki.[4] In what follows, advantage will be taken of some concepts, like those of "learning-by-doing" and "decomposability in social systems", and a conceptual framework will be put forward on the conditions for creativity from below. This framework will then be applied to the specific model of the Marshallian Industrial District (MID).

According to Rosenberg, there are three types of learning which may contribute to productivity growth: the first is R&D, that is, the specialized arrangement of specific facilities and scientific skills for the production of new economically useful knowledge; the second type is "learning-by-doing", that is the development of knowledge or skills for a productive process as a by-product of practising that process; the last type is "learning-by-using", that is the development of knowledge regarding a product (improvements, etc.) which is linked to the use of that product.[5] "Learning-by-doing" or "learning-by-using" do not necessarily have a creative content. For example, there is no creativity at all (in learning) when a worker "learns" to perform a given productive action with a predetermined standard of accuracy and speed; neither can creativity be inferred when the practice of doing or using is only a means by which R&D receives feedback on the working of planned processes and products.[6]

In some cases, however, learning may have a creative content, more or less interdependent with R&D: for example, when the information which workers transmit to R&D is enriched by suggestions; or when new ideas spring directly from productive practice, and their development is sustained by technical education and/or by circulation and comparison of ideas among producers,[7] with the possible support of R&D. It is proposed to describe these opportunities collectively using the term Decentralized Industrial Creativity (DIC), with "decentralized" denoting that the sources of new knowledge are not concentrated in specialized divisions with a few isolated scientists, but also distributed among the crowd of producers; and "industrial" to exclude the cases of creativity associated with the activity of isolated craftsmen.

II. CONDITIONS FOR MANIFESTATION OF DIC

The building block of DIC is practical knowledge.[8] In comparison with formal knowledge, practical knowledge is less systematic in method and content, less articulated and thus harder to transmit in formal and general terms. Conversely, formal knowledge "is removed, in both time and space, from the experiences and the events it describes".[9] Not all the relevant circumstances of production and product-using can be understood by means of accepted systematic methods, nor communicated in formal and general terms (for example, by means of textbooks, blueprints, written instructions, etc.). Certain circumstances can be more effectively and more economically grasped by producers and accumulated as practical knowledge.

That part of practical knowledge which is not encompassed in formal knowledge may have economic value in itself; this is the specific advantage of DIC over separate R&D.[10] The producers may directly draw data from practical knowledge and combine them with personal endowments of imagination, technical education, other experience, etc. The combination may bring about new viewpoints and allow new hints, that is, new approaches to the process of production and use of products. Specialization allows for the identification of distinctive approaches. But an excessive degree of specialization of labour limits the identification of meaningful and original approaches which suggests that Tayloristic-like organizations are at odds with DIC.

Three other important conditions that reinforce the learning and creative effects of specialized practical knowledge are the coexistence of several approaches to problem solving, their mutual interactions, and the decomposability of the production process. First of all, "the coexistence of different approaches creates the condition for a number of challenges in the formulation of any given problem".[11] But coexistence can be useful only in so far as the different approaches and the related knowledge and personal endowments do interact. Finally, the decomposability of a production process into partially autonomous production components makes room for single events of DIC, within a single component, even when the overall process is highly complex.[12] Then, those events may extend to other parts of the process, for example, through tensions and disequilibrium effects which concentrate creative energies and mutual interactions.[13]

When coexistence, mutual interaction and decomposability contribute effectively to creating a large body of practical knowledge not encompassed in formal knowledge, the stage is set for systematic manifestations of DIC. Like R&D, the systemic character of DIC denotes a regular promotion of innovation, even if, of course, no individual manifestation of creativity can be forecast. Unlike R&D, however, this systemic character does not extend to the quality of innovation. DIC's results have in themselves a bent for lack of generality, for variation and differentiation. Finally, while single manifestations of DIC have, in general, an incremental character, their accumulation has possible major effects on economic performance.

III. THE INDUSTRIAL DISTRICT

The foregoing framework can be applied and some general relations drawn between DIC and a specific model of industrial district proposed by Giacomo Becattini,[14] i.e. a "socio-economic entity" which is characterized by the "active coexistence" of an open community of people and a segmented and specialized population of firms. The community of people and the population of firms live in the same geographical area. The population of firms is specialized in the sense that there is a principal industry which dominates the economy of the district. The segmentation means that different phases of the principal industry, and eventually of the auxiliary and complementary industries, are divided among the firms, each of which specializes in one industry and in one or a few phases.

Some studies have identified almost 60 local systems in Italy which seem to approximate this model.[15] The principal industries of these districts are largely characterized by the production of customized, differentiated, highly styled goods, where centralized R&D has usually large shortcomings. The segmentation of the population of the firms is usually interrelated with the (quasi)-decomposability of the production processes carried out in the district. Following Becattini's terminology, I will refer to this specific model as the Marshallian Industrial District, or briefly as the MID.

IV. DECENTRALIZED INDUSTRIAL CREATIVITY WITHIN THE MARSHALLIAN INDUSTRIAL DISTRICT: FEASIBILITY

A first remark concerning DIC within MID relates to the segmented nature of the population of firms. The MID characteristic translates into a large population of entrepreneurs, more or less small and independent. As the small entrepreneur is not separated from practical knowledge concerning production processes and use of products, he can take advantage of new ideas which are suggested by, and/or emerge from, his collaboration with skilled employees.

The presence of skilled workers within the MID is sustained by both supply and demand factors. On the supply side, the overlapping of community and industry makes the formation of a local skilled workforce easier. Similarly, the production of customized and highly styled goods which prevails in these districts raises demand for a skilled workforce. Furthermore, the existence within the district of a large number of specialized firms, which supply a range of intermediate goods and services related to a given set of activities, facilitates the formation of spin-off firms, which absorb creative energies not accommodated within the incumbent firms.

At first sight, the predominance of a single industry within a district would appear to restrict severely the possibility of different approaches, practical knowledge and personal endowments. However, as different phases of the principal industry are divided among different firms, the presence of a principal industry is still consistent with the coexistence of subsidiary, complementary and secondary industries within the same district. This coexistence implies a differentiation of the practical knowledge prevalent among the firms which, in turn, promotes a differentiation of approaches.

The feasibility of interaction among the different approaches is directly sustained by three important defining properties of the MID: the geographical proximity of the population of firms; its segmentation; and the overlapping of daily life and production activities. Generally speaking, face-to-face contacts are an effective means for the communication of practical knowledge and for the interaction of approaches. Proximity facilitates a frequent and not strictly planned realization of contacts.[16] Division of labour among firms demands coordination, which constitutes the general context for the realization of contacts. Finally, the socio-economic overlapping promotes the formation of local traditions and standards of communication regarding the core production processes within each district.[17]

V. INCENTIVES FOR DECENTRALIZED INDUSTRIAL ACTIVITY

The characteristics of MID act also as incentives for DIC. Innovation, in general, and DIC, in particular, are supported, on the one hand, by market conditions of active competition within the industry, and, on the other, by the social acceptance of rules restricting the most harmful forms of competition. Two defining properties of the MID are consistent with the presence of healthy competition: first, the localization of an industry or a few industries, to which a population of several firms contributes, may bring about a high potential for competition by means of largely (if not perfectly) substitute products; secondly, proximity helps in the detection of different options for buyers.

The overlapping of industry and community supports the formation of rules concerning typical transactions. If - and the emphasis is on the "if" - rules restricting competition are rightly directed towards growth, and if competition within the rules is lively, the incentives for mobilizing the creative energies of individuals within the district are strong. When such rules are set and accepted, their enforcement is sustained by face-to-face contacts (which facilitate a quick assessment of moral attitudes), by the burden of social penalty (like exclusion from the community), and by the social reward for a well-merited success. A final question concerns the compatibility of individual incentives with those for cooperation in creative processes. I skip here this question, which in any case presents various solutions.[18]

VI. EXAMPLES

Among the specific manifestations of DIC within the MID, the following are of particular relevance. The first case concerns the process of diffusion of innovation. In this case, proximity works through the support of inter-firm mobility of workers, bandwagon effects and, more generally, through the intensification of informal contacts. Imitation resulting from the diffusion of innovation, when coupled with specific practical knowledge and differentiated market opportunities, acts as a creative stimulus, which may bring about new variations.[19]

A second case concerning DIC and the circulation of ideas has to do with the interplay between DIC and formal R&D. This may take different forms: first, local public and private joint ventures for the promotion of large research projects; secondly, the results of private R&D in some complementary industry, for example, by firms making specialized machinery for the principal industry of the district, are directly tested and adapted within some subset of the firms of the district; finally, there can be indirect exchanges of ideas between manufacturers through the activity of local suppliers of knowledge services, for example, software houses.

A third case is connected with the interplay between local final-product firms and local subcontractors in product development. Quite often this interplay is a characteristic of the transactions in the Italian industrial districts. Brusco says: "In the industrial district, the (final)-firm normally has a rather vague idea of what it wants. Its technical offices, which often coincide with the manager, define the new product along general lines....The definitive plan is perfected in talks between management and the most skilled workers, and especially between management and subcontractors...".[20]

VII. DYNAMIC INDUSTRIAL DISTRICTS

The previous discussion has supported the assertion that the MID, as an idealized form of some important types of local systems of small firms, presents properties which are consistent with the regular working of DIC.

However, consistency does not mean necessity. A number of difficulties may arise which can constrain and even bring to a halt

DIC within an industrial district. The previous reflections may help us to assess and classify these difficulties. An industrial district is truly dynamic and has growth potential when it has the capacity to cope systematically with such difficulties. Let me conclude by referring to a specific feature that has characterized dynamic industrial districts. This is a rich activity of institution-making by both private and public agents who aim through organized collective action to overcome the systemic effects of broad internal and external changes. In turn, institution-making is supported by the exercise of DIC, since the practice of mutual collaboration in creative events is in itself an act of participation. The latter, however, is at odds with any rigid and centralized planning. Thus, industrial policy at the local level[21] has to be adapted to differentiated and changing sets of interests. It has to be intended as a purposive and skilled contribution to the institution-making activity of the local agents. When either the propensity to institution-making or the supporting political culture is lacking in an industrial district, the basic conditions which sustain DIC are easily impaired, and the life-expectancy of such a district is relatively short.

REFERENCES

Aoki, M., 1988, *Information, Incentives and Bargaining in the Japanese Economy*, Cambridge University Press, Cambridge.

Amin, A. and M. Dietrich, 1991, "From hierarchy to 'hierarchy': the dynamics of contemporary corporate restructuring in Europe", in A. Amin and M. Dietrich (eds.), *Towards a New Europe*, Edward Elgar.

Becattini, G., 1990, "The industrial district as a creative milieu", in G. Benko and M. Dunford (eds.), *Industrial Change and Regional Development*, Belhaven Press, London.

Bellandi, G., 1991, "The industrial district in Marshall", in E. Goodman and J. Bamford with P. Saynor (eds.), *Small Firms and Industrial Districts in Italy*, Routledge, London.

Bellandi, G., 1992, "The incentives to decentralized industrial creativity in local system of small firms", in *Revue d'économie industrielle*, no. 59, 1992.

Bianchi, P. and N. Bellini, 1991, "Public policies for local networks of innovators" in *Research Policy*, no. 4.

Brusco, S., 1986, "Small firms and industrial districts: the experience of Italy", in D. Keeble and E. Wever (eds.), *New Firms and Regional Development*, Croom Helm, London.

Brusco, S., 1991, "The idea of the industrial district: its genesis", in F. Pike, G. Becattini, W. Sengerberger (eds.), *Industrial Districts and Inter-firms Cooperation in Italy*, International Institute of Labour Studies, Geneva.

Cohendet, P., P. Llerena, and A. Sorge, 1992, "Technological diversity and coherence in Europe: an analytical overview", in *Revue d'économie industrielle*, no. 59.

Cowling, K., 1990, "A new industrial strategy", in *International Journal of Industrial Organization*, no. 8.

Dei Ottati, G., 1991, "The economic bases of diffuse industrialization" in *International Studies of Management and Organization*, vol. 21, no.1, pp.53-77.

Dijk, M.P. van, 1992, "The interrelation between industrial districts and technological capabilities development", mimeo, 1992.

Garofoli, G., 1991, "Local networks, innovation and policy in Italian industrial districts", in E.M. Bergman, G. Mayer and F. Todtling (eds.), *Regions Reconsidered*, Mansell, London.

Marshall, A., 1927, "Industry and Trade", Macmillan, London (1st edn., 1919).

Marshall, A., 1986, *Principles of Economics*, reprint from the 8th edn., Macmillan, London (1st edn., 1890).

Nelson, R., 1980, "Production sets, technological knowledge and R&D: Fragile and overworked constructs for analysis of productivity growth", in *American Economic Review*, vol. 70, May, pp.62-67.

Nelson, R. and S. Winter, 1982, *An Evolutionary Theory of the Firm*, Macmillan, London.

Rosenberg, N., 1982, *Inside the Black Box: Technology and Economics*, Cambridge University Press, Cambridge.

Russo, M., 1989, "Technical change and the industrial district: the role of inter-firm relations in the growth and transformation of ceramic tile production in Italy", in E. Goodman and J. Bamford with P. Saynor (eds.), *Small Firms and Industrial Districts in Italy*, Routledge, London.

Sabel, Ch., 1982, *Work and Politics*, Harvard University Press, Cambridge, Mass.

Sforzi, F., 1990, "The quantitative importance of Marshallian industrial districts in the Italian economy", in F. Pike, G. Becattini, W. Sengerberger (eds.), *Industrial Districts and Inter-firm Cooperation in Italy*, International Institute for Labour Studies, Geneva.

Simon, H.E., 1981, *The Sciences of the Artificial*, MIT Press, Cambridge, Mass. (1st edn., 1969).

Stohr, W.B., 1991, "On the theory and practice of local development in Europe", in W.B. Stohr (ed.), *Social Relations and Spatial Structures*, Macmillan, London.

Trigilia, C., 1990, "Work and politics in the Third Italy's industrial districts", in F. Pike, G. Becattini, W. Sengerberger (eds.) Industrial *Districts and Inter-firms Cooperation in Italy*, International Institute for Labour Studies, Geneva.2

NOTES

1. Brusco (1986).

2. On the definition of industrial variety (or technological diversity), see Cohendet, Llerena & Sorge (1992); on the definition of development from below, see Stohr (1991); on the concept of "internal and external hierarchies", see Amin and Dietrich (1991) and Cowling (1991).

3. Van Dijk, 1992, para. 4.7.

4. According to Aoki (1988), the weight assigned to local information in the Japanese firm is an important factor in the competitive strength of this form of big firm.

5. Rosenberg (1982, p.122).

6. Obviously, these cases are prevalent when the organization of work is dominated by mass-production and bureaucratic, top-down relations.

7. The generic term "producer" distinguishes here those in charge of the productive process or of the use of products from the researchers employed in separate R&D divisions.

8. Practice is the prerequisite of practical knowledge. Practice permits a broad sensorial contact with reality; and the sensorial data can be registered consciously and unconsciously by the agent in his/her routines of action and thought. This type of routine constitutes practical knowledge. See, for example, Nelson & Winter (1982).

9. Thrift (1985).

10. R&D is, in itself, a separate activity, whose approach to economic events is based on formal knowledge. See Nelson (1980, p.67).

11. Becattini (1991), p.108).

12. According to Simon (1981, pp.209-229), a general condition which facilitates copying with the complexity of a system is the eventual decomposing of the system itself into quasi-autonomous components.

13. Such types of effects could be subsumed within various concepts referred to by some economists and historians as effective sequences, technological convergences, serendipity, creative symbiosis, etc.

14. Becattini (1990).

15. Sforzi (1990) has reported the existence of several industrial districts in Italy which show, according to an analysis of census data (years 1971 and 1981), a well-defined principal industry. According to Porter (1990, pp.155, 443), a large part of Italy's industries with an international competitive advantage are centred in local clusters; the list of these clusters includes a good subset of the industrial districts reported by Sforzi.

16. Examples of informal contacts are the exchanges of ideas within social institutions, like families, clubs, and so on.

17. Alfred Marshall (1927, p.287) referred to effects like these in coining the term "industrial atmosphere". For the interplay of market and community within industrial districts, see Bianchi & Bellini (1991), Dei Ottati (1991), Trigilia (1990).

18. A set of related conditions which defines a possible solution is as follows: (a) the creative outcome is constituted by a stream of incremental innovations, variations, adjustments; (b) no strategic information leaks out from the cooperative efforts; (c) there is a

good number of agents who can be sequentially involved in the process, and they have some similar or connected exigencies; (d) reiterated opportunistic behaviour is punished. See Bellandi (1992).

19. Alfred Marshall (1986, p.227) discussing processes of this kind wrote: "If one man starts a new idea, it is taken up by others and combined with suggestions of their own; and thus it becomes the source of further ideas". See Bellandi (1989) for a review of Marshall's thoughts on this matter.

20. Brusco (1986, p.188). See also Russo (1989) and Sabel (1982, p.222).

21. Brusco (1991), Cowling (1990, p.182).

PART TWO

INDUSTRIAL DISTRICTS, INTER-FIRM COOPERATION AND ENDOGENOUS TECHNOLOGICAL DEVELOPMENT: THE EXPERIENCE OF DEVELOPED COUNTRIES [1]

Bjørn T. Asheim[*]

INTRODUCTION

Technological capabilities are perhaps the single most important differentiating factor concerning the development and future prospects of industrial districts. However, technological capability cannot be regarded as a prerequisite for the emergence of industrial districts. The rationale for industrial districts rests on the creation of "external economies of scale" (i.e. economies that are external to the firm but internal to the area) for groups of small firms as a competitive alternative to the "internal economies of scale" of big companies. This is achieved by inter-firm cooperation resulting from functional specialization of the production process within networks of small firms, and by the localization of these firms in particular localities (i.e. industrial districts).

The economies of product specialization and externalization through subcontracting to small, specialized firms within industrial districts do not necessarily involve any particular degree of technological capability as they can be achieved in many different ways (i.e. from the practice of "putting-out" (Lazerson, 1993) to the use of advanced, computerized production equipment (Storper 1992)). Thus, one can observe industrial districts with different levels of development. Brusco confirms this, in describing industrial

---

[*] Department of Human Geography, School of Cultural and Social Studies, University of Oslo, Norway.

districts in the Third Italy, by saying that "some are more developed and capable of innovations, others are more backward, with low wages, without steady relations with foreign markets and exposed to the competition of the newly industrialized countries" (Brusco 1986, 195).

The present paper uses existing literature on industrial districts in developed countries to analyze the role of inter-firm cooperation for endogenous technological development. Section I first argues for a definition that restricts the use of the term to specific types of agglomerates of small and medium enterprises. Industrial districts are then further distinguished in terms of their capabilities for endogenous technological development and the role played by policy intervention in promoting these capabilities. Section II sets up the analytical framework for discussing the role of inter-firm linkages in development of technological capabilities. Section III provides empirical illustrations from developed countries. Section IV summarizes the growth problems and prospects of industrial districts in developed countries and, finally, section V draws some conclusions concerning policy in this area.

I. INDUSTRIAL DISTRICTS AND TECHNOLOGICAL CHANGE

A. Towards a definition of industrial districts

An "industrial district" is "essentially a territorial system of small- and medium-sized firms" (Goodman 1989, 21), which more precisely could be described as a network of small- and medium-sized firms within geographically defined (local) production systems. According to Brusco "what is relevant is no longer the characteristics of one single firm, but the characteristics of the industrial district of which the small firm is a part" (Brusco 1986, 187).

Looking more systematically at the structural characteristics of industrial districts, they could be summarized in the following way (Garofoli 1991a, 95):

(a) An extensive division of labour between firms in the local production system, which represents the basis for a close network of intra- and inter-sectoral input-output relations;

(b) A strong product specialization at the firm and company level, which limits the production spectrum, stimulates the acquisition of specialized knowledge, facilitates the introduction of new technology, thus leading to an increased independence of the production systems of the district;

(c) The existence of an effective information network at the district level, which guarantees a wide and fast circulation of information about markets, alternative techniques, new raw materials, components and other input goods used in the production process, and also new administrative techniques, which all contribute to convert individual knowledge to collective competence for the district as a whole. These processes are facilitated by geographical proximity which provides good opportunities for frequent "face-to-face" contacts, especially between suppliers and users of means of production and various producer services; and

(d) The high competence level of the workforce, which partly is a result of inter-generational transfer of informal knowledge about labour processes and production techniques, and partly is a result of formal training in technical schools, etc.

1. What constitutes an industrial district?

According to Marshall, industrial districts are constituted by two dimensions. They can be separated analytically: the *functional* dimension of *external economies*, on the one hand, and the *territorial* dimension of *agglomeration economies*, on the other. Of the four structural characteristics described in the previous paragraph, the first two refer to the external economies and the last two to the agglomeration economies. What distinguishes an industrial district from other industrial agglomerations with strong external economies such as the Perrouxian development poles or the Japanese just-in-time production systems is precisely the existence of agglomeration economies. Thus, writers like Scott have misunderstood Marshall's concept of industrial district when they define an industrial district as "a localized network of producers bound together in a social division of labour, in necessary association with a local labour market" (Scott 1992, 266). Apart from the erroneous equation of the notion of external economies with social division of labour, Scott's definition is too broad and analytically imprecise, thus making it difficult to distinguish between qualitatively different territorial production complexes such as, for example, a Perrouxian development pole like the Southern Californian aircraft industry, the (just-in-time) production system of Toyota City and the territorial concentration of small- and medium-sized firms of the Third Italy. To avoid such general concepts, it is necessary to formulate a more specific definition of industrial districts, and to use other concepts to identify different forms of "new industrial spaces".

Another important factor supporting the emphasis on the *territorial* dimension in the definition of industrial districts is the fact that Marshallian industrial districts are characterized by many independent small firms, a factor which ensures that no single big company acts as a centre for strategic decision-making. In contrast, in the "Perrouxian development poles", the "key" or "motor" industries are the large firms which, due to their higher innovative capacity as compared to the smaller firms in the pole, account largely for the higher rate of output growth of the "pole" as compared to the rest of the economy. Thus, once more Scott's definition of industrial districts is in opposition to the Marshallian one, when he argues "that we need to extend any generalized definition of industrial districts to include large production units, and that the latter often play a major part in the initiation, development and growth of industrial districts" (Scott 1992, 266).

The achievement of external economies of scale is not conditioned by a territorial agglomeration of the production system. According to Perroux, it is possible to talk about growth poles in an "abstract economic space", i.e. firms which are linked together with a "key industry" to form an industrial complex. The growth potential and level of economic activity of the growth pole may be intensified by territorial agglomeration (Haraldsen 1988, Perroux 1970).

However, as Haraldsen emphasizes, a *localized* growth pole in what Perroux calls "banal" or "geonomic" space, cannot be seen as a growth pole simply because of the territorial agglomeration of economic activity. Territorial agglomeration of economic activity, in which none of the industries can be characterized as "key industries", cannot be defined as a growth pole, since the agglomeration of economic activity as such is not the driving force behind the growth of the firms (Haraldsen 1988, 47). In this context agglomeration economies are used as a *functional* concept to describe the intensification of the external economies of a production system resulting from the geographical concentration of economic activity. This also represents the conventional use of the concept of agglomeration economies in traditional regional economics (e.g. normally specified as localization and urbanization economies).

By contrast according to Marshall, the external economies are normally obtained through the geographical concentration of economic activity "or, as is commonly said, by the localization of industry" (Marshall 1891, 325). In this case, external economies are considered as "one of the most important factors in explaining the efficiency of the industrial system of a district" (Bellandi 1989, 139) but they do not fully explain the advantages of agglomeration. To accomplish that, Marshall provides us with his particular definition of agglomeration economies.

2. Agglomeration economies and territorial "embeddedness"

In contrast to traditional regional economics, Marshall attaches a more independent role to agglomeration economies as the specific *territorial* aspects of a geographical agglomeration of industrial production. Marshall focuses on traditional socio-cultural factors, which concern the quality of the social milieu of industrial districts, and which only indirectly affect the profits of firms. Among such factors, Marshall emphasizes, in particular: the "mutual knowledge and trust" that reduces transaction costs in the marketplace; the "industrial atmosphere" which facilitates the generation of skills required by the industry; and the effect of both these aspects in promoting innovations and innovation diffusion among small firms within industrial districts.

The "industrial atmosphere" of industrial districts can enhance the potential of small firms to acquire knowledge and skills in order to support the development, adoption and diffusion of innovations. Such processes are strongly conditioned by the spatial proximity and cultural homogeneity of industrial districts. The transactional problem of the diffusion of innovations among competitive firms requires the setting up of formal or informal arrangements allowing innovative cooperation. This may be facilitated through the relatively high degree of trust and consensus among and between firms, employers and workers, often present in an established industrial district (Bellandi 1989).

Referring to Marshall, Bellandi emphasizes that the economies of the districts originate from the thick local texture of interdependencies between the small firms and the local community (Bellandi 1989). Thus, it is necessary to conceive of industrial districts as "a social and economic whole ... . The success of the districts, then, lies not just in the realm of the 'economic'. Broader social and institutional aspects are just as important" (Pyke, Sengenberger, 1990, 2).

What is expressed here is the idea of "embeddedness" as a key analytical concept in understanding the formation as well as the functioning of industrial districts (Granovetter 1985). Harrison points out that "the industrial district model posits a very strong form of the embedding of economic (business) relations into a deeper social fabric, providing a force powerful enough to provide for the reproduction of even so apparently paradoxical a practice as cooperative competition" (Harrison 1991, 34). Fua emphasizes that "the continuity with local history and traditions is doubly valuable. It is something positive in itself, and it is a source of strength in achieving other positive results. Hence the system's merits" (Fua 1983, 376). He concludes by stressing that "in this model, industrialization finds fertile soil in the local (if still latent) supply of entrepreneurial energies, labour and saving, and in the existence of a well-run society with its institutions, its culture and material infrastructures. The success of the model relies on its capacity to combine all the strong points and resources of the existing organization and harness them to modern development" (Fua 1983, 355). According to Harrison, this mode of theorizing is fundamentally different from the one found in conventional regional economics or in any other neoclassical-based agglomeration theory (Harrison 1991). It is precisely this embeddedness in broader socio-cultural factors, originating in a pre-capitalist civil society that is the material basis for Marshall's view of agglomeration economies as the specific *territorial* aspects of geographical agglomeration of economic activity (Asheim 1992a).

B. Agglomeration economies and technological capabilities

According to Piore and Sabel, such agglomeration economies constituting "the fusion of productive activity, in the narrow sense, with the larger life of the community" represent "the common solution" to the problems of "the reconciliation of competition and cooperation" as well as of "the regeneration of resources required by the collectivity but not produced by the individual units of which it is composed" (Piore, Sabel 1984, 275). The development of industrial districts confirms that such "fusion" can solve the first problem, but it is much more doubtful whether it has the potential to solve the second problem, where the question is normally that of the need for permanent innovation and adoption of new technologies.

Indeed, as already pointed out, the "industrial atmosphere" of industrial districts can support the imitation, adaptation and diffusion of innovations among small- and medium-sized firms. In the same way, the presence of trust can bring about the introduction of new technology into industrial districts, since mutual trust - in addition to reducing transaction costs - seems to be crucial for the establishment of non-contractual inter-firm linkages. Becattini conceives of this as a social process of collective self-awareness in which the decision to introduce a new technology, partly owing to the common system of values and attitudes prevailing in the districts, is perceived as "an opportunity to defend an already acquired position" (Becattini 1990, 47). One of the most important channels for information and diffusion of new technology among small- and medium-sized firms is other firms (i.e. epidemic diffusion), thus emphasizing the importance of interaction between firms within formal and informal networks. In this way, technological development within one firm stimulates development in other firms of the industrial district. In addition, such industrial districts in their capacity as innovative milieux can be situated higher up in the central place system than the size of their population would indicate. This increases the chances of firms in these districts to become early adopters in a process of hierarchical diffusion (Asheim 1990). Storper argues that "agglomeration ... facilitates efficient operation of a cooperative production network ... combining the advantages of specialization and flexibility, which are key to technological learning" (Storper 1992, 84, 60). However, it is questionable whether the intentional creation of trust between networking firms, as argued by Lorenz (1990) and Sabel (1992), can be "embedded" in the same way as the original form of "mutual knowledge and trust" found in Marshallian industrial districts.

However, the importance of territorial embedded agglomeration economies in promoting innovations concerns largely *incremental* innovations.[2] This is due to several specific features of the industrial districts:

(a) External economies are normally secured through vertical cooperation, most typically between commissioning and subcontracting firms; this limits the potential for horizontal technological cooperation;

(b) normally there is fierce horizontal competition in strongly competitive markets between firms producing the same products or carrying out the same production functions;

(c) A characteristic of industrial districts is that they are made up of independent small firms with no single big firm acting as a centre for strategic decision-making. The problem, in this respect, is that they lack innovative capacity owing to a shortage of both human and financial resources to build up and support a necessary level of research and development capacity.

Therefore, as Marshall was already aware, agglomeration economies as such do not give any guarantee for the promotion of product and process innovations originating from formal R&D. However, as Marshall also noted, "industrial districts can generate innovations by incremental steps, through a gradual improvement of the final product [i.e. product innovations], of the processes [i.e. process innovations] and of the overall production organization [i.e. organizational innovations] (Bianchi, Giordani 1993, 31). Thus, territorially embedded economies represent important basic conditions and stimulus to *incremental* innovations through informal "learning-by-doing" and "learning-by- using". As Bellandi suggests, such learning, based on practical knowledge (experience) of which specialized practice is a prerequisite, may have significant creative content. Thus, as a result of what Bellandi calls "decentralized industrial creativity" (DIC), the collective potential innovative capacity of small firms in industrial districts is not always inferior to that of large, research-based companies (Bellandi, present volume). It must also be emphasized that even if such incremental innovations individually have no major impact, their combined effect can be extremely important for product design and productivity growth in different branches, especially in relation to the overall economic performance of small- and medium-sized firms.

C. Small firms, industrial districts and technological development

As R&D-oriented units are a marginal phenomenon among small- and medium-sized firms within or outside industrial districts, complex systems of product and process innovations (i.e. *new technological systems*) or breakthroughs in technological development (i.e. changes in the *techno-economic paradigm*), which are primarily the concern of national systems of innovation, very seldom take place within these firms as well as in the industrial districts. As Brusco argues, "industrial districts are slow to adopt new technologies, lack expertise in financial management, have little of the know-how required for basic research, and are unable to produce epoch-making innovations" (Brusco 1992, 196). Similarly, owing to the relatively low level of scientific competence and technological know-how of small- and medium-sized firms within industrial districts, *radical* innovations tend to be diffused more slowly. The collective innovative capacity of industrial districts in the long run, however, can be raised if the original qualities of the social milieu of the districts are supplemented by managerial and technological professional expertise. This will be seen in some of the examples discussed in the following sections.

Therefore, the question of endogenous technological capability-building by small- and medium-sized firms within industrial districts concerns the following:

(a) the development of *incremental* and *radical* product and process innovations, which means that firms inside the districts actually carry out innovations by themselves;

(b) the adoption, adaptation and application of *incremental* and *radical* innovations generated externally; and

(c) the imitation and implementation of *incremental* innovations made by more innovative firms both inside and outside the districts.

Accordingly, firms in industrial districts can be distinguished as those with low or high internal resources and competence with respect to technological capability-development on the basis of their access in the districts to professional competence. Thus, firms which only have command of artisanal competence or informal knowledge acquired through working-life experience will be categorized as firms with *low* internal resources and competence. Firms having command of professional competence through the employment of engineers or other university trained staff, i.e. in possession of "formal knowledge" are considered as firms with a *high* level of internal resources and competence. *Formal* knowledge is made up of codified scientific or engineering knowledge in contrast to *tacit* knowledge, which is embodied in skilled personal and technical routines (Smith 1992). The tacit dimensions of technical learning "require involvement with a particular production process or product use distinguishing between learning-by- doing and learning by using" (Kozul-Wright 1993, 4). However, in a dynamic perspective, a change towards greater emphasis on formal knowledge can be achieved by replacing or supplementing the tacit knowledge of local entrepreneurs by the formal knowledge of professional managers in the running of small- and medium-sized firms.

Relating the level of internal competence of firms to the different types of innovation described earlier, it is argued that firms with low internal resources and competence can adopt, develop or imitate mainly *incremental* innovations. To be able to adopt, adapt, and develop *radical* innovations firms must have access to intrafirm-based professional technological competence, which through inter-firm cooperation can also enhance the technological competence of the districts. While *radical* innovations normally lead to more incremental innovations, it is also possible that the "decentralized industrial creativity" associated with the more-or-less complex "learning-by-doing" and/or "learning- by-using" processes of *incremental* innovations can also, in exceptional cases, result in *radical* innovations (Bramanti, Senn 1991, 101).

Turning to the question of innovation diffusion, it is argued that the latter relates more to the collective technological capacity of the industrial district, i.e. to resources that are external to the firm but internal to the area. According to Brusco, it is "the fact of being a 'system' rather than being a 'single firm' that defines the degree of sophistication of these industrial structures" (Brusco 1986, 194). The "system" quality may or may not be supported through local structures outside the firm. Thus, Brusco distinguishes between industrial districts without external local government intervention, which he calls "industrial district Mark I", and industrial districts with considerable government intervention, which he calls "industrial district Mark II" (Brusco 1990).

The diffusion of innovations in industrial districts Mark I is stimulated "by fostering interaction between the skilled workers and small entrepreneurs of the 'final-firms' and their subcontractors" (Brusco 1990, 15). In this way, the internal skill and competence of firms are strengthened through inter-firm collaboration. This strategy could be characterized as "learning-by-interacting", which "reflects a network of relations embracing the educational and technical infrastructure, interaction between different stages of the production process and sharing of information between many different economic and non-economic institutions" (Kozul-Wright 1993, 4). The interactions between producers and users of intermediate products and between suppliers and users of machine tools and business services are the main forms of cooperation in industrial districts Mark I, increasing the overall efficiency of the local production system (Brusco 1990, Garofoli 1992).

This *vertical* form of inter-firm cooperation or linkages promotes primarily the adoption and diffusion of *incremental* innovations, while the adoption and diffusion of *radical* innovations depend to a larger extent on *horizontal* inter-firm cooperation within the field of research and development (Håkonsson 1992). The lack of the latter form of cooperation, which requires the existence of firms with a high level of internal resources and competence, is one of the problems of the traditional industrial districts of model Mark I in the Third

Italy. Håkonsson argues that "collaboration with customers leads in the first instance to the step-by-step kind of changes [i.e. incremental innovations], while collaboration with partners in the horizontal dimension is more likely to lead to leap-wise changes [i.e. radical innovations]" (Håkonsson 1992, 41). However, according to Garofoli, the increasing importance of horizontal diffusion of innovations between sectors facilitates "the introduction of innovations outside the enterprises and sectors which invest in R&D", resulting in a largely improved innovative capacity of small firms within industrial districts (Garofoli 1992, 60).

The spatial proximity of interacting firms which characterizes an industrial district is an important enabling factor in both forms of cooperation. In fact, it could be argued that "geographical and cultural distance might play an even more important role" in the case of *radical* innovations than in the case of *incremental* innovations. The lack of standard criteria for selecting the best paradigm implies that "'subjective' elements in user-producer relationships ... will become important" (Lundvall 1990, 19). This is supported by Håkonsson, who claims that "the importance of proximity is particularly noticeable in horizontal relationships, but it is not altogether absent in the case of vertical relations" (Håkonsson 1992, 125).

The need for public intervention, and thus for a transition of industrial districts to a Mark II model, has been the result of the development of new markets and new technologies since the end of the 1970s, representing a challenge for both large and small firms. The increased demand from the market for customized products necessitates frequent (design) changes of - and a search for new and original - models, which, if they are to be carried out successfully, require outside experts' assistance, even if the innovations must still be labelled as *incremental*. These rapid product innovations lead, in turn, to a demand for *incremental* process innovations. However, as new, computerized production equipment is becoming increasingly complex and sophisticated, "the introduction of new technologies calls for a professional expertise inherently different from the traditional professions" (Camagni, Rabellotti 1988, 20).

While a majority of large firms already have carried out a process of restructuring, many small firms in industrial districts are either just about to engage in this process or are in the midst of it. Unlike large firms, where the hierarchical decision-making process makes it relatively easy to introduce new technology, this is a much more difficult process for small firms in industrial districts (Brusco 1990). This is partly because of the lack of professional competence in small firms, and partly because of the network (hence not hierarchical) structure of industrial districts. According to Brusco, industrial districts are:

> "characterized by a sort of strong, heavy inertia. The district goes on learning the technology in a deep, personal and creative way, but it is very difficult to move this huge mass of people - not just the dependent workers, but the whole competence of all the people. Therefore, industrial districts eventually face the problem of how to acquire the new technological capabilities which are necessary to revive the process of creative growth. It is here that the need for intervention appears" (Brusco 1990, 17).

Some regions in the Third Italy have tried to solve this problem by setting up centres for real services in order to offer the small- and medium-sized firms the assistance they need in "real" terms (i.e. information about markets, technology, finance etc.), rather than giving them direct financial help (Brusco 1990).

Table 1 provides a schematic presentation of the preceding discussion. It will be noted that a distinction is made between "adoption of" which is considered spontaneous, and corresponds to the Mark I type, and "development of" which requires the stimulus of external intervention and corresponds to the Mark II type districts.

Table 1

Minimum requirements of firms' internal competence and different models of industrial districts with respect to application, adaptation and diffusion of innovations

Strategy of innovation			
Category of innovation	Application	Adaptation	Diffusion
Incremental (adoption)	Low internal competence	Low internal competence	Mark I industrial district
Incremental (development)	Low internal competence	Low internal competence	Mark II industrial district
Radical (adoption)	High internal competence	High internal competence	Mark I industrial district
Radical (development)	High internal competence	High internal competence	Mark II industrial district

Since technological change is the principal competitive strategy for both product and process innovations, the development of professionalism is bound to have a crucial role in the revitalizing strategy of small- and medium-sized enterprises (Camagni, Rabellotti 1988, Cooke, Morgan 1991). According to Lundvall "the long term competitiveness of firms, and of national economies, reflects their innovative capability, and, moreover, firms must engage in activities which aim at innovation just in order to hold their ground" (Lundvall 1992, 8). However, in this process, most small- and medium-sized firms are particularly vulnerable and, thus, dependent on outside local and regional institutions for support "in order to speed up innovation, expand into new markets and thus consolidate regional growth" (Schmitz 1992, 115). Therefore, small- and medium-sized firms, in order to overcome innovative-related problems, "need organizational support throughout the entire adoption and adjustment process" (Camagni 1992, 1). According to Cooke and Morgan, in their study of Emilia-Romagna, "the main impetus for creating a regional system of institutional support was the widespread recognition that small firms, left to themselves, were simply not equipped to cope with the challenges of accelerated technological change, higher quality products and more globalized markets. The mono-industrial culture of the districts was a further stimulus because, if a sector went into terminal decline, it could well drag an entire area down with it" (Cooke, Morgan 1991, 53). As pointed out by Smith, "the success of any national or regional economy relies in part on its ability to create firms which become the 'bearers' of new technologies" (Smith 1992, 19). Thus, following Goddard, "in such a highly competitive situation the regions that will succeed will be those that have developed their institutional capacity in support of local RTD" (i.e. research and technological development) (Goddard 1992, 8). Such a development cannot, however, be fully successful without an industrial policy strengthening linkages and interactions between the *regional* systems of innovation, typically consisting of the DIC of small- and medium-sized firms within industrial districts, and the larger, R&D-based *national* system of innovation, made up of large TNCs, small high-tech firms, universities, research institutions, and central and local public agencies (Kozul-Wright 1993). In this process, centres for real services can play an important role. A step in this direction seems to have been taken by the regional authorities of Emilia-Romagna in "proposing that the ERVET system [Regional Development Agency of Emilia-Romagna] becomes much more integrated with the new regional technological poles (at Bologna, Parma and Piacenza) so that the benefits of applied research projects can be diffused more widely throughout the region. In addition, ERVET has been enjoined to develop synergies with the regional university system because these links are relatively underdeveloped" (Cooke, Morgan 1993, 33).

II. INTER-FIRM LINKAGES IN INDUSTRIAL DISTRICTS AND ENDOGENOUS TECHNOLOGICAL CAPABILITY-BUILDING:TOWARDS AN ANALYTICAL FRAMEWORK

We have now developed the theoretical dimensions necessary for undertaking the analysis of inter-firm linkages and endogenous technological capacity of industrial districts. These dimensions are the following three:

(a) Weak *versus* strong local cooperative environment, i.e. the question of the degree of "embeddedness" of agglomeration economies;

(b) Low *versus* high level of internal resources and competence of small and medium-sized firms with respect to technological change; and

(c) Industrial districts of model Mark I vis-à-vis model Mark II; i.e. industrial districts without and with public intervention, respectively.

By using dimension (a), it is possible to isolate which agglomerations of small- and medium-sized firms could be called "industrial districts". The two analytically separable dimensions constituting industrial districts - external economies and agglomeration economies - can be specified as *necessary* and *sufficient* conditions, respectively, for the formation and growth of industrial districts. Thus, the existence of territorially embedded agglomeration economies is the key variable determining whether or not a local agglomeration is an industrial district. This constitutes the basis for the existence of a local cooperative environment with strong ties, that is, stable and permanent relations where mutual trust is a dominant feature. Industrial agglomerations without embedded agglomeration economies have a local cooperative environment with weak ties (occasional and unstable relations) and, thus, cannot be said to represent industrial districts (Vatne 1992).

When this dimension is combined with dimension (b), industrial districts and other industrial agglomerations are differentiated with respect to the internal resources and competence of the firms within the different areas. It is important to distinguish between firms with a low *versus* high level of internal resources and competence given that "the basic economic unit of the market economy is the firm, and that this is where - for the most part - technology is translated into economic results" (Smith 1992, 19). The same is also basically true for industrial districts even when the significance of the inter-firm collaboration within the districts is taken into consideration. A high level of internal resources in the form of professional competence is, for example, needed for small- and medium-sized firms to be able to apply advanced, computerized, flexible, multi-use production equipment, which has given these firms the opportunity to engage in diversified quality production (i.e., the flexible specialization model) as well as to enter into horizontal inter-firm cooperation (Asheim 1992a). Thus, as Brusco emphasizes, "the capacity of a system of firms to innovate depends absolutely on the collaboration between hundreds of firms and thousands of people in different roles and with different skills. It also depends, therefore decisively on the level of competence and knowledge of the production process by these thousands of protagonists" (Brusco 1989, 264). However, the opportunity of employing "professionals" (managers and civil engineers) to secure the innovative capacity of the firm is more or less restricted to the largest and/or most economically viable of the small- and medium-sized firms.

Before introducing the third dimension of industrial districts of Mark I and Mark II models, a couple of examples of industrial agglomerations which do not qualify as industrial districts owing to a weak local cooperative environment have been set out in figure 1 and, thus, will not be dealt with in the subsequent analysis.

As an example of an industrial area with a weak local co-operative environment, consisting of firms with a low level of internal resources and competence, one can mention the area of Stella in Naples discussed by Amin elsewhere in this volume. Areas like Stella could be described as consisting of traditional, local-market-oriented artisan firms with a strong dependence on the informal economy.

Figure 1

Industrial districts and other types of industrial agglomerations

Local cooperative environment	SMEs' internal resources and competence	
	Low	High
Weak	Traditional, local market oriented artisan firms (Ex. Stella, Naples)	Science Parks; Large firms dominated production systems (Ex. Canavese, Turin)
Strong	Industrial districts (see Figure 2)	

Source: Adapted from Vatne (1992).

The "Science Parks" could be mentioned as an example of a local cooperative environment with weak ties combined with firms having a high level of internal resources and competence. According to Morgan "stand-alone science parks" can be considered "the technological equivalent of cathedrals in the desert" (Morgan 1991, 9, Massey, Wield 1992). Another example which could also fit in the latter category concerns the Canavese and Turin areas in Italy where "the network of small firms already formed in the area ... differ from the ones which are typical to industrial districts, because their basis is not a territorial community, but rather a 'professional community'. This means that the values at the basis of this community of innovative entrepreneurs [values linked to professionalism, continuous learning and innovation] are not necessarily shared by the other groups with which they come into contact. Consequently, these values cannot establish a system of economic regulation such as that found in industrial districts, which must instead be organized in such a way as to satisfy special interests" (Michelsons 1989, 443). The latter area could be characterized as a production system dominated by large firms but also including highly specialized, small subcontracting firms without any independent network of their own.

In principle, there are two alternative ways of solving the problem of raising the level of professional competence of the small-firm sector in industrial districts, these are:

(a) Through reliance on collective capacity-building by, for example, setting up centres for "real services" which could systematically assist firms in the industrial districts in keeping pace with the latest technological developments. This could be done either through a networking strategy between firms and public and private agencies, or through public intervention; or

(b) Through "cooperation" with big companies (ranging from simple cooperation with subcontractors to takeovers), which in one way or another can give the small firms access to research and development capacities and financial resources.[3]

As the last "model" involves the danger of the small firms ending up as dependent subcontracting firms, the first "model" of establishing centres of "real services" must be considered the most adequate and beneficial strategy for building up technological capabilities and improving the innovation capacity of industrial districts, thus transforming them into Mark II districts. It should be underlined that "the inclusion of these services in the production process allows a structural change - for example, the reshaping of processes, or the differentiation of products, or a change in market coverage" (Bianchi, Giordani 1993, 33). This is also confirmed by the Italian experience, where, according to Brusco, "in some places, real services have certainly been successful in encouraging growth, and have had an important effect in moving districts towards new technology and towards upper segments of the market" (Brusco 1990, 17-18).

It would appear, therefore, that the creation of local or regional institutions promoting innovative cooperation could provide a solution to the problem of ensuring or maintaining an optimal technological dynamism in industrial districts, so as to avoid technological stagnation or retardation. According to Smith, "the production infrastructure will be an important shaping factor in the *technological* competitiveness and capabilities of firms. Even at a simple level, the scale and scope of the infrastructure affects the ability to diffuse and apply technologies, access to information, international linkages, and the supply of skills. All of these are central elements in innovative performance" (Smith 1992, 8-9).

Figure 2 provides a schematic summary of the potential for endogenous technological capability-building for different types of industrial districts, conceptualized as "local production systems" which are understood as a "collection of operating units linked technologically and organizationally in the manufacture of final goods" (Sheard 1983, 65).

Square I in Figure 2 -- industrial districts of model Mark I with small- and medium-sized firms characterized by a low level of internal resources and competence -- represents, in fact, the original Marshallian model of an industrial district. When continuing with the analysis, it is important to remember that "industrial districts - when they are successful - are creative, display originality, are often able to discover new markets, continuously introduce incremental innovations, some of which may prove important, and enhance social mobility and worker participation" (Brusco 1992, 196). According to Becattini, it is in this sense that "a MID [Marshallian industrial district] is either creative or it is not a (true) MID" (Becattini 1991, 102). However, the problem with these industrial districts is their relative *low* potential for endogenous technological capability-building. As an example of such a district, reference will be made to Gnosjö in Småland (Sweden).

Figure 2

Different models of industrial districts with respect to technological capability-building

Internal resources and competence	Strong local cooperative environment	
	Industrial district Mark I	**Industrial district Mark II**
Low	I Local production systems with a *low* potential for technological capability-building (Ex. Gnosjö, Sweden)	II Local production systems with *some* potential for technological capability-building (Ex. Carpi and Reggio-Emilia in Emilia-Romagna, Italy)
High	III Local production systems with a *good* potential for technological capability-building (Ex. Jæren, Norway; Sassuolo, Emilia-Romagna, Italy)	IV Local production systems with a *high* potential for technological capability-building (Ex. Modena, Emilia-Romagna, Italy; Baden-Württemberg, Germany)

In square II of figure 2, we find local production systems with *some* potential for technological capability-building. This potential is due to the collective resources of the industrial districts as they belong to the Mark II model, which to some extent compensates for the low level of internal resources and competence of the small- and medium-sized firms of these districts. Carpi, in Emilia-Romagna of the Third Italy, will serve as the main example of this type of industrial district.

Square III in figure 2 represents local production systems with a *good* potential for technological capability-building. The positioning of these industrial districts as having a greater potential than districts in square II is due to the strong *horizontal* inter-firm cooperation normally found in these districts between firms with high levels of internal resources and competence. Such cooperation is of strategic importance in promoting technological development, for example, "substantial synergy may be obtained from a close, door-to-door cooperation by the producers and the users of capital equipment" (Sengenberger, Pyke 1992, 15). The districts of Jæren (Norway) and Sassuolo in Emilia-Romagna (Italy) will be used to exemplify the workings of such industrial districts.

The last model of industrial districts, square IV in figure 2, is characterized by a *high* potential for technological capability-building due to the combined effect of the presence in the district of small- and medium-sized firms with high levels of internal resources and competence and the level of intervention (Mark II model). Such industrial districts characterized by a strong innovative capacity could be defined as "technology districts", understood as a particular type of industrial district (Michelsons 1989, Storper 1992). According to Storper, "the concept of Marshallian industrial district, while significant in its own right, needs additional specification to distinguish those agglomerations that today lie at the heart of advanced economic development from other territorial collections of economic activities" (Storper 1992, 90). The district of Baden-Württemberg (Germany) will be used as the major example of this type of district.

III. EMPIRICAL ILLUSTRATIONS OF THE ROLE OF INDUSTRIAL DISTRICTS IN ENDOGENOUS TECHNOLOGICAL CAPABILITY-BUILDING

The following empirical illustrations are not meant to give a general overview of the above-mentioned industrial districts, but will one-sidedly focus on aspects of importance in the analysis of their endogenous technological capability-building.

Local production systems with a low potential for technological capability-building (square I of figure 2)

In the literature on industrial districts "the Swedish metalworking producers in Småland" have been mentioned as illustrating an example of "new industrial spaces", where a development analogous to that of small- and medium-sized firms in the Third Italy is said to have taken place (Sabel 1989, 22). Gnosjö, which is the main location for this metalworking industry of small- and medium-sized firms, is the most industrialized rural commune in Sweden with more than 300 enterprises and a population of about 9,000 inhabitants. A large majority of the firms belong to the metalworking industry; the average firm size is between 10 and 20 employees, with the largest firm employing 160 persons.

Gnosjö must be defined as an industrial district owing to the presence there of both external economies as well as agglomeration economies. The district is characterized by typical branch specialization, including some producers of simple capital equipment. Subcontracting is prevalent but most of the subcontractors serve several clients, and, therefore, they are not normally dependent on only one or a few large customers for their sales. Thus, Gnosjö can be considered an industrial district (Asheim 1992b).

Nevertheless, the endogenous capacity for technological development must be characterized as relatively limited (Asheim

1992b). This is due to an industrial structure dominated by highly labour-intensive and price-competing manufacturing industries (Karlsson, Larsson 1993). Furthermore, Gnosjö has a surprisingly low formal educational level, particularly with regard to the university level, as well as a negative attitude towards higher education which, consequently, leads to a poor level of formal technological competence. Although most of the small firms have a reasonable level of informal (tacit) technical knowledge, this is not sufficient to keep pace with general technological development (Asheim 1992b), since, as has already been discussed earlier, "the early adoption of new technology by enterprises is heavily dependent on the formal educational level of their employees" (Karlsson, Larsson 1993, 126). Most of the products for the final market are very simple; there is an overall lack of core technological competence. In addition, local and regional authorities have not been very active in compensating for this lack of competence of small firms, the blame for which, must, to a large extent, be laid on the inhabitants' extremely favourable view of the entrepreneur (Asheim 1992b, Ørjasæter 1989). Consequently, "the attempts to develop the knowledge-intensive sector in the Gnosjö region have up till now not been very successful" (Karlsson, Larsson 1993, 136).

The explanation for this situation is, in part, historical, as the original formation of the Gnosjö industry is an example of proto-industrialization (Asheim 1992b). The consequences of the low level of internal resources and competence have already been demonstrated by the difficulties confronting subcontractors in the autocar industry to maintain their competitiveness. These difficulties have been the result of the combined effect of the stiff foreign competition faced by Swedish domestic car producers, in general, and the changes in these firms' subcontracting networks towards a greater degree of European sourcing, in particular. In this situation, the subcontracting firms in Gnosjö, as a result of their incapacity to generate *radical* innovations, will have to rely on cost- and price-reducing strategies, only in part obtained through the adoption of *incremental* process innovations (Asheim 1992b, Ørjasæter 1989). Thus, the much needed "restructuring of the manufacturing industry in the Gnosjö region will be seriously hampered by a lack of the relevant labour supply" (Karlsson, Larsson 1993, 136).

The problems identified above which are typical of traditional industrial districts have to do not only with the relatively low level of professional competence and qualifications of the small firms but also with the insufficiently developed regional institutional support mechanisms which means that the district must be considered a Mark I model industrial district. Thus, *incremental* innovations dominate the innovative activities of the region. The result has been a relative slow move up the price-quality curve into the production of higher quality products. It has also meant a limited ability to diversify into new industries manufacturing higher value-added products.[4]

In some industrial districts of this type, the stagnation in the traditional sectors and the increased foreign competition from low-cost producers have forced small- and medium-sized firms to start sourcing outside the district for cost reasons (as, for example, in the industrial district of Santa Croce in Tuscany (Amin, Thrift 1992)). Such developments could result in a break-up of the local subcontracting networks, with an increasing number of production units being located outside the region in cheap labour areas, and a growing penetration of imports. This could eventually lead to the local economies becoming tertiarized, leaving only higher value-added activities such as design within the original industrial district at the expense of direct production activities. In the case of Santa Croce there is, according to Amin and Thrift, "already some evidence to suggest that, into the 1990s, the organization of industry ... will be "post-Marshallian", that is, less locally confined and less vertically disintegrated" (Amin, Thrift 1992, 580).

Local production systems with some potential for technological capability-building (square II of figure 2)

The characteristic of industrial districts of this category, such as Carpi and Regio-Emilia in Emilia-Romagna, is that they have been transformed into Mark II industrial districts by regional political intervention. In this way, the low level of internal resources and competence of the small firms has been compensated through the establishment of different types of "centres of real services". In Carpi, the well-known regional innovation centre, Textile Information Centre for Emilia-Romagna (CITER), was established by a supportive regional council. CITER is considered "the prototype and pride of the network of business services centres in Emilia-Romagna" (Bellini *et al.* 1990, 178). This centre has had an extremely positive impact on the performance of the small knitwear firms of Carpi, of which the majority are subcontractors to a few leading firms, in the fields of (i) fashion (product innovations), by providing information on "trends and changes in colour, fabrics, lines for knitwear and clothing"; (ii) technology (process innovation), by providing information on "the state of the art and trends in textiles, technologies, regulations governing the use of machinery, production techniques and technologies"; and (iii) marketing, by providing "commercial information in the form of summaries of the important data concerning domestic and foreign markets" (Bellini *et al.* 1990, 179). According to Brusco and Righi, the role of CITER "has been a determining element in moving the sector towards the more sophisticated segments of the market, where quality is as important as price, or even more important, and where the danger of NIC competition is less worrisome" (Brusco, Righi 1989, 419).

Concerning the diffusion of technology within the industrial district, "computerized numerically controlled (CNC) equipment is widely used in weaving, embroidering, and certain types of cloth cutting; but garment assembly, ironing, packaging, and inspection tasks remain labour-intensive" (Lazerson 1993, 211). Furthermore, CITER has offered the small- and medium-sized firms of the industrial district a locally developed CAD (computer aided design) technology called CITERA, which through a more rapid introduction of new styles and samples and considerable cost-savings in the production process enhances the firms adaptability to market trends and customers demands (Cooke, Morgan 1993). CITERA users see CAD as an important part of their strategy to move into the production of more sophisticated products selling on higher quality markets. This represents the "high road" to competitiveness (i.e. strong competition (Storper, Walker 1989)) in contrast to the "low road" of shifting production to low wage areas within Italy and other South European countries, which some of the larger firms in the district have started to do (Cooke, Morgan 1993).

Cooke and Morgan report that some of the early users of the CITERA system have "refused to share the benefit of CAD with their subcontractors, *despite* the fact that this would enhance both versatility and quality. ... If this is the case then the task of promoting more innovative forms of corporate collaboration in the 1990s might prove to be more difficult than is often imagined" (Cooke, Morgan 1993, 28).

Correspondingly, the Centre for Mechanized Services to Agriculture (CESMA) has supported the agricultural machinery industry of Reggio Emilia by supplying services in the following areas: market studies, certification and standardization and technological innovation (Bellini *et al.* 1990, 178). However, the lack of horizontal cooperation between small- and medium-sized firms within the district prevents the innovation and diffusion of any basic core technology, even though since the beginning of the 1980s there has been "a growing conviction that existing businesses should be consolidated and strengthened through the creation of business services centres, whose main task is technology transfer and the provision of specialist services with a high value added value" (Bellini *et al.* 1990, 172).

Local production systems with a good potential for technological capability-building (square III of figure 2)

An illustrative example of square III, local production systems with a good potential for technological capability-building, can be taken from an industrial district south of Stavanger in the south-western part of Norway. Here, an organization called TESA (Technical Cooperation) was established by local industry in 1957, in collaboration with the local technical schools and later with the regional and national R&D institutions, with the aim of supporting technological development among the member firms, which are medium-sized, export-oriented firms producing mainly farm-machinery. This has, among other things, resulted in the district being today the centre for industrial robot technology in Norway. The close, horizontal inter-firm cooperation, resulting in the development of core technologies (*radical* process innovations), existing in this district is rather unique in an international context. The technological cooperation is strongly dependent on the high level of internal resources and competence of the firms. It must also be mentioned that Jæren is a small industrial area (for example, only 10 to 15 companies have been/are members of TESA, albeit the most important and technologically advanced ones). In addition, the region is characterized by strong common values (i.e. the Protestant work ethic, which also is dominant in Gnosjö) and close family ties in the communities (Asheim 1992a, 1992b).

This example can be used to focus on structures enabling the successful development of horizontal inter-firm technological cooperation within industrial districts (Asheim 1992a, 1992b). These can be summarized as follows:

- The collaboration within TESA is on *process innovation* and not on *product innovation*. This factor further strengthens the qualitative dimension of cooperation through the significant but delicate dualism of competition and collaboration by stressing technological development of common interest to all participating firms (i.e. new production techniques);

- The production system is characterized by horizontal specialization or complementarity in products. Brusco, as well, has pointed out that cooperation and collaboration, especially concerning technical innovations, are credited with creating less difficulties between firms doing different things (Brusco 1986, 1990);

The initiative to establish TESA was taken by the local industry, which corresponds to Brusco's recommendation of involving individual entrepreneurs in the development of such centres (Brusco 1989).

Another example of this model can be found in the ceramic-tile industrial district in and around the small town of Sassuolo in Emilia-Romagna, where a concentration of hundreds of small firms involved in this industry is located. This industrial district has experienced a process of technological change which has to be understood in the perspective of "the interrelationships between firms operating in the ceramic-tile industrial districts" (Russo 1989, 198). Russo argues that such a complex phenomenon as a process of technological change "cannot easily be understood if we attribute to one particular source complete responsibility for that process, whether it be the innovative firm or the large corporation". She proposes, "instead, to focus on a group of closely related firms - in particular, the firms' operation in an industrial district" (Russo 1989, 201). However, Sassuolo is not defined as a Mark II industrial district as the level of public intervention is not considered strong enough. Partly the main business service centre of the industry, the Ceramic Centre, which was founded in 1976 by a consortium of the University of Bologna, regional agencies and various ceramic industry associations, supplies very *specific* technical services to the industry, concentrating on research on various types of clay for ceramic tile production, production processes, and chemical and mechanical analyses of finished products, and partly it is located in Bologna, i.e. *outside* the industrial districts in question. According to Brusco and Righi "other centres have a much wider field of interest and their activities run from product design and production to marketing" (Brusco, Righi 1989, 417).

In Sassuolo, the small ceramic-tile firms do not normally themselves carry out the innovation of new machines or new production methods, and must have them explained as a result of their lack of professional technical competence. New products and processes have instead been largely developed outside the ceramic-tile firms by a group of small engineering firms which build machines for tile producers (process innovation), and by factories which introduce the new colours and products (product innovations). There are only a few innovating firms among the machine producers; the rest of the manufacturers are only imitators. However, the capacity for imitating/modifying has, in fact, promoted *incremental* process innovations in tile production (Russo 1989). "Innovations were usually known in days or weeks and copied in a few months. Firms seeking technical leadership had to improve constantly to stay ahead" (Porter 1990, 216). This has resulted in a greater variety of choices among different versions of the same machine, implying that the ceramic-tile firms can adopt precisely the machine that solves the firms' particular technical problems, thus, making them more competitive in the marketplace. In this way, technology producers can offer customized products through close user-producer relations, which also stimulates the diffusion of new technology to other ceramic firms in the district (Russo 1989). According to Porter, "Italian equipment producers worked continuously with the manufacturer to improve production machinery" (Porter 1990, 213).

This close relationship and frequent contacts between the equipment manufacturers and the tile producers - often stimulated by being located close to each other - allow the tile producers to use the specialized staff of the engineering firms as their own internal technical staff to solve production or design problems. The machine firms, on the other hand, can make use of ceramic firms to test the prototypes of new machinery instead of having to carry out such tests in laboratories. As a consequence of this relationship, the industrial district also becomes what could be called an "integrated district", in the sense that the district in addition to the industry producing a given final product includes firms which manufacture production equipment, supply intermediate products and provide various forms of business services related to that product (Russo 1989).

Russo concludes by emphasizing the central "role played by the interrelationships between firms and their proximity to each other. Together these provide the basis for the process of generation and adoption of new techniques, and, moreover, it is within the network of interrelationships between the ceramic-tile firms of the industrial district that the effects of technical change on the structure of the industry are felt" (Russo 1989, 215). This implies that "foreign firms must compete not with a single firm, or even a group of firms, but with an entire subculture. The organic nature of this system is the hardest to duplicate and therefore the most sustainable advantage of Sassuolo-firms" (Porter 1990, 225).

Local production systems with a high potential for technological capability-building (square IV of figure 2)

Storper argues that Modena, in Emilia-Romagna, can be included in what he calls "technology districts"; that is, industrial districts characterized by a high degree of innovative capacity (Michelsons 1989, Storper 1992). Modena is the centre of the metalworking and mechanical engineering industry, in general, and a centre of luxury car production (Ferrari, Maserati and Lamborghini), in particular; it has long benefited from a pool of trained entrepreneurs and workers in mechanics. In addition, Modena offers a considerable number of public technical consulting services to the small- and medium-sized firms of the district (Sabel 1989). Recently, the public services provided have included a centre of "real services" for technological upgrading of the metalworking and mechanical engineering industry as well as a centre for technology transfer in industrial automation (Cooke, Morgan 1991, 36). This local and regional public intervention has, according to Zeitlin, contributed to the fact that "the metalworking districts of Modena and Bologna have maintained or even enhanced their competitive position, while the textile districts of Prato and Carpi have experienced greater difficulties in readjustment" (Zeitlin 1992, 283).

It is noteworthy that, in Emilia-Romagna, the Italian ex-Communist Party (the party in local government) and the trade unions have been favourable towards the system of small- and medium-sized firms and have played an important role in assisting the regional economy through public intervention. In contrast, in Tuscany, the same party and trade unions have, until recently, provided very little supportive institutional framework to the small firms of, for instance, Prato and Santa Croce, because it was considered that small firms were backward and opposed to the interests of the working class (Cooke, Morgan 1991). Thus, it is an intriguing question, how Prato will be able to meet the new international competition "in its rather hostile governmental environment" (Cooke, Morgan 1991, 40).

Baden-Württemberg is a successful industrial region, but it cannot be characterized as a small-firm economy. Indeed, there are some inter-industry variations in size structure; for example, large firms are much less dominant in the machine tool industry than in the electrical and electronics industries, and especially in the autocar industry. According to Cooke and Morgan, most of the machine-tool firms are small- and medium-sized firms employing typically 100 to 200 persons (Cooke, Morgan 1993). Consequently, there exist some smaller industrial agglomerations which, in size and structure, look more like the industrial district model (Schmitz 1992). This also implies that it would be more correct to talk about *several* industrial districts *within* Baden-Württemberg than to refer to the whole of Baden-Württemberg as *one* industrial district. However, even in the machine tool industry, large firms dominate the system of subcontracting and inter-firm networking (Cooke, Morgan 1990). Thus, the inclusion of the industrial agglomerations in Baden-Württemberg among the industrial districts presents conceptual problems (Gaffard 1992), particularly, since the industrial structure of the region is basically an outcome of the growth of Fordist mass-production industries after the Second World War (Herrigel 1993).

However, characteristics of the regional systems of production in Baden-Württemberg are (a) close inter-firm cooperation;

(b) extensive public-private networking; and (c) an active role of local and regional government in strengthening the innovative capacity of the local industry. In this system of innovating by networking (Morgan 1991), the large firms play a decisive role by investing substantially in local purchasing and training, and establishing extensive subcontracting relations with regional industry (Cooke, Morgan 1990). One of these large firms, Bosch, practices a policy of limiting any given subcontractor's sales to Bosch to about 20 per cent of its turnover to prevent these firms from becoming dependent subcontractors (Sabel et al 1989). In this way, the large companies could be looked upon as "tutors" for the rest of the industry in Baden-Württemberg (Cooke, Morgan 1990).

In this type of inter-firm networking, which involves large companies and mostly medium-sized firms, vertical cooperation between customers and suppliers is the dominant feature. Specific technological collaboration seems not very common, even if Bosch has started to adopt a strategy of transferring certain forms of technological know-how to outside firms. However, there are also many examples of horizontal cooperation, a much more effective form of cooperation in promoting technological development. Such collaboration in R&D, design, marketing, common-purchasing policy and staff training typically takes place between medium-sized firms in the machine-tool industry (i.e. the *Mittelstand* of small- and medium-sized firms) involved in activities that are complementary rather than in direct competition with each other (Cooke, Morgan 1993, Gaffard 1992).

Through both intermediary private institutions and local and regional government, Baden-Württemberg is well provided with technical consulting services and vocational and technical educational training. The regional government has employed an active innovation policy with "a well-developed strategy to improve the conditions for innovation and industrial growth in the region" (Schmitz 1992, 108). Overall, both public and private R&D budgets are very high in Baden-Württemberg and there is a strong emphasis on stimulating the diffusion of know-how through technology transfer programmes and institutions (Cooke, Morgan 1990). The Steinbeiss Foundation, formally privately owned but, in fact, entirely controlled by the Government of Baden-Württemberg, "has the primary role of matching the technological needs of small- and medium-sized producers" (Herrigel 1993, 231). However, in sectors dominated by large firms, the policy of regional and local government has less influence on the performance of the industry (Schmitz 1992).

In evaluating the efficiency of the technology policy, it must be remembered that the industrial and economic success of Baden-Württemberg in the 1970s and 1980s preceded or coincided with this policy. However, "it would be unreasonable entirely to discard claims that the regional government helped industry to cope with the challenges of the 1990s" (Schmitz 1992, 108). Therefore, although regional technology policy did not by itself strengthen the collective innovation capacity, it may be assumed that it played an important role in making local industry more consolidated and competitive in the 1980s (Schmitz 1992).

In conclusion, as has been shown by these empirical examples, "not all the established regional economies have institutionalized cooperation among specialists as extensively as Baden-Württemberg or Modena" (Sabel 1989, 27). Furthermore, it is also necessary to emphasize that such strategies can be accomplished in different ways. When comparing the administrative systems of the Third Italy with Baden-Württemberg, a different balance of power between regional and municipal governments may be observed. In Baden-Württemberg, political initiative originates from the regional government, whereas in the Third Italy municipal authorities play a more important role as the policy formulating agencies (Schmitz 1992). Also concerning industrial structures, important differences exist between the small- and medium-sized firms in the industrial districts of the Third Italy compared to the industrial agglomerations of Baden-Württemberg which are dominated by large firms. However, concerning "systemic innovation, which requires strong synergies between industry, finance and the science and technology base, Emilia-Romagna is not as well placed as regions like Baden-

Württemberg, where these synergies have existed for much longer" (Cooke, Morgan 1993, 36).

IV. POLICY IMPLICATIONS FOR PLANNED INDUSTRIAL DISTRICTS

The European experience of industrial districts has become a major point of reference in the recent international debate on industrial policy promoting endogenous development (Schmitz, Musyck 1993). According to Garofoli "endogenous development is ... the ability to innovate at a local level" thus making "networks and innovation ... the crucial factors for the strengthening of endogenous local development" (Garofoli 1991b, 125, 136).

However, all the available empirical evidence presented in the preceding sections suggests that "the *emergence* of the industrial districts does not result form consciously pursued local or regional industrial strategy" (Schmitz, Musyck 1993, 32). On the contrary "the collaborative relationships generally evolve organically. They originate when a number of factors happen to coincide in an appropriate manner" (Håkansson 1992, 126-27). The central problem is, then, whether it is possible, through planned intervention, to create the sufficient conditions - represented by the presence of agglomeration economies - for the development of an industrial district (Asheim 1992a). Pyke and Sengenberger ask in a similar way, if such conditions could "be repeated using different social and economic arrangements", and they suggest that "the question of replicability takes on a different light if the focus is put not so much on the specific character of social and economic institutions as on the functions that they carry out" (Pyke, Sengenberger 1990, 5).

In this discussion it is necessary to distinguish between *specific* and *general* factors explaining the formation and development of industrial districts. The more important the specific factors are, the more difficult it is to transfer experiences from one region to another. On the one hand, the most specific socio-cultural factors, which are historically embedded in a particular region, cannot be "repeated" in another region. On the other hand, the general lessons derived from the working of external economies through inter-firm networking as well as the promotion of private-public cooperation should, in principle, be much easier to transfer from region to region. In addition, it should also be possible to transfer the potential lessons to be learned from the more "general" aspects of the embedded, socio-cultural factors from one region to another, that is, above all the presence of a positive attitude towards modernization.

Let us illustrate this discussion by returning to figure 1, where two examples of industrial agglomerations which did not qualify as industrial districts are shown, and examine what kind of industrial policy would be needed to convert them into local production systems of an industrial district type.

Spontaneous, unplanned growth of clusters of small firms

In this case, the policy aim must be to transform clusters of small firms with important elements of informal economies into industrial districts. The strategy must be to localize areas embedded in socio-cultural structures favourable to modernization and economic development. Especially important is the question of a positive attitude towards cultural modernization (e.g. peasant-rationality would be an example of cultural-ideological factors with a negative attitude towards economic and cultural modernization) (Asheim 1993). If such areas are identified, the policy question would be how to transform these areas into industrial districts of model Mark II (square II in figure 2); that is, to formulate public policies which can promote the formation of inter-firm horizontal and vertical cooperation between small firms within the local clusters, and to provide the institutional support framework needed for the necessary upgrading of products and processes of the small firms (e.g. the establishment of centres for real services). Mark I industrial districts must in fact be "jumped over" since they have evolved "organically" and unplanned.

Planned development of industrial agglomerations

In this category of industrial agglomerations, we find typically "science parks", development poles, etc., where the lack of horizontal inter-firm cooperation is the main problem. The policy question, in this case, is to formulate strategies that can transform these agglomerations into industrial districts of model Mark II (square IV in figure 2) by establishing agencies, for example, such as centres for real services, which can introduce a networking strategy between small- and medium-sized firms.

Sabel and Lorenz have provided some evidence of how it would be possible to initiate trust-building processes, that is, to create intentionally mutual trust between networking firms within industrial agglomerations. Lorenz has, in a study on the Lyon region of France, showed that trust and cooperation among firms can be intentionally created through a "partnership" strategy, which is based on the merit of establishing long-term relations concerning the amount, price and quality of work between the client firms and their subcontractors (Lorenz 1990). In a study from the United States, Sabel points to the possibilities of creating trust by bringing in consultants in order to help groups of firms redefine their collective interests so as to pave the way for what Sabel calls "studied trust" (Sabel 1990). According to Gelsing, "in industrial policy, programmes to promote networking are now becoming frequent. Denmark, Sweden, Spain, Portugal, even the United States, where 'industrial policy' is a curse, and, not to forget Italy where some claim it all started, have networking programmes today" (Gelsing 1992, 127).

However, collective efficiency cannot be expected to be an immediate result of programmes of institutionally enhanced growth. The industrial district experience therefore has the greatest relevance to industrial areas which already have a critical mass of small firms (Schmitz, Musyck 1993). "In other words, to the extent that policy implications can be drawn from this experience, they are not concerned with the emergence of industrial districts but with the path they took once they existed" (Schmitz, Musyck 1993, 32).

V. CONCLUSION: INDUSTRIAL DISTRICTS AND TECHNOLOGICAL DEVELOPMENT - PROBLEMS AND PROSPECTS

What makes the industrial districts so successful, but at the same time so vulnerable to changes in the international capitalist economy, is that they are characterized by the combination of functional and territorial integration. A "productive" balance between these modes of integration is the key to the success of the districts.

The balance between functional and territorial integration of the 2industrial districts is exposed to at least two fundamental threats that would need to be overcome in order to ensure continual reproduction. First, there is the threat from changing external relations by an extension of the time-space-distanciation of the production system through increased external ownership and control of local industry (Asheim 1992a). This can diminish the autonomy of individual firms as well as reduce the role of the industrial districts as such in the national and international markets. Such extensions can either be the result of large national and international corporations buying up successful small enterprises in the districts, and making them into branch plants or subsidiaries, thus transferring "final" decision-making to agencies external to the region (Tolomelli 1990); or it may occur as a result of the substitution of local subcontractors by firms outside the industrial districts in order to squeeze costs (Amin, Thrift 1992).

Take-overs are often a result of lack of financial resources and/or marketing capabilities of small- and medium-sized firms, which restrict their innovative capacity with respect to both new products and production technology. Often there are only two alternative ways of solving this problem for the small-firm sector: either through endogenous - private and public - support by setting up centres of real services; or through the take-over by a big company. Such acquisitions by big firms may of course represent a satisfactory solution to the individual small firm, but "it is important to observe how, by means of such operations, groups of enterprises not only are taking over individual firms, but through them can enter the web of relations between firms within the districts and integrate them into their corporate network" (Tolomelli 1990, 366).

The second category of change is the formation of more formalized groups of firms, sometimes controlled by larger companies outside the industrial districts, but most commonly the groups are formed by small firms under competitive pressure aiming to stay competitive (Zeitlin 1992). This change towards the formation of groups may be observed in several industrial districts in the Third Italy; for example, in Sassuolo the financial crisis in the late 1970s resulted in a concentration of firms within groups (Russo 1989); in Prato, there are now more than 400 groups of firms (Zeitlin 1992), while in the Carpi knitwear industry, four large groups are operating (Cooke, Morgan 1991); in Bologna five major groups now control much of the automatic packaging machinery sector (Zeitlin 1992). Thus, the production system of the Third Italy is undergoing changes, and firms which appear small often actually belong to a hierarchical structure of companies (Bellini *et al.* 1990, Bianchi, Gualtieri 1990). According to Cooke and Morgan, "these new corporate hierarchies appear to be emerging in the region's industrial districts as a result of a growing concentration of capital" (Cooke, Morgan 1993, 24). In addition to helping small- and medium-sized firms to solve the financial problems they face because of the need for increased R&D expenditure for securing better access to international markets, the establishment of groups is a strategy for supplying small firms with professional competence on a formalized inter-firm cooperative basis.

From the previous discussion, it would appear that the increased degree of integration into the world economy (i.e. international markets, corporate hierarchies and networks, and global production systems) is strengthening the importance of functional integration at the expense of territorial integration (i.e. the "embedded" agglomeration economies), which is the sufficient condition for the formation of industrial districts (Asheim 1992a). The small- and medium-sized firms of the industrial districts are increasingly being squeezed between "more aggressive and more flexible strategies on the part of the large firms on the one hand, and, on the other, by increased competition from low-wage countries" (Cooke, Morgan 1993, 22). As a result, the transformation of industrial districts takes place either through take-overs of small- and medium-sized firms by TNCs, or by a process of re-positioning involving a change from square I via squares II or III to square IV (for example, through the formation of larger groups of firms). In this necessary process of restructuring, "the small firms' network", in order to survive, "will have to modify some of its basic characteristics and evolve toward a more concentrated structure, in which a limited number of leading firms or firm associates will perform a key role in both strategic and commercial terms" (Malerba 1991, 39). This trend has characterized the development of industrial districts in the beginning of the 1990s, and will have a decisive effect on the future prospects of this form of territorially organized industrial agglomeration. The chances of continual growth of the ideal type version of industrial districts, consisting of independent small firms balancing functional with territorial integration, are steadily decreasing.

Thus, the ultimate question still remains: How much long-term strategic planning can be introduced into the decentralized industrial systems of small- and medium-sized firms and be undertaken by new corporate leaders without totally destroying the innovative milieu, flexibility and consequent economic dynamism of industrial districts?

132

REFERENCES

Amin, A. (1989), "Specialization without growth: small footwear firms in Naples, in Goodman, E., J. Bamford (eds.), *Small firms and industrial districts in Italy,.* Routlege, London, 239-256.

Amin, A. and N. Thrift (1992), "Neo-Marshallian nodes in global networks", *International Journal of Urban and Regional Research*, 16,4, 571-587.

Asheim, B. (1985), "Capital accumulation, technological development and the spatial division of labour: a framework for analysis", *Norsk Geografisk Tidsskrift*, 39,2, 87-97.

Asheim, B. (1990), "Innovation diffusion and small firms: between the agency of lifeworld and the structure of systems", in Alderman, N., E. Ciciotti, A. Thwaites (eds.), *Technological Change in a Spatial Context: Theory, Empirical Evidence and Policy*, Springer-Verlag, Berlin, 37-55.

Asheim, B. (1992a), "Flexible specialisation, Industrial Districts and Small Firms: A Critical Appraisal" in Ernste, H., V. Meier (eds.), *Regional Development and Contemporary Industrial Response. Extending Flexible Specialisation*, Belhaven Press, London, 45-63.

Asheim, B. (1992b), "Industrielle distrikt og fleksibel spesialisering i Norden ? En komparativ analyse av industriregionene Jæren og Gnosjö", *Occasional Papers*, o. 6, Department of Human Geography, University of Oslo.

Asheim, B. (1993), "Industrial districts and technological development: The European experience", paper presented at the Conference on New Tendencies in Urban and Regional Development in Europe, Durham, United Kingdom, March.

Becattini, G. (1990), "The Marshallian industrial district as a socio-economic notion", in Pyke, F., G. Becattini, W. Sengenberger (eds.), *Industrial Districts and Inter-Firm Co-operation in Italy*, International Institute for Labour Studies, Geneva, 37-51.

Becattini, G. (1991), "The industrial district as a creative milieu", in Benko, G., M. Dunford (eds.), *Industrial Change and Regional Development*, Belhaven Press, London, 102-114.

Bellandi, M. (1989), "The industrial district in Marshall", in Goodman, E., J. Bamford (eds.), *Small Firms and Industrial Districts in Italy*, Routledge, London, 136-152.

Bellandi, M. (1992), "The incentives to decentralized industrial creativity in local systems of small firms", *Revue d'Economie Industrielle*, no. 59, 99-100.

Bellini, N. et al (1990), "The industrial policy of Emilia-Romagna: the business service centres", in Leonardi, R., R. Nanetti (eds.), *The Regions and European Integration: The Case of Emilia-Romagna*, Pinter Publishers, London, 171-186.

Bianchi, P. and G. Gualtieri (1990), "Emilia-Romagna and its industrial districts: the evolution of a model", in Leonardi, R., R. Nanetti (eds.), *The Regions and European Integration: The Case of Emilia-Romagna*, Pinter Publishers, London, 83-108.

Bianchi, P. and M.G. Giordani (1993), "Innovation policy at the local and national levels: the case of Emilia-Romagna, *European Planning Studies*, 1,1, 25-41.

Bramanti, A. and L. Senn (1991), "Innovation, firms and milieu: a dynamic and cyclic approach, in Camagni, R. (ed.), *Innovation Networks: Spatial Perspectives*, Belhaven Press, London, 89-104.

Brusco, S. (1986), "Small firms and industrial districts: the experience of Italy, in Keeble, D., E. Wever (eds.), *New Firms and Regional Development in Europe*, Croom Helm, London, 184-202.

Brusco, S. (1989), "A policy for industrial districts", in Goodman, E., J. Bamford (eds.), *Small Firms and Industrial Districts in Italy*, Routledge, London, 259-269.

Brusco, S. (1990), "The idea of the industrial district: its genesis", in Pyke, F., G. Becattini, W. Sengenberger (eds.), *Industrial Districts and Inter-Firm Co-operation in Italy*, International Institute for Labour Studies, Geneva, 10-19.

Brusco, S. (1992), "Small firms and the provision of real services", in Pyke, F,. W. Sengenberger (eds.), *Industrial Districts and Local Economic Regeneration*, International Institute for Labour Studies, Geneva, 177-196.

Brusco, S. and E. Righi (1989), "Local government, industrial policy and social consensus: the case of Modena (Italy)", *Economy and Society*, 18,4, 405-24.

Camagni, R. and R. Rabellotti (1988), "Technology, innovation and industrial structure in the textile industry in Italy", paper presented at the Conference on the Application of New Technologies in Existing Industries: Prospects for Regional Industrial Regeneration and Employment in Europe, Newcastle upon Tyne, United Kingdom, March.

Camagni, R. (1992), "New innovation policies at local level", paper presented at the Conference on Science, Technology and Community Cohesion, Louvain-la-Neuve, Belgium, December.

Cooke, P. and K. Morgan (1990), "Industry, training and technology: the Baden-Württemberg system in perspective", *Regional Industrial Research Report*, no. 6, Department of City & Regional Planning, UWCC, Cardiff.

Cooke, P. and K. Morgan (1991), "The intelligent region: industrial and institutional innovation in Emilia-Romagna", *Regional Industrial Research Report*, no. 7, Department of City & Regional Planning, UWCC, Cardiff.

Cooke, P. and K. Morgan (1993), "Growth regions under duress: renewal strategies in Baden-Württemberg and Emilia-Romagna", Department. of City & Regional Planning, UWCC, Cardiff.

Freeman, C. and C. Perez (1986), "The Diffusion of technical innovations and changes of techno-economic paradigm", paper presented at the Conference on Innovation Diffusion", Venice, Italy, March.

Fua, G. (1983), "Rural industrialization in later developed countries: the case of northeast and central Italy", *Banca Nazionale del Lavoro Quarterly Review*, 147, 351-377.

Gaffard, J.-L. (1992), "Territories in Europe and innovation", paper presented at the Conference on Science, Technology and Community Cohesion, Louvain-la-Neuve, Belgium, December.

Garofoli, G. (1991a), "The Italian model of spatial development in the 1970s and 1980s", in Benko, G., M. Dunford (eds.), *Industrial Change and Regional Development*, Belhaven Press, London, 85-101.

Garofoli, G. (1991b), "Local networks, innovation and policy in Italian industrial districts", in Bergman, E.M. et al (eds.), *Regions Reconsidered*, Mansell, 119-140.

Garofoli, G. (1992), "Industrial districts: structure and transformation", in Garofoli, G. (ed.), *Endogenous Development and Southern Europe*, Avebury, Aldershot, 49-60.

Gelsing, L. (1992), "Innovation and the development of industrial networks", in Lundvall, B.-Å. (ed.), *National Systems of Innovation*, Pinter Publishers, London, 116-128.

Goddard, J.B. (1992), "Research and development in the community: debate on the inequalities, paper presented at the Conference on Science, Technology and Community Cohesion, Louvain-la-Neuve, Belgium, December.

Goodman, E. (1989), "Introduction: the political economy of the small firm in Italy, in Goodman, E., J. Bamford (eds.), *Small Firms and Industrial Districts in Italy*, Routledge, London, 1-30.

ranovetter, M. (1985), "Economic action and social structure: the problem of embeddedness, *American Journal of Sociology*, 91, 481-510.

Haraldsen, T. (1988), "Vekstpol og utvikling", *Meddelelser fra Geografisk institutt, Universitetet i Oslo, Ny kulturgeografisk Serie*, no. 22, Oslo.

Harrison, B. (1991), "Industrial districts: old wine in new bottles? *Working Paper 90-35*, School of Urban and Public Affairs, Carnegie Mellon University.

Herrigel, G.B. (1993), "Power and the redefinition of industrial districts: the case of Baden-Württemberg, in Grabher, G. (ed.), *The Embedded Firm. On the Socioeconomics of Industrial Networks*, Routledge, London, 227-251.

Håkonsson, H. (1992), *Corporate Technological Behaviour: Co-operation and Networks*, Routledge, London.

Karlsson, C. and J. Larsson (1993), "A macro-view of the Gnosjö entrepreneurial spirit, *Entrepreneurship and Regional Development*, 5,2, 117-140.

Kozul-Wright, Z. (1993), "Organizing complexity: innovation in the Marshallian industrial district of Brianza", DESD, United Nations, New York.

Lazerson, M. (1993), "Factory or putting-out? knitting networks in Modena", in Grabher, G. (ed.), *The Embedded Firm. On the Socioeconomics of Industrial Networks*, Routledge, London, 203-226.

Lorenz, E. (1990), "The social construction of trust: informal networks of subcontracting in French industry", discussion paper for the Workshop Flexible Specialisation in Europe, Zürich, Switzerland, October.

Lundvall, B.-Å. (1990), "User-producer interactions and technological change", paper presented at the Conference on Technological Change, organized by the TEP Program of the OECD, Paris/La Vilette, France, June.

Lundvall, B.-Å. (1992), "Introduction", in Lundvall, B.-Å.(ed.), *National Systems of Innovation*, Pinter Publishers, London, 1-19.

Malerba, F. (1991), *Italy: the National System of Innovation*, Universita L. Bocconi, Milan.

Marshall, A. (1891), *Principles of Economics*, 2nd edn. Macmillan, London.

Massey, D., D. Wield (1992), "Science parks: a concept in science, society, and "space" (a realist tale)", *Environment and Planning D: Society and Space*, 10, 411-422.

Michelsons, A. (1989): "Local strategies of industrial restructuring and the changing relations between large and small firms in contemporary Italy: the case of Fiat Auto and Olivetti", *Economy and Society*, 18,4, 425-447.

Morgan, K. (1991), "Innovating-by-networking: new models of corporate and regional development", paper presented at the Conference on the Development of Technology and Regional Change, Aalborg, Denmark, November.

Ørjasæter, E. (1989), "Innovasjonskapasitet i Gnosjø Kommune", *Meddelelser fra Geografisk Institutt, Universitetet i Oslo. Ny kulturgeografisk serie*, no. 24, Oslo.

Perroux, F. (1970), "Note on the concept of 'Growth Poles'", in McKee, Dean, Leahy (eds.), Regional Economics: Theory and Practice, New York, 93-103.

Piore, M., C. Sabel (1984), *The Second Industrial Divide: Possibilities for Prosperity*, Basic Books, New York.

Porter, M.E. (1990), *The Competitive Advantage of Nations*, Macmillan, London.

Pyke, F. and W. Sengenberger (1990), "Introduction", in Pyke, F., G. Becattini, W. Sengenberger (eds.), *Industrial Districts and Inter-Firm Co-operation in Italy*, International Institute for Labour Studies, Geneva, 1-9.

Russo, M. (1989), "Technical change and the industrial district: the role of inter-firm relations in the growth and transformation of ceramic tile production in Italy", in Goodman, E., J. Bamford (eds.), *Small Firms and Industrial Districts in Italy*. Routledge, London, 198-222.

Sabel, C. (1989), "Flexible specialisation and the re-emergence of regional economies", in Hirst, P., J. Zeitlin (eds.), *Reversing Industrial Decline? Industrial Structure and Policy in Britain and her Competitors*, Berg Publisher, Oxford, 17-70.

Sabel, C. (1992), "Studied trust: building new forms of co-operation in a volatile economy", in Pyke, F., W. Sengenberger (eds.), *Industrial Districts and Local Economic Regeneration*, International Institute for Labour Studies, Geneva, 215-250.

Sabel, C. et al (1989), "Regional prosperities compared: Massachusetts and Baden-Württemberg in the 1980s", *Economy and Society*, 18,4, 374-404.

Schmitz, H. (1992), "Industrial districts: model and reality in Baden-Württemberg, Germany, in Pyke, F., W. Sengenberger (eds.), *Industrial Districts and Local Economic Regeneration*, International Institute for Labour Studies, Geneva, 87-121.

Schmitz, H. and B. Musyck (1993), "Industrial districts in Europe: policy lessons for developing countries? *Discussion Paper*, 324, IDS, University of Sussex, Brighton.

Scott, A. (1992), "The role of large producers in industrial districts: a case study of high technology systems houses in Southern California, *Regional Studies*, 26,3, 265-275.

Sengenberger, W. and F. Pyke (1992), "Industrial districts and local economic regeneration: research and policy issues, in Pyke, F., W. Sengenberger (eds.), *Industrial districts and local economic regeneration*, International Institute for Labour Studies, Geneva, 3-30.

Sheard, P. (1983), "Auto-production systems in Japan: organisational and locational features", *Australian Geographical Studies*, 21, 49-68.

Smith, K. (1992), "The role of the science and technology infrastructure in national economic performance", Notat 17/92, *Future-Oriented Technology Policy*, Royal Norwegian Council for Scientific and Industrial Research, Oslo.

Storper, M. and R. Walker (1989), *The Capitalist Imperative: Territory, Technology, and Industrial Growth*, Basil Blackwell, New York.

Storper, M. (1992), "The limits to globalization: technology districts and international trade, *Economic Geography*, 68,1, 60-93.

Tolomelli, C. (1990) "Policies to support innovation in Emilia-Romagna: experiences, prospects and theoretical aspects, in Alderman, N., E. Ciciotti, A. Thwaites (eds.), *Technological Change in a Spatial Context: Theory, Empirical Evidence and Policy*, Springer-Verlag, Berlin-Heidelberg, 356-378.

Vatne, E. (1992), "Local resource mobilization and internationalization strategies in small- and medium-sized enterprises", paper presented at the 13th Nordic Symposium on Critical Human Geography, Oslo, Norway, September.

Zeitlin, J. (1992), "Industrial districts and local economic regeneration: overview and comment", in Pyke, F., W. Sengenberger (eds.), *Industrial Districts and Local Economic Regeneration*, International Institute for Labour Studies, Geneva, 279-294.

NOTES

1.   I should like to thank Eirik Vatne, Centre for Research in Economics and Business Administration, Norwegian School of Economics and Business Administration in Bergen, the participants in the UNCTAD/GATE symposium and, in particular, Helen Argalias from the Technology Programme of UNCTAD, who organized the symposium.

2. Using the Freeman-Perez classification, the following four categories of innovations are distinguished: (a) incremental innovations which are more or less continuously on-going improvements in existing products and processes;   (b) radical innovations which are discontinuous events such as new production technologies or new consumer products. This category of innovation is based on formal R&D;   (c) new technological systems which consist of clusters of radical and incremental innovations which are technologically and economically interrelated; and (d) a new "techno-economic paradigm" which involves many clusters of radical and incremental innovations, but may also embody many new technological systems with a pervasive effect on the economy as a whole (e.g. introduction of steam power and electric power, information technology) (see Freeman and Perez 1986).

3. Sabel points out that in order to "gain access to technical expertise and, sometimes, the capital necessary to apply it, small and medium-sized firms in the industrial districts appear to be seeking long-term, collaborative relations with larger partners inside or outside the industrial district. Sometimes these relations take the form of long-term subcontracting arrangements; sometimes the larger firm purchases equity in the smaller" (Sabel 1989, 26-27).

4. It is argued that new industries normally have "a greater capacity for technical innovations and a greater control of the market" (Garofoli 1992, 53), thus supporting a more robust industrial structure in the local economy. This improves "the position of the local productive systems in the regional and international division of

labour" resulting in "a greater ability to defend the local system against outside competition" (Garofoli 1992, 53).

TECHNOLOGICAL INNOVATION AND INDUSTRIAL DISTRICTS: SOME COMMENTS AND EVIDENCE

Fernando Villarán *

Introduction

Coming from a continent where stabilization and structural adjustment programmes are being widely implemented and dominate the official economic and social agenda, it is very important to highlight the contribution made by the symposium (and the paper commented upon) towards the recognition of the crucial role of technology and industrial organization for the purpose of obtaining growth and development.

In recent years, both topics have been put aside by mainstream economics, not only in the academic world, but also in the concerns of many international organizations, governments and even public opinion. Stabilization and structural adjustment programmes have been stimulated (and sometimes subtly imposed) worldwide, particularly in developing countries. Government expenses, fiscal deficit, minimum wages, taxes, exchange rates, interest rates, social security expenses, commercial balances, among other macroeconomic variables, are pervasive topics; there is little or no place for technology, science, education, innovation and industrial policies. In certain circles, the latter group may even be considered bad words, simply because they may imply State or external intervention and/or alteration in "free market forces".

It is difficult to explain why mainstream economics and official policies derived therefrom resist so stubbornly any recognition of the

* PEMTEC, Lima, Peru.

link between innovation and growth, at least in developing countries (this would be a good theme for a seminar). Why is it so difficult to understand that macroeconomic policies, being important, only determine the general conditions? They are only the frame within which economic and social agents act and take decisions; they can never replace the driving force of development that starts at the firm level. To discuss what happens at this level, and to try to understand what conditions determine and stimulate technological innovation will always be an essential and valuable exercise.

That is why I consider the paper by Bjørn Asheim so relevant or, as we say in our country, "on the right track". It offers a good frame in which to examine, organize and discuss all these extremely important issues. Certain conceptual differences highlighted below by no means diminish its general value. The symposium has provided a gratifying and rare opportunity to discuss these topics freely and fruitfully.

In order to contribute to the debate and avoid the very strong temptation to stray beyond the agenda, I will proceed first to confirm my agreement with Dr. Asheim's thesis and, secondly, to discuss some differences and, finally, offer some conclusions.

Agreements

The definition of industrial district as a "network of small- and medium-sized firms" seems more adequate and analytically workable than other definitions which include the "the big firm variant". In the flexible specialization paradigm, the relation between small and big firms, as demonstrated by Japanese industry, is extremely important, but its relative importance is reduced if the geographical and social dimension is introduced.

One of the major contributions of the paper is the highlighting and development of the concept of "embeddedness". Among other things, this concept implies "mutual knowledge and trust", "high degree of trust and consensus", the creation of a social and cultural atmosphere that promotes the generation and diffusion of innovations. This concept is useful because it focuses on these issues and gives clues to understanding the social, cultural and institutional roles, relations and networks; it also helps in overcoming the simplifications often seen in the literature where industrial cooperation is reduced to market relations. This distinction has important implications for research, policy design and implementation of promotion programmes. The concept can help in defining the proper questions for research as well as to ascertain the roles of the different institutions and social organizations involved in small-scale enterprise promotion.

This concept, and others indicated in the paper, provides a better understanding of one of the traditional secrets (in both senses, i.e. explanation of their success and recognition of ignorance) of industrial districts, i.e. the existence of "a complex mix of competition and cooperation". The reference made to process innovations as being more co-operation-biased as opposed to product innovations that contribute to incentive competition between firms, offers very important insights that can be pursued further. The positive role played by external institutions, as cited in the cases of Stavanger (Norway) and Emilia Romagna (Italy), show some fine tuning in respect of this issue that is not common in other promotion institutions. Nevertheless, there would seem to be plenty of room to continue research into this "mysterious" and apparently contradictory relation.

The three dimensions proposed in the analytical framework -that is, (a) weak *versus* strong local cooperative environment (embeddedness); (b) low *versus* high level of internal resources and competences with respect to technological development; and (c) industrial districts without or with public (and private intervention) - are useful for determining the design of policies and the direction of promotion actions for small enterprise groups, or even whole sectors. In this sense, figures 1 and 2 are useful for characterizing industrial districts and agglomerations.

The proposed policies to foster technological dynamism in the industrial districts through setting up centres of real services, through public or private initiative, and co-operation with big companies, backed by important empirical evidence (in Italy, Germany and other countries), can be taken as quite adequate.

However, the fears about the subcontracting relationship between small and big firms seem exaggerated; in many developed and developing countries, this relationship has proved to be very convenient, both for small and big firms. The definition adopted for industrial districts must not surpass its analytical limits, which would overlook the potential benefits.

Throughout the text, the author refers repeatedly to the concept of technological innovation, both to explain processes and situations found in reality as well as to make it a key actor in intervention policies, as can be seen in the following citation: "Since technological change is the principal competitive strategy, for both product and process innovations, the development of professionalism is bound to have a crucial role in the revitalizing strategy for small- and medium-sized enterprises". This uncommon technological-innovation-centred stance is one of the major contributions of the paper.

The paper contains several proposals for both the policy level and the promotion level. I would like to focus on the following two:

(a)   "The creation of local or regional institutions promoting innovative cooperation could provide a solution to the problem of ensuring or maintaining an optimal technological dynamism in industrial districts, so as to avoid technological stagnation or retardation".

The question may be raised about the type and nature of the institutions necessary to reach these objectives. It seems that there is no single formula to create industrial districts, since local tradition, including institutional tradition, plays a major role.

(b)   "A high level of internal resources in the form of professional competence is, for example, needed for small- and medium-sized firms to be able to apply advanced, computerized, flexible, multi-use production equipment, which has given these firms the opportunity to engage in diversified quality production (i.e., the flexible specialization model) as well as to enter into horizontal inter-firm cooperation".

Both proposals are of a general nature so they can be widely implemented even in different environments.

Since the purpose of this exercise is not primarily to point out the points of agreement, but rather to contribute to the debate, I shall make an effort to find some differences.

Differences

Problems begin when the author asserts: "the importance of territorial embedded agglomeration economies in promoting innovations concerns largely *incremental* innovations". For me, this type of technological dynamism is good enough; such innovation is responsible for economic growth and that is what small industries can and must do. Expecting that they systematically (or with regularity) would perform radical, history-making innovations is not reasonable.

Concerning the classification "innovation" itself, which the author takes from Freeman and Perez, the discussion about the differences between minor and major innovations is an old one. It can be tracked right back to Schumpeter, since it was major innovations that he had in mind when he formulated his definition. This distinction has been partially useful for research and academic purposes, since it permits scholars to classify and study innovations in *ex post* analysis. However, the relation between type of innovation and growth has never been clarified. Nobody has proved that major or radical innovations produce growth or that minor and incremental ones do not, or even that the first produce more growth than the second type. Such an assertion cannot be sustained by historic facts. Japan, in the 1950s and 1960s, and the four Asian "tigers" in the 1980s showed high growth rates with little or no major innovations. The same can be said of other developing countries, such as Brazil in the 1970s and Chile in the 1980s.

Even a very important innovation - the personal computer - can be considered an incremental innovation, since it did not entail creation of any new component, taking in consideration that the microprocessor, memory chips, keyboards, monitors, diskettes, input-output devices and software existed before the personal computer arrived. What the Silicon Valley entrepreneurs did was to put the components together in a package affordable to a wide range of people. Its economic impact and contribution to growth is beyond doubt.

On the other hand, if one insists on considering the personal computer as a major or radical innovation, then the theory that small firms (even clusters of small firms) do not produce this type of innovation runs aground because the product was produced by small firms in 1975 in California. The same argument can be applied to many other innovations, like the cheap automobile (Henry Ford) at the beginning of the century.

That is why it is difficult to classify innovations, and even more difficult to say something about their growth potential, while it would be outright dangerous to design promotion policies around such a classification.

From what has been said above, one can conclude that table 1 is not so useful. The vertical axis has been questioned (categories of innovation) and the horizontal axis also presents its own problems. At the firm-level, there are three possibilities (not just two): in addition to the application and adaptation of innovations, one must consider the creation of innovations. The fourth strategy of innovation (diffusion) arises from any of the three previous ones and is an inter-firm process. Hence, setting these elements out in linear fashion may not be a good idea.

An effort must be made to avoid misleading conclusions such as the following: "The problem [with small firms] in this respect is that they lack innovative capacity due to shortage of both human and financial resources to build up and support a necessary level of research and development capacity". The line of thinking is as follows: small-scale industries do not have financial and human resources for R&D, so they have no innovative capacity. While the first part of the affirmation may be correct, the second part does not necessarily follow: to accept this logic is to accept that the only types of innovation come from R&D; this is not true in general (considerable literature supports this point) and is less true for small enterprises.

This observation does not imply that R&D is not important. It is very much so. However, it is not the principal source of innovation for small- and medium-scale enterprises. This brings us to another important issue: the sources of innovation. They are intimately interrelated with the topic under discussion: a high quality workforce, cooperation between firms, access to information, adaptation, imitation (and outright copying) and conglomeration, among others. All of these factors influence positively the generation of innovations. In conclusion, the acceptance of the classification used by the author could limit drastically the perception of the potential of industrial districts to foster innovation, which can be promoted consciously.

By way of a conclusion

This section will depart somewhat from the framework of the paper - which is limited to cases in developed countries - and comment on the situation in the developing countries.

I could not end without alluding to some doubts about the pertinence and convenience of using the concepts presented in the paper, bearing in mind the economic reality in countries such as Peru. The six structural characteristics for industrial districts (Mark II type) that can be traced in different parts of the paper are:

(a) Extensive division of labour between firms;
(b) Strong product specialization;
(c) Effective information network;
(d) High competence-level of the workforce;
(e) Socio-cultural "embeddedness";
(f) Existence of support institutions (public or private).

It is difficult to find all of these characteristics present in the agglomerations and groups of small-scale industries existing in developing countries.

Table 1 shows the presence of these characteristics in the known agglomerations of small enterprises in Peru. As may be seen, none of these cases fulfils completely the definition of an industrial district given in the paper. The most frequently occurring of the structural characteristics are "strong product specialization" and "existence of support institutions", while the least frequent are: "socio-cultural embeddedness", "extensive division of labour" and "effective information network" and "high competence level of the workforce".

This simple table allows some policy measures to be inferred: concentrating efforts on information, capacity-building of the workforce, encouraging division of labour and promoting institutional and organizational strengthening offer positive possibilities.

Bearing in mind the characteristics of Latin American and many African countries, it does not make too much sense to search for industrial districts, and even less sense to classify them. This concept, alone or as a part of the concept of flexible specialization,[1] can act as a paradigm, as a north star to navigate by, but probably not much more than that.

Table 1

Groups	No. of firms	Characteristics					
		a	b	c	d	e	f
Gamarra	(3,000e*)	*	*				
Trujillo	(1,000e)		*				*
Cuzco	(16e)				*		*
CBK	(32e)			*	*		
APIC	(800e)		*				*
APEMEFAC	(200e)		*				*
Caqueta	(300e)	*	*			*	
Paruro	(150e)			*			
TOTAL		2	5	2	2	1	4

In developing countries, the challenge is not to search for or to characterize the industrial districts (if any exist), but to use this concept and its policy implications to promote technological dynamism (innovation) in the small-scale sector. Clustering of small firms is one of the most important ways of maximizing their contribution to development.

The following facts bear consideration:

(a)   Small-scale industry is a very extended phenomenon in developing countries;

(b)   Important segments of small-scale industry have demonstrated dynamism, flexibility, capacity to adapt to external changes and to react to policy measures;

(c)   The formal and over-protected industrial sector of many developing countries, based on big enterprises, is in crisis[2] and undergoing a deep restructuring process.[3]

The picture can also be turned around: instead of searching for industrial districts in developing countries, probably a difficult and frustrating task, the industrial district lesson must be used to guide policy measures and promote suitable tasks and institutions.

From the experience of industrial districts, one can extract the following proposals:

(a)   Promote the clustering of small firms; support the clusters already existing;

(b)   Promote horizontal cooperation (division of labour and product specialization) between small firms;

(c)   Create real service centres (both public and private);

(d)   Involve and strengthen existing institutions that can support and transfer technology to small firms, e.g. research centres and universities;

(e)   Assure that adequate professionals may offer and give direct or indirect advice to small firms;

(f)   Assure the possibility of permanent training for personnel and owners;

(g)   Foster process, machinery, input and forms of organization innovation, that strengthen the cooperative forces and diminish the competition forces among small enterprise groups.

NOTES

1. "From a third world perspective, the flexible specialization thesis is an evocative idea rather an empirical generalization, and largely untested. However, stating that mass production and the factory system are not necessarily the one and only way to upgrade production facilities, the flexible specialization thesis opens a range of new perspectives on industrial development" (Sverrisson 1992).

2. "Sudan is a classical case of a [mass-production] industrialization crisis. While one can argue whether there really is a mass-production industry crisis in the industrialized countries, there can be no doubt that there is such a crisis in Sudan" (Hansohm 1992).

3. "If one should identify one major trend in this development, it is the retreat of large-scale mass production (which never operated very efficiently in the African setting anyway) and of direct government involvement in production" (Aeroe 1992).

TECHNOLOGICAL DIFFUSION IN THE ITALIAN
MARSHALLIAN INDUSTRIAL DISTRICT OF BRIANZA

Zeljka Kozul-Wright *

"There exists throughout the universe an astonishing activity which no cause can
diminish, and everything which exists seems constantly subject to necessary change."

LAMARCK (1844)

INTRODUCTION

The growing importance of new technologies to the determination
of competitiveness is widely recognized in current economic research.
Much of this research concentrates on the pivotal role of the TNCs
as agents of technical change (TCMD, 1992), emphasizing the
networking system among large TNCs, as a distinct feature of the
global economy (Hagerdoorn and Schakenraad, 1991). This paper
explores similar relations between technology and organization
among SMEs in local geographical clusters.

The Marshallian industrial district (MID) of Brianza in northern
Italy represents a highly successful case of incremental technological
diffusion, particularly of product development arising from the
complex interplay of inter-firm and intra-firm relations, characterized
by continuous and repeated interactions among the firms inside a
small-firms-network system. Extensive linkages between the core
R&D system of innovation at the *national* level and the small-firms-
networks system at the *regional* level allow for enhanced speed of
technological diffusion and for the associated improvements in

* The paper was prepared while the author was with the United Nations Centre
for Science and Technology for Development.

innovative performance of the sector's furniture firms, as proven by the Italian furniture sector's unparalleled competitive performance.

Although the firm is perceived as an essential component of any innovative system, the evolutionary perspective adopted in this paper requires an analytical framework which can more fully embrace the interactive nature of the innovative environment. In this respect the concept of a *productive system* is of particular relevance. A productive system describes a set of complementary and competitive relations through which wealth is produced and distributed. Any successful productive system must use its labour force effectively and combine a system of managerial control, marketing and distribution strategies. It must also possess an industrial structure that continuously reduces the costs of production (Wilkinson, 1983). However, the capacity to sustain innovation and technical advance will determine its longer-term competitiveness and prosperity. This paper focuses on the dynamic elements of productive systems and particularly the conditions of *innovation* and *learning,* suggesting that it is in the interaction of the different components of a system rather than the isolation of one particular feature that success or failure lies.

Modern industrial productive systems are essentially mixed systems in which private and public institutions provide a rich and diverse pattern of competition, cooperation and trust that stimulates economic performance (Wilkinson, 1983; Hodgson, 1988; Rosenberg, 1988). There is now considerable evidence at the national level which supports the conclusion that mixed systems best encourage innovation and technological development (Andersen and Lundvall, 1988; Nelson, 1986; Nelson, 1993). The concern of this paper is to reinforce this conclusion at the industrial level. In this respect, we suggest that the industrial district, symbolized by Brianza, represents one possible type of a *productive system* conducive to rapid diffusion of incremental innovation. In particular, the externalities associated with the concentration of industries in a spatially defined area and marked by a high degree of user-producer interactions encourage *learning* among different but mutually dependent productive activities.

The interactive relationship between technology and the environment in which it operates forms the *leitmotif* of the *evolutionary* theoretical paradigm adopted in this paper.[1] This contrasts with the linear view of technical change adopted by the orthodox neo-classical Walrasian paradigm. The latter interprets economic growth as a series of causally unconnected equilibria determined by given preferences, fixed property rights and an *exogenous* rate of technical progress. Seen from this perspective, it is the availability of given resources, including scientific knowledge, which determines economic performance and constrains increases in output.

By contrast, an evolutionary perspective assumes the *endogeneity* of technical change: technical change does not merely happen to the system but is determined by it. Although the limits of the static perspective have been recognized by economists of differing theoretical persuasions, and there is in addition considerable agreement that economic growth and long-term prosperity imply the development of new products and processes which lead to productivity growth and economic progress, innovation remains an elusive concept (Rosenberg, 1988).

The lack of a clear approach to innovation is apparent in the Schumpeterian tradition which has contributed the most to the economic analysis of technical change. Despite Schumpeter's own description of different types of economic innovation - "new consumer goods, new methods of production or transportation, new markets, new forms of industrial organization that capitalist enterprise creates" (Schumpeter, 1987, p.83) - his own and much later analysis focused almost exclusively on cost-reducing technological innovation. This already narrow focus was further restricted by making a rigid distinction between invention, innovation and diffusion, which Schumpeter believed to be mutually exclusive processes. In addition, Schumpeter associated the innovative process with the capabilities of isolated individuals making a radical break with an existing technological regime.

Innovation, I would argue, represents the commercial application of new knowledge or the combination of old knowledge in radically novel ways. Such activity, while disrupting existing economic routines - and the associated firms, practices and factors of production - will improve the competitive position of the firm or the broader productive unit in which it is introduced by creating new markets, advancing the technological regime or establishing new linkages between producers and users. Recognizing that technical change is an evolutionary process implies that invention, innovation and diffusion occur *simultaneously* rather than *sequentially*, and that much change is of a dynamic and incremental nature. Unlike Schumpeter, we believe that innovation is a permanent feature of economic development. In the more recent literature, the superior effects of incremental innovation associated with *learning-by-doing* and *learning-by-using*, on productivity performance and product developments have been widely acknowledged.

While the definition of innovation encompasses a variety of different economic activities, it is nevertheless useful to accept as an initial starting point the distinction between product and process innovation. Following recent research by Rosenberg(1988), and Lundvall (1988) and in the particular context of the furniture industry, emphasis is placed on *incremental product innovation* via continual improvements in design, both of an aesthetic and engineering character. This type of innovation has not only improved the performance of the final products but also considerably reduced production costs.[2]

This approach gives *learning* a central role in the innovative process. Moreover, learning is itself recognized to be a complex social process embodying both formal knowledge acquisition as well as more informal processes implied by the tacit nature of much knowledge tied to a particular time and place, which is, in turn, dependent upon inherited skills. A growing body of literature on learning-by-doing and learning-by-using has explored these aspects (Arrow, 1962; Rosenberg, 1982; Lundvall, 1988a, Kozul, 1992). I will emphasize *learning-by-interacting* as a condition of successful innovation. An emphasis on learning implies that technological choices and systems of production are interdependent, inseparable and *path-dependent* phenomena. Moreover, the *tacitness* and *uncertainty* surrounding innovation highlight the importance of continual adaptation, modification and improvement. Innovation is an incremental and cumulative process of continual modifications, not only to the product, but equally to process technologies and organizations which support production and diffusion.

Once the idea of a perfect market is rejected as the most appropriate environment for innovation the strategic role of the firm assumes increasing importance. According to Schumpeterian reasoning, the dynamic entrepreneur - as a basic agent for innovation - carries an important, but far from exclusive, weight in the innovation process. Rather, the increasingly collective nature of innovation suggests a more broadly conceived pattern of organizational involvement (Reich, 1990).

I. ITALIAN SYSTEMS OF INNOVATION

Franco Malerba (1993), in describing the contemporary Italian national system of innovation, highlights the coexistence of two distinct "systems of innovation"; the former is represented by the "small firms network" and the latter by the more traditional "core R&D system of innovation". Although the two systems are constantly and intensively interacting and supporting one another, they are nevertheless distinct. While the small firms' network system is made up of many SMEs (small and medium enterprises) operating in industrial districts (such as Brianza) that interact at the *regional* level, the "core R&D system" is composed of those firms with formal R&D labs and potent external linkages (universities, technical institutes, public research centres) at the *national* level. Malerba claims that the small firms' networks is far more effective and successful (in terms of the innovative output) than the latter due to the dynamic scale economies associated with learning through accumulated expertise and continual upgrading. The core formal R&D system, on the other hand, despite substantial R&D growth during the 1980s, has not been as successful for historical reasons associated with the characteristics of the Italian industrialization process. However, it would be quite misleading to see these two systems as functioning in isolation from each other. An array of linkages between the national, regional and local level has evolved, often with considerable public support. A number of innovation centres (such as CESTEC in Lombardy), supported by private firms, industrial associations, financial organisations, research institutes and regional government bodies, disseminate technological information and provide necessary training. Also an array of fiscal incentives and favourable credit conditions has been used to diffuse the latest technologies, especially among SMEs.

During the 1970s, Italy emerged as the world's leading furniture exporter, a position that it sustained in the subsequent decade. (In 1980, its share of world exports, in value terms, was 22.7 per cent). In the 1990s, Italy has remained the unchallenged world leader in furniture-making, especially for upholstered furniture, living-room furniture and contemporary chairs (ITC, 1990). Unprecedented growth of the industry over the past two decades was due to profound changes in technological structures and application of new materials as well as to the adoption of new systems of production. Underlying the transformation of a traditional, low value-added, labour-intensive, craft-based industry into a capital- and knowledge-intensive industry, has been a restructuring process through the flexible and highly innovative industrial structure described by the MID, of which Brianza is the most successful case in furniture-making (Bellandi, 1989).

The range of organizational structures utilized by Italian furniture producers has evolved over time in response to major changes in their macro-economic and technological environment. Three leading trends that characterize the restructuring process of the 1970s were the predominance of the small firm (Bellandi, 1989; Beccattini, 1987), decentralization of production, known generally as *decenttramento produttivo* (Silvestrelli, 1979; Florio, 1982), and increased use of subcontracting (Brusco, 1982; Silvestrelli, 1979; Florio, 1982).

During its rise to global export pre-eminence, the Italian furniture industry has had to adapt to adverse external conditions, although this sector has fared better than most of the other Italian industries. Between 1970 and 1980, the industry's annual growth rate was over 9 per cent (three times the national industrial average). During the same period, the industry's overall output increased by 118 per cent, while labour productivity almost doubled (+ 92 per cent). Throughout the 1970s, the Italian economy experienced very slow growth in industrial activity in general. Although the furniture industry did not escape the negative impact of the oil crisis and subsequent fall in demand in the early 1980s (particularly between 1982-1985), it nevertheless quickly recovered in the post-1985 period. Throughout the 1980s, productivity per employee increased by almost 40 per cent (CSIL, 1988).

The expansion of Italian furniture production was principally export-driven, largely owing to increased demand from neighbouring European Community countries and the Middle East. Despite severe international recession in the mid-1970s, the value of Italian furniture exports increased by 1000 per cent over the decade. From 1970 to 1988, the Italian share of global furniture exports nearly doubled in value, rising from 10.9 per cent in 1970 to 19.8 per cent in 1988.

The Italian furniture industry never embraced a Fordist pattern of productive organization nor Taylorist structures of work organization and has remained dominated by its traditional craft heritage. However, the 1960s did witness an absolute drop in the number of artisanal firms and a noticeable increase in large firms. Both trends were reversed in the 1970s, with the firms in the 10 to 49 employee category making the greatest gains. Only two firms employed over 500 employees out of the total number of 33,936 productive units. Employment rose by 14 per cent in the 1970s. Despite a set-back in the early 1980s, the industry quickly re-established itself and between 1970-1986 the average annual growth rate was 9 per cent (three times the national average). This trend continued throughout the 1980s. The rationalization of the furniture sector, which began in the latter part of the 1960s and became fully established in the 1970s is intimately associated with *decenttramento produttivo* or productive decentralization (Silvestrelli, 1979; Florio, 1982) or externalization of production via massive increases in external sub-contracting at all stages of production and distribution. This comprises the principal type of organizational innovation which has accompanied the process of technical change. Furniture in Italy is made predominantly within industrial districts of which Brianza is the most illustrative and successful example. Brianza has approximately 4,500 firms, that, on the average, employ five people. The district is made up largely of small firms, (craft-based artisan firms employing under 10 people), a small core of market leaders (four to five firms), a moderate number of medium-sized firms but practically no firms employing over 500 employees.

Throughout the 1970s, a new vertical division of labour emerged among the furniture firms within industrial districts such as Brianza. The small craft workshop producing a variety of products, usually in wood and with traditional technologies, became a specialized unit often working for a larger firm and on standardized semi-finished components (particle-board) with highly automated, small-scale, high-tech machines. The finished components were then assembled by the large companies. This facilitated a process of industrial reorganization combining the principles of mass production and greater product customization. A number of prominent firms emerged which dictated the standards, particularly with respect to design and the fashionable qualities associated with furniture - these included Cassina, B&B and Zanotta. Although precise statistical data on the productive structure of the sector according to the pattern of final output, that is, the distribution of firms by size of final output (or the degree of concentration by output) is not available, the breakdown of the share of manufacturing output has been estimated by the Centre for Light Industry Studies (CSIL) to be approximately as follows: 40 per cent of total final output is produced by the large firms (between 50-500 employees); 30 per cent of output by medium-size firms (between 20-49 employees), while the remaining 30 per cent is produced by the mini firms and the handicrafts (under 20 employees).

Table 1

An international comparison of firm size in the furniture industry (1976)

Countries	Firms with >10 employees	Average no. of employees in firms with >10 employees	Percentage of firms employing >100 employees
USA	5 250	57.1	.....
Italy	3 476	31.1	3.8
Germany	1 730	87.9	12.2
France	1 600	53.3	10.1
UK	1 480	57.1	18.0
Spain	1 717	...	0.8
Sweden	280	42.8	7.0

Source: Florio, 1982, p.47.

The second aspect of productive decentralization has involved the externalization of production via the effective and extensive subcontracting of horizontal and vertical activities. While subcontracting was undoubtedly present in the previous craft structure of industry, it increased substantially in the 1970s. Although firms in Brianza vary considerably in the degree of subcontracting, all firms now engage in some form of subcontracting along the value chain. This not only includes the relation between the larger firms engaged in assembly and retailing and those (mostly small) firms finishing particular components but also among the smaller firms themselves engaged in the various specialized activities in the production cycle. According to one set of measures of decentralization of production, the share of subcontracting expenditure in the furniture industry between 1971 and 1981 increased by close to 250 per cent compared to the average rise in the rest of the Italian manufacturing sector of around 75 per cent (Ferri, 1985, pp. 24-25).

II. INDUSTRIAL RESTRUCTURING IN THE ITALIAN FURNITURE INDUSTRY

Restructuring in the 1970s refers to the innovative corporate strategies of the large firms that was demanded by the changing production requirements of the times, namely, multi-plant investments, collaboration agreements, flexible automation and increased reliance on subcontracting or externalization of production. Underlying this process was the evolution of the industrial sector towards a fragmentation of its supply structure, with increasing prominence of firms employing fewer than 50 employees at the expense of the larger firms with more than 500 employees. The last element formed an important component of the strategies evolving within the leading furniture firms which were faced with daunting challenges, such as increased power of the trade unions, growing competition from the NICs and declining domestic demand. Similar processes were occurring in other segments of the Italian economy. The 1971 and 1981 censuses revealed a fragmentation of the productive process.

Decentralization of the productive cycle has also signified restructuring of the industry from the larger-scale, long-batch production of the 1960s and 1970s to the small-scale, short-batch production of the 1980s which has proved more profitable. The most noticeable organizational innovation, supportive of process and product innovations, has occurred via widespread use of subcontracting and through external acquisition of semi-finished parts and components, previously performed internally. This trend, which had begun in the 1960s, took root in the 1970s and was almost universally applied by the 1980s.

Table 2

Structure of the Italian furniture industry
(distribution of firms by number of employees)

Size	1961 Firms	Per cent	1971 Firms	Per cent	1981 Firms	Per cent
1-9	26 609	92.8	27 515	88.6	29 207	86.3
10-49	1 815	6.3	3 013	9.7	395	11.7
50-99	195	0.7	393	1.3	364	1.1
100-499	69	0.2	132	0.4	149	0.4
500+	1	0.0	4	0.0	2	0.0
Total	28 769	100.0	31 072	100.0	33 858	99.5

Source: Based on ISTAT statistics and calculations by the author.

The key product- (and simultaneously, process-) innovation underlying these processes was particle-board and an appropriate technology to fashion it. This enabled the production of a customized product at mass-production prices. Such developments reinforced changes in the product itself towards the evolution of furniture from an article of utility to an article of fashion which encouraged corporate responses based on the production of small-batch, high quality, customized goods produced in unprecedented variety. Though not incompatible with Fordist production techniques, these changes have allowed the possibility of transcending the furniture industry's dualistic structure (Silvestrelli, 1979). The basis of the successful restructuring process in the furniture sector has been a high-price/high-quality product gaining market share, manufactured within a flexible and highly innovative industrial structure in an industrial district of which the best known is Brianza. Competition based on such a high-price product in itself indirectly suggests an improvement in quality and consequently a transition towards higher market segments characterized by product differentiation.

Brianza is unquestionably the most important of all furniture MIDs in Italy, contributing over 25 per cent of total Italian output in furniture, particularly in the upholstered furniture segment (requiring highly skilled craftsmen) and kitchens for the higher market segment. By 1981, over one-quarter (26 per cent) of the Lombardian labour force was employed in wood-related industries. In Lombardy, 410 industrial firms (each with over 20 employees) were registered, engaging 17,042 workers. In the 1970s, the average non-artisan firm employed 41.6 employees. There were nearly 200 artisan firms in the region employing approximately 1,580 workers, the average-sized firm employing eight workers (Silvestrelli, 1982). Close to a quarter (22.09 per cent) of Italy's investments in furniture were in Lombardy, making this region the nation's leading area for furniture making. By the 1980s, the industrial region of Brianza had approximately 4,500 furniture firms whose average size was five employees, with a small core of market leaders (five firms of approximately 200 employees), and a moderate number of medium-sized firms (200 to 400 employees). Brianza supplies the great consumption centres around Milan and northern and central Italy. Product innovation and differentiation formed the leading strategies for this purpose. These market leaders have set up their own research centres, closely studying related technological developments in similar industries in Italy and abroad in order to keep abreast of the state-of- the-art techniques and processes. While the artisan and small firms (productive units employing fewer than ten employees) were favoured by their physical proximity to larger firms, it was their social interaction (institutionalized through their artisan association - CNA-FNALA and informal channels of information-sharing cultural associations, etc.) which had expanded in recent years to embrace professional and technical societies, business associations, research centres, trade fairs, export consortia and exhibits, thereby modernizing a traditional craft district into a genuine industrial district. In the furniture sector, 30 per cent of all firms were artisan-type (employing fewer than 20 employees) producing approximately 35 per cent of the total sector's output.

III. THE SURVEY

The data presented in this paper are based upon survey evidence from interviews with owners and key-decision makers and other representatives of the furniture industry in Italy, collected by the author in the spring of 1989, on the basis of questionnaires administered to a random sample of 20 furniture firms of differing sizes.

During the interviews, the respondents were asked to evaluate the consequences and effects of the factors listed below related to the introduction of innovations in their firms, to which the following responses were provided (see table 3). These factors are ranked by the mean score, in order of importance, by our respondents (found in column one *rank*). The second column names the particular *factors* being evaluated). The factors are ranked by the *mean score*, on a *0 to 10* point scale which is located in the third column. The fourth column supplies the *acceptance rate*, or the percentage of respondents who rated these factors with at least a 4 point score, indicating their estimation of the factor to be at least of medium influence.

Product innovation through design can be classified in two varieties: *development of new products*, or innovations based on industrial design, and *incremental innovations*, or improvement via continuous refinement, adaptation and modification to standard models, namely *product differentiation*. The creation of the modern furniture industry has largely converged on the latter. The respondents were asked to assign a value to each type of technological innovation which occurred in their firms in order of importance. Their responses are presented in table 3.

As table 3 indicates, our respondents have confirmed that *product innovations* (mean score = 7, acceptance rate = 90 per cent), and *improvement in existing processes* (mean score = 6; acceptance rate = 80 per cent) ranked higher than new *process innovations* and *improvement in existing products*.

Table 3

Types of innovation in Brianza

Rank	Factor*	Mean score (0-10)	Acceptance rate, percentage of firms (*rounded*)
1	c	7.0	90
2	d	6.0	80
3	e	5.0	74
4	f	5.0	68

*
c= Product innovation
d= Improvement in existing processes
e= Improvement in existing products
f= Process innovation

Scoring system (0-10):
      0-3 = Weak influence
      4-6 = Medium influence
    7-10 = High influence

Number of missing observations: 0 (n=20).

Source: Survey.

The findings from our research established that the Italian furniture industry was highly innovation-conscious. The firms in our sample readily identified the following process innovations as central to their activity: (a) the use of specialized machinery and new computer-based technologies; (b) the further use of robots for industrial purposes; (c) the introduction of prefabricated panels into furniture making; (d) the insertion of new man-made materials and products into furniture making; (e) contracting from outside the firm. If not already introduced, such innovation was expected to be further diffused in the near future and firms were responding accordingly. Both product innovation and improvement in the quality of existing products were recognized as central by producers in Brianza in which respect market research and understanding consumer preferences were considered highly influential, though in conjunction with the demands of leading firms and distributors (as table 3 indicates).

As table 4 suggests, factor (c) consumers' preferences plays a critical role in the process of new product creation for 95 per cent of the respondents, while in response to another question, up to 40 per cent of the respondents interpreted innovation as a direct result of *demand by the final users*. New products are continually being created

Table 4

Factors influencing creation of new products in Brianza

Rank	Factor*	Mean score (0-10)	Acceptance rate, percentage of firms (*rounded*)
1	d	7.6	89
2	c	7.4	95
3	f	5.7	74
4	g	5.6	74

*
d= Market research
c= Changes in consumers' preferences
f= New products in leading firms
g= Changes in distributors' preferences

Number of missing observations: 0 (n=20).

Source: Survey, Q.13, \d\, \c\, \f\, \g\.

to suit consumers' needs and even to create them, illustrated by the high ranking provided to the effect of *demand-inducing* (supplied to another question in the survey). This implies that leading firms in the district are not simply responding passively to market signals but acting strategically to defend their market position through active product development. As table 4 also shows, leading firms in Brianza have played a critical part in this process by engaging in demand-inducing types of innovations in order to ensure future demand. Such a strategy is coupled by considerable **market research** (mean score = 7.6, acceptance rate = 89 per cent), and close contact with - but not excessive dependence upon - the **distributors** (mean score = 5.6, acceptance rate = 74 per cent).

Table 5 presents the key innovations in products in the narrow sense, as judged by our respondents, according to the answers provided to the survey.

<u>Table 5</u>

Key innovations in products, in the narrow sense, introduced in firms in the last 20 years

Rank	Factor*	Mean score (0-10)	Acceptance rate, percentage of firms (*rounded*)
1	a	9.0	95
2	b	8.0	68
3	c	8.0	65
4	d	7.0	56
5	e	7.0	80

*
a= Use of chipboard which enabled assembly-line production
b= Use of MDF (medium-density fibreboard) for wood panelling
c= Combining quality, design and functionality
d= Use of polyurethane for upholstery
e= Transition from traditional to modern styles of furniture

No. of missing observations = 0   (n=20).

<u>Source</u>: Survey, Q. 15 \a\.

Internal learning (inside company) was ranked as the leading channel of technological diffusion (mean score = 8, acceptance rate = 100 per cent); this was followed by *integration with more successful companies* (mean score = 8, acceptance rate = 60 per cent); via *informal channels* (mean score = 4, acceptance rate = 53 per cent), and only in fifth place, via *imported technologies* (mean score = 3, acceptance rate = 23 per cent). This would confirm a high degree of national technological development and low dependence on foreign technology sources (see table 6).

Table 6

**Channels of diffusion in Brianza
respondents' ratings of channels of technology diffusion**
(Percentage of firms)

Rank	Factor*	Mean score (0-100)	Acceptance rate, percentage of firms *(rounded)*
1	a	100	8.0
2	c	100	8.0
3	b	60	5.0
4	e	53	4.0
5	d	23	3.0

*
a = Internal learning in company
c = Integration with more successful companies
b = Personnel mobility in firm
e = Through informal channels
d = Through imported technologies

No. of missing observations: 1 (n=19).

Source: Survey, Q. 19

Determinants of innovation

As table 7 suggests, **learning** from both formal and informal sources was recognized as important to the process of innovation; however, **technical innovations acquired from other firms** (informal source, including imitation) was ranked higher than **internal R&D** (formalized source) by the respondents. Given the low rating of contractual acquisition (patents and licences), the critical importance of inter-firm, user-producer relations and inter-industry technological interdependence is underscored. Not surprisingly, **outside job orders** were only considered to be an influential factor for the handicrafts and the mini firms. Given the significance of learning through informal channels, one would expect the ability to diffuse innovations to be high in Brianza.

Despite a certain ambivalence towards the extent of vertical disintegration, *decenttramento produttivo* was itself recognized as a major stimulant to innovation by survey. Such evidence would strongly suggest that organizational factors play a considerable role in the innovative process. The pattern of interrelationship between firms encountered in Brianza can be characterized by a well-established system of relations of informal *networking* and powerful *user-producer interactions*. Innovation within this context is the result of networking not only by the group of leading firms but also throughout the entire industrial district. Productive networking not only encourages learning for each firm, but also increases the firms' interdependence thereby encouraging collective learning. This is facilitated by horizontal supply regimes and non-hierarchical decision-making processes. The resulting multiple sources of innovation and diversity of production techniques further facilitate the diffusion of entrepreneurial skills, creativity and the rapid adoption of new innovations.

Table 7

Factors determining innovation in Brianza

Rank	Factor*	Mean score (0-10)	Acceptance rate, percentage of firms (*rounded*)
1	n	6.0	60
2	g	5.0	48
3	a	4.0	50
4	i	3.0	42
5	b	3.0	28
6	k	2.0	25
7	h	2.0	24
8	l	2.0	19
9	m	2.0	18
10	c	1.0	12
11	f	1.0	6

*
n= Acquired from other firms in same sector
g= Technological innovations from abroad embodied in
materials and components
a= R&D in own laboratories
i= Innovations acquired from other firms
b= Innovations developed in own firm but not in R&D laboratories
k= Innovations acquired by Italian producers
h= Innovations from Italy embodied in materials and components
l= Innovations acquired through human capital
m= Innovations acquired from universities and research centres
c= Outside job orders
f= Innovations transmitted through capital ventures

Number of missing observations: 0 (n=20).

Source: Survey, Q. 25.

Innovations in materials

Materials used for the production of furniture in Italy have undergone a total transformation in the last 40 years. Up to the 1960s, the Italian furniture industry was a traditional industry using solid wood as its primary input. The increasing diversity of inputs and their gradual adaptation and improvement has been a central component in the modernization of the Italian furniture industry. The substitution of particle-board for timber has enabled substantial natural-resource saving activities. This literally invisible innovation has transformed furniture-making.

The domestic manufacture of particle-board using a much reduced volume of solid wood has meant that over 60 per cent of all of the primary material used for furniture production in Italy is now domestically produced. Moreover, the particle-board is itself undergoing constant improvement - the latest form, medium-density fibreboard (MDF), is already being extensively used in Brianza.

Wood substitutes represent only one of the new materials in furniture production. The use of metals and plastics with respect to both the final product in, for example, office furniture and equally new fittings and joiners, has been a noticeable feature of the past two decades and a source of ongoing innovation. In fact, part of the success of firms in Brianza has undoubtedly been their ability to combine these different materials. Another significant material around which Italy has built a particular reputation is leather. Significantly, the adaptation of these new inputs has involved close relations between the furniture industry and other industries (such as chemicals, automobile, and electronics industries).

The application of particle-boards has itself required complementary innovation, particularly in the area of *finishing*. Undoubtedly, the adaptation of an appropriate machine-technology has been essential to the successful spread of particle-board use. Without the emergence of numerous and widely diverse small-scale specialized CN/CNC machines adapted from metal manufacture, vertical disintegration and decentralization of production would not have been feasible. As the technology evolved in the past two decades, concomitantly the productive processes were revolutionized, exerting strong pressure on the organizational and commercial features of the industry. Close-knit links between furniture producers and wood-working machine suppliers have been decisive in enabling the necessary degree of flexibility in furniture-making. The furniture producers often "contract" out their orders to the machine producers for a particular type of machine/technology (machines made to order) in response to their specific needs (CSIL, 1988). The wood-working machine suppliers not only provide credit and finance for the purchase of the new technologies and machinery, but also engage in the training of labour, offer quality post sale service, willingly trade in old models and effectively coordinate an active second-hand market (Ferri, 1985; CSIL, 1988).

Innovation in design

Furniture design falls into two basic categories: period reproduction and modern furniture. While the latter category lends itself more readily to industrial design, as it is based on the use of the particle-board, the former tends to be made of solid wood and is less subject to mechanized treatment. Increasingly, modern furniture is taking the form of systems furniture, providing even greater opportunity for design modification, not only with the furniture itself but in relation to corresponding appliances and furnishings.

The development of modern Italian furniture is closely related to the development of industrial design. Over time, but particularly since the early 1920s, design has developed as an independent economic variable. However, as such, it embodies significant problems. Essentially, design requires experimentation and creativity the product of which rapidly becomes a public good. These characteristics are difficult to combine as the latter tends to undermine the former. Two additional considerations need to be recognized in assessing the application of design to industry. First, it usually requires a considerable degree of *tacit knowledge*, embodied in a "tradition" of design acquired through numerous formal and informal channels and established over many years. Secondly, it is likely to require considerable interaction between various groups involved in the production of the final product. The appropriate combination and development with respect to these different facets of design is likely to determine its successful application to industry.

Design in the furniture sector is a highly interactive process characterized by rapid response to changes from market leaders which are quickly diffused across the industry and built upon a wide network of human resources with knowledge and experience across all activities in the industry. Product design in Italy embodies a centuries-old tradition fostered by the local aristocracy whose demands extended across the product range and, more recently, with the emergence of a conforming bourgeois class. Italian furniture designers see themselves as innovators in life-styles and as trend-setters for fashion-conscious consumers rather than purely producers of functional commodities. Exclusivity and individuality account for much of the appeal of the prestigious Made in Italy brand name. Italian furniture is famous for design excellence which serves a primary strategy for Italian competitiveness. Brianza's proximity to Milan, arguably the world's leading centre of design, has in this respect been of critical significance to the success of the district.

With respect to the place of design, it is important to distinguish between the development of new products, i.e., radical innovations based on industrial design and incremental innovations, or improvement via continuous refinement, adaptation and modification to standard models, i.e. product differentiation. The creation of the modern furniture industry has largely converged on the latter. Moreover, design typifies the increasingly collective nature of innovation. Previously, design was the result of individual designers and/or master craftsmen. Presently, the sources of design are largely twofold: professional designers and architects; and individual manufacturers who often establish themselves on the basis of a new design. The former tends to predominate in the larger size firms often through commonly shared design centres (such as the original

Centro Ricerche of C&B Italia). However, with respect to both types and sources of innovation stemming from design, networking plays an essential role between designers and furniture producers (external partners with specialist expertise) who must respond to new materials (new man-made materials, colours, dyes, plastics, etc.) and grasp the manufacturing processes before they can invent and implement new designs. Design is increasingly a team effort, employing collective skills often using the latest computer technology. Moreover, the close association between a highly skilled labour force and their product constitutes an additional source of furniture design. With the advent of Computer-Aided-Design (CAD), design has become an integral part of the productive system, highlighting the role of networking, or "coupling" between science, technology, production and consumption.

Finally, the importance of incremental product innovation has meant significant changes in marketing and distribution. In this respect, furniture fairs, exhibitions and stylish catalogues have taken on importance and the presence of a highly decentralized distribution network (25,000 distributors in total) has ensured that producers are not dictated to by a few powerful distributors but remain highly responsive to volatile consumer tastes.

Design in Italy is a highly interactive process characterised by rapid response to changes from market leaders which are quickly diffused throughout the industry and set in a wide network of human resources with knowledge and experience across all activities in the industry. As such, networking and interactive learning are essential conditions for successful design. Not only the subcontracting system itself but also other channels of information such as trade fairs, handicraft associations and catalogues have been important in encouraging design values.

Our data shows that design has served as a primary component of innovation in the Italian furniture sector. *Learning in design* occupies the paramount role in product development for the great majority of the Italian respondents and is noticeably more important than more formal channels of innovation (see table 8).

<u>Table 8</u>

**Factors determining innovation and diffusion
in Brianza**

Rank	Factor	Mean score (0-10)	Acceptance rate percentage of firms (rounded)
1	d	6.0	84
2	e	6.0	79
3	c	5.0	63
4	b	5.0	63
5	a	3.0	26

*
d= learning in design
e= learning in machine use
c= by level of investment in R&D by companies operating in Italy
b= by opportunities offered by technical and scientific progress
a= opportunities offered by foreign technological opportunities

Number of missing observations: 0 (n=20).

<u>Source</u>: Survey, Q.33.

Innovation and work organization in Brianza

Genuinely new technological systems, of which flexible manufacturing is a case par excellence, necessarily signify alternative internal
structures within firms. There is much evidence to suggest that such
systems within successful firms present a noted tendency toward
horizontal and decentralized control structures, as opposed to vertical
hierarchical Taylorist labour practices (OECD, 1988). This has been
confirmed by our study. Evidence witnessed inside the most
successful firms, where labour moves freely from firm to firm within
the district and fluid internal market structures within the firms
themselves, diffusing generic knowledge and thereby increasing the

collective learning potential of the district as a whole. With personnel mobility, information moves freely as well, transmitting generic information and tacit knowledge at a rapid pace, acting as a key transmission of technology diffusion. The opening up of new channels of communications is crucial in the most innovative firms, thereby informally democratizing the firms' control strategies and promoting collective learning capabilities of the district as a whole.

The effect of new information technologies upon the system of work organization, however, has not been only one-sided, as there is evidence of both up-skilling and down-skilling occurring at all levels of the system, accompanying disturbances in the existing types of processes when major changes in job designs occur. Such changes are most evident in cases of process innovations (that is, the introduction of particle-board and of CAD/CAM processes), but does not characterize the predominant type of incremental product innovation occurring in this sector, where gradual changes are usually accompanied by up-skilling and job-broadening.

In all these respects, appropriate involvement of the labour force is essential. In Brianza, a flexible yet highly skilled workforce is favoured by the existence of a labour market internal to the industrial district rather than specific to the firm. This guarantees the provision of transferrable skills while the costs of training labour are socialised within the district. Moreover, the benefits of innovation are readily recognized by the workforce and the costs are minimized through continued high levels of employment inside the district.

Workers in the small- and medium-sized firms tend to be multi-skilled and have relations of professional camaraderie, despite the relatively low degree of unionization (Trigilia, 1990). Due to the family-related nature of much employment, the informal (non-institutionalized) nature of relations among workers and the managers is reinforced. Moreover, the family structures enhance mobility and support investment in acquiring additional skills. The process of learning new skills is made more secure by the recognition that they will not be made redundant if their particular firm is forced into liquidation. The managers of the small firms (often brothers or close relatives) are themselves generally former workers and qualified skilled artisans who are still performing many different tasks within the handicrafts.

The Italian furniture industry carried through a successful process of restructuring in response to cost pressures, technical opportunities and changing patterns of demand and consumer tastes. The result has been a cumulative process of growth supported by important organizational changes described by an industrial district and characterized by a diversity of coordinating mechanisms particularly favourable to *interactive learning* and the diffusion of incremental innovations.

The industrial district of Brianza provides a very stimulating environment for innovation, due to (a) an appropriate incentive structure for innovation combining cooperative and competitive attitudes; (b) the nature of the community-based relations which provide the appropriate mixture of autonomy and integration; (3) a "loose" hierarchy guaranteeing appropriate managerial authority with elements of shop-floor responsibility. Institutions must, with respect to innovation reduce uncertainty by ensuring appropriate channels of information, enhancing learning, encouraging experimentation and mediating conflict through appropriate incentives and tenable forums for discussion between the affected parties.

The price mechanism acts as an integrating force; however, it does not act alone. The community market works well in Brianza but the quest continues for an appropriate balance between market and non-market coordination. The essence of the innovative ingenuity of this system lies precisely in its organizational and technological diversity, within a decentralized, non-hierarchical production process, based on a system of production displaying multiple sources of innovation and relying on *ex-post* market selection to shake out "the wheat from the chaff" (Nelson, 1982, 1986). While unsuccessful firms are subject to the pressure of bankruptcy, the assets released have plenty of opportunity to be redeployed in similar establishments or through the formation of new units; local substitution of all factors

Table 9.

Factors stimulating innovation in the furniture firms of Brianza

Factor	Influence
Learning in design	medium
Learning in machine use	medium
Market research	high
Changes in consumer preferences	high
Changes in distributors' preferences	medium
New products in leading firms	medium
Opportunities offered by foreign technological achievements	weak
Opportunities offered by technical and scientific progress	medium
Level of investment in R&D by domestic companies	medium
Favourable market prospects in more advanced countries	medium
Possibility of satisfying needs of domestic market	medium
Lower unit costs in country relative to competitors' country	medium
Technological innovations acquired from other firms in same sector	medium
Technological innovations from abroad embodied in materials & components	medium
Technological innovations acquired via imports	weak
R&D in own labs within firms	medium
Technological innovations acquired from firms in other sectors	weak
Product innovation	high
Improvement in existing products	medium
Process innovations	medium
Improvement in existing processes	medium
Possibility of imitation abroad	weak

Source: Survey

of production is readily available. However, entry is limited by informal social networks and high degrees of tacit knowledge. The community itself represents a repository of such knowledge reinforced by inherited family commitment to a particular craft tradition. Indeed the family structure, at least in Brianza, has wide significance for the success of the district.

The family is only one among a number of coordinating institutions that support economic activity within the district. The large firms are often the instigators and defenders of higher standards, particularly in the area of research and industrial relations. Public support is also important, especially with respect to training. The presence of several distinguished technical schools in the area exercise an important function in the information-transmission process. Moreover, the local state has often provided support to information centres and export consortia within industrial districts, though perhaps less so in Brianza where the accumulation of managerial, technical, professional and commercial expertise in furniture-making stretches back over 200 years.

The establishment of linkages and an appropriate pattern of interaction between activities constituting the broad process of furniture-making has been identified as the central story behind Brianza's successful competitive performance. In this context, it is necessary to highlight the close-knit relationship between the wood-working machine producers and the furniture producers (Ferri, 1985).

Despite the remarkable success of Brianza, the ongoing problems relating to labour training, promotion and access to external markets inherent in this pattern of industrial organization suggest a continual role for public coordination and support as well as joint intra-firm action. Indeed, to sustain incremental innovation of the kind discussed in this paper requires continuing institutional adaptation and the need for more, not less, constructive public policies.

REFERENCES

Andersen, E.S. and B. A. Lundvall (1988) (eds), "Small national systems of innovation facing technological revolutions: an analytical framework", in Freeman and Lundvall.

Arrow, K. (1962a), "The economic implications of learning by doing", *Review of Economic Studies*, 29 (June), vol. 80, pp. 155-73.

Arrow, K. (1962b), "Economic welfare and the allocation of resources for invention", in Lamberton, D.M. (1971), *Economics of Information and Knowledge*, Penguin, Harmendsworth, pp. 141-159.

Beccattini, G. (1987), *Mercato e Forze Locali, Il Distretto Industriale*, Il Mulino, Bologna.

Bellandi, M. (1989), "The Industrial District in Marshall", in Goodman et al.

Best, M. (1990), *The New Competition, Institutions of Industrial Restructuring*, Polity Press, Oxford.

Brusco, S. (1982), "The Emilian Model: productive decentralisation and social integration", *CJE*, no. 6.

CSIL, (1988), *Rapporto sulla struttura produttiva del settore legno-arredamento*, Milan.

Ferri, A. and A. Zini (eds.) (1985), *Il Parco maccine per la lavorazione del legno in Italia*, ERVET, Bologna.

Dosi, G., Freeman, C., Nelson R., Silverberg, G. and L. Soete (eds.) (1988b), *Technical Change and Economic Theory*, Frances Pinter, London.

Florio, M. (1982), *Il Falegname e l'Economia Politica*, Il Mulino, Bologna.

Freeman, C. and B.A. Lundvall (eds.) (1988), *Small Countries Facing a Technological Revolution*, Pinter, London.

Hagdoorn J. and J. Schakenraad (1991), "The Internationalization of the Economy, Global Strategies and Strategic Technology Alliances", *Nouvelles de la Science et des Technologies*, vol. 9, no. 2, 29-41.

Hodgson, G. (1988), *Economics and Institutions*, Polity Press, Blackwell, Cambridge.

ISTAT, (various years), Rome.

ITC (1990), *Wooden Household Furniture: A Study of Major Markets*, UNCTAD/GATT, Geneva.

Kozul, Z. (1992), "Organizing flexibility: a comparison of the Italian and Slovene Furniture Industries", *Economic Analysis and Worker Management*, vol.3, XXVI, pp. 216-243, Zagreb.

Lundvall, B.A. (1988a), "Innovation as an interactive process: from user-producer to the national system of innovation", in Dosi, *et al.*

Lundvall, B.A. (1988b), "Institutional learning and national systems of innovation", paper presented at Conference, Roskilde University.

Malerba, F. (1993), "Italy, the national system of innovation", in Nelson, R. and N. Rosenberg, *National Innovation Systems*, Oxford University Press, New York.

Nelson, R. and S. Winter (1982), *An Evolutionary Theory of Economic Change*, The Belknap Press of Harvard University Press, Cambridge.

Nelson, R. (1986), "Incentives for entrepreneurship and supporting institutions", in Ronen.

Nelson, R. and N. Ronenberg (1993), National Systems of Innovation, Oxford University Press, New York.

OECD (1987), *Structural Adjustment and Economic Performance*, Paris.

OECD (1988), *New Technologies in the 1990s: A socio-economic strategy*, Paris.

Pyke, F., Beccattini G. and W. Sengenberger (1990), *Industrial Districts and Inter-firm Cooperation*, International Institutue for Labour Studies, ILO, Geneva.

Reich, R. (1991) "Entrepreneurship Reconsidered: the team as a hero," *Participative Management*, Harvard Business School, Cambridge Massachussets.

Ronen, J. (ed.) (1986), *Entrepreneurship*, Lexington Books, Lexington, Massachussets.

Rosenberg, N. (1982), "Inside the Black Box", *Technology and Economics*, Cambridge University Press, Cambridge.

Rosenberg, N. (1988), "Technology and growth experiences: some lessons for the developing countries", Stanford University, paper prepared for the World Bank Seminar (November).

Schumpeter, J. (1942, 1987), *Capitalism, Socialism and Democracy*, Unwin, London.

Silvestrelli, S. (1979), *Lo Sviluppo Industriale delle Imprese Produttrici di Mobili*, Angeli, Milan.

Silvestrelli, S. (1982), "L'organizzazione del lavoro", *Il Settore del Mobilio e Arredamento Problemi e Prospettive*, Lorenzon, F. et al. (eds.), Treviso, October.)

Trigilia, C. (1990), "Italian industrial districts, neither myth nor interlude", in Pyke, *et al.*

United Nations, Transnational Corporations and Management Division, (TCMD), (1992), *World Investment Report*, United Nations, New York.

Wilkinson, F. (1983), "Productive systems", *CJE*, 1983, vol. 7, pp. 413-429.

Wright, R. (1991), *Three Essays in Comparative Economic Analysis*, (Ph.D. thesis) Cambridge University, Cambridge.

NOTES

1. While its origins can be traced to the ideas of Smith, Marx, Schumpeter and Marshall, the work of Kaldor, Nelson, Winter, Murrell, Rosenberg, Pasinetti, Dosi, Freeman and Lundvall provides a more contemporary reference point.

2. The evolutionary approach used in this paper builds upon the following crucial assumptions: (a) the focus of analysis shifts from a single productive unit ruled by a monolithic interest to a network of firms often found in different industries cooperating together and mutually stimulating each other into innovative and competitive behaviour. The dynamics of interactions between firms with different types of expertise assume the spotlight, i.e., the social organization of the firm and the market structure matters. In contrast to more orthodox approaches, the system of industrial organization (including the organization of the market) plays a critical role in fostering or impeding the evolution of the process of qualitative change and development; (b) technical change and innovation, unlike other produced commodities, contains a significant degree of *tacit knowledge* (or know-how), which cannot be simply codified and transferred through formal channels but must, in part, consist of accumulated experience and skills acquired though practical experience. Moreover, such knowledge and the associated learning processes involved are likely to require complex social channels of support if it is to be fully utilized. From our perspective, *diffusion* or the spread of new products and processes between firms in an industry and across industries is often of far greater importance than the inventive process. The rates of diffusion are affected not only by the structure of the market but even more so by the nature of inter-firm relationships; (c) innovation represents progress in knowledge, which is not always immediately recognizable (or measurable) owing to its cumulative nature. Consequently, innovation often occurs, not only from additional R&D expenditure, but as a result of experience acquired through time, whereby learning acts as a critical source of gains in productivity. The notion of innovation adopted here implies

that the savings commonly associated with the learning effect, that is, labour costs, and the removal of bottlenecks (Davies, 1979), are extended to other activities including management, marketing and distribution. Innovation is not easily susceptible to quantitative measurement precisely owing to this characteristic.

PART THREE

INDUSTRIAL DISTRICT EXPERIENCES
IN DEVELOPING COUNTRIES

Khalid Nadvi *

INTRODUCTION

The current crises in large-scale "Fordist" systems of industrial manufacturing has revitalized interest in small-scale manufacturing, in general, and small-firm industrial districts (IDs), in particular.[1] Although the idea of industrial districts dates back to Alfred Marshall, it has become widely associated with the contemporary success of regional small-firm industrial economies in various parts of Europe, and in the United States and Japan.[2] In addition, the concept has been identified as the small-firm variant of the flexible specialization paradigm (Piore & Sabel 1984), as constituting "regional production systems" (Storper & Harrison 1990) and as "historically and geographically specific technological-institutional systems" (Scott & Storper 1992).

Essentially, industrial districts are understood as consisting of clusters of small- and medium-sized enterprises within a specific industrial sector; they are usually process-specialized and interlinked with each other through production subcontractual arrangements, located in close proximity to one another within a well-defined geographical space and bound together by various sets of common social categories and values.

Such a system of industrial organization is felt to be resilient in the face of economic crises, to have a socially embedded and indigenous growth potential and to be conducive to innovation

---

* The paper was written while the author was with the Technology Programme of the UNCTAD secretariat.

(Schmitz 1989). Consequently, small firms are no longer perceived as marginal categories but as integral components of regional patterns of industrial and technological development.

The original Marshallian view of industrial districts has been extended in four important directions. First, through recognition that the State (particularly at the local level) and sectoral associations can play a pivotal role in fostering and assisting industrial districts. Secondly, through a greater emphasis on the regionally specific socio-cultural and political environment that strengthens the functioning of industrial districts. Thirdly, through the stress on innovation and the dynamics of technical learning resulting from user-producer interactions within process-specialized inter-firm cooperation. Fourthly, for its particular relevance to the context of incipient industrialization (Schmitz 1989).

This paper reviews the contemporary experience of industrial districts in developing countries with a particular focus on the technology dimensions of the model. Within this framework, four broad themes are examined. The question of how each impacts upon innovation and technological development will be considered. The first concerns the nature of inter-firm relations, both vertical and horizontal variants as well as with large enterprises, and the effect of such inter-firm networking on skill and technology development and innovatory behaviour through user-producer interactions. Secondly, the character of the "social milieu" within which IDs operate and which provides them with what has been termed as local "agglomerative economies", and the social regulatory mechanisms that serve to mediate inter-firm cooperation and competition within the clusters. Thirdly, the role of national and more importantly regional levels of the State, as well as sectoral and societal institutions, associations and consortia which assist small firms clusters through various "real services", including informational, technological, market and financial support (Brusco 1992). Fourthly, the implications of operating under labour surplus conditions (Sengenberger & Pyke 1991, Schmitz 1989). Are developing country industrial districts likely to follow the "low road" growth path, characterized by a strategy aimed at reducing wage costs in a price competitive manufacturing environment with sweatshop working conditions? Or will they take the "high road" where emphasis is placed upon product quality and sustained innovation as the basis for achieving a competitive edge? Alternatively, is there a middle path where competition based upon product innovation, quality and price coexist with labour surplus conditions? If so, how can small-firm clusters be motivated to move towards it, if not onto the "high road" itself?

Prior to reviewing the developing country case experiences, a few points of caution need to be noted. First, the current literature on industrial districts in developing countries is limited and uneven in detail.[3] Consequently, this paper cannot aim to provide an exhaustive survey of what may well be a fairly widespread phenomenon, given the magnitude of small-scale manufacturing in developing countries. Instead, it tries to draw out some common threads from the disparate evidence, in order to stimulate further discussion and inquiry.

Secondly, there is much confusion and conceptual weakness in the literature on industrial districts. Alongside the notion of industrial districts, dissimilar ideas associated with the model, such us flexible specialization, collective efficiency, diffuse industrialization, social milieu, economies of scale and scope need to be clarified. This task, which lies beyond the scope of our paper, has recently been attempted by several authors (Powell 1990, Asheim 1992, Pecquer & Silva 1992, Schmitz 1992b).

Thirdly, and allied to the above point, caution should be used regarding the way in which the industrial district concept is applied in contexts with which it has not been directly associated. The contemporary "ideal type" image of industrial districts has largely emerged from the Third Italy experience. A number of recent studies have stressed the diversity in industrial districts within the Third Italy, as well as across Europe as a whole (Amin 1989, Amin & Robins 1990, Murray 1987, Schmitz 1992a). Thus rather than attempting to "fit" diverse developing country experiences with small-firm clusters into the supposed ideal type framework, we will emphasize that there are likely to be different types of industrial districts and that they undergo different stages of development. What is critical is to be aware of the importance of contextual and historical specificities that have influenced the way in which industrial districts have taken shape and currently function; then what is common and generalizable as well as what is specific may be sought.

Finally, given the novelty of this approach and the manner in which it relates to a number of themes concerning small-scale manufacturing in developing countries, it may be useful to clarify what this paper is not about. The informal manufacturing sector (Bromley, ed., 1978; Sethuraman, ed., 1981; Portes *et al.*, ed., 1989), small/large firm subcontracting linkages (Watanabe 1983, Mead 1984, Lazerson 1990), new and appropriate technologies for small firms (Carr 1985, Kaplinsky 1990) are only touched upon in so far as they fall within the framework of spatially clustered small firms. Industrial estates, offshore industry, export zones and science parks lie outside the scope of the paper.

The paper is structured as follows: Section I briefly sets out the core elements of industrial districts which are pertinent to the developing country environment. The concerns expressed regarding the overall relevance of the concept to incipient industrialization are also mentioned. Section II reviews a number of developing country case studies. In addition, to a descriptive overview of the broad features of small-firm clusters, the discussion is structured around the implications for technology and technological innovation and the four associated themes outlined above. The final section summarizes the broad findings of the developing-country review. With respect to policy implications, it questions whether an industrial district, which encompasses both social and economic space, can be replicated by planned intervention from above, or whether it is essentially an endogenous development which can at best be fostered from below. Brusco's notion of stages of development of industrial districts would seem to indicate that, whereas in a number of cases potential industrial-district type formations have evolved, their further progress requires external intervention and support. This raises the question of modalities for articulating such support. The paper concludes with some additional questions regarding the relationships in inter-firm collaboration, the social fabric and technological progress within developing-country industrial districts.

I. CORE ELEMENTS OF THE INDUSTRIAL DISTRICT CONCEPT

At the level of production, industrial districts are characterized by a multi-skilled and dexterous craft labour force, a tendency to target niche markets, an accent on quality and continuous product and process innovation, an ability to exploit multi-task production technologies and a capacity to respond swiftly to shifting market conditions (Piore & Sabel 1984). Use of new flexible production technologies, notably the supposedly scale-neutral microelectronics,[4] and changes in the organization of production, both at the micro (individual firm) and the meso (cluster or sector) levels are all elements of the flexibly specialized view of small-firm industrial districts. Furthermore, inter-firm cooperation in production allows individual units to become process-specialized but yet avail themselves of external economies of scale and scope which would not be feasible had they been operating in isolation. In such settings of collective gains, "a small firm in an industrial district does not stand alone; a condition of its success is the success of the whole network of firms of which it is a part" (Sengenberger & Pyke 1991, p.1).

In sharp contrast to alternative analytical frameworks for small-scale manufacturing (Anderson 1982), the industrial district concept emphasizes four points: first, the spatial and sectoral clustering of small- and medium sized firms; secondly, interrelations between such small firms; thirdly, the growth dynamism of small-firm clusters primarily rooted in local and endogenous capabilities within the district and fourthly, the need for holistic analysis incorporating the social, economic and political dimensions that influence the way in which clusters of small firms organize, function and develop (Sengenberger & Pyke 1991).

At the heart of the industrial district concept is the notion that a substantial degree of inter-firm networking in production relations can take place when small firms cluster together in sector-specific agglomerations. Thus, clusters constitute an essential building-block of an industrial district. Production networks within the cluster are further accentuated by a thick web of social relations that tie firms together, and provide the basis for relations of trust and reciprocity necessary for the smooth functioning of network arrangements (Granovetter 1973).[5]

Production networks can consist of the following set of relations: (a) vertical patterns of production subcontracting, whereby individual enterprises are either process and/or product specialized; (b) horizontal patterns of subcontracting, whereby firms expand individual capacity at critical periods and take on large orders collectively; (c) sharing of tools, technology and skilled labour across enterprises; (d) formal and informal exchange of "generalized" information regarding market trends, prices, technological developments, product and process innovations, skills and access to factor markets; as well as "particular" knowledge of contacts, clients, workers and private and state institutions.

Through such forms of production networking, a number of external economies arise for firms within the cluster. These include: a specialized labour market within the confines of the cluster, thereby reducing job search costs; a specialized "information bank" as a result of the concentration of expertise and the sharing of generalized and particular knowledge; and the use of specialized machinery and skills through inter-firm division of labour. Similarly, ancillary trades and support services collect around the district providing, among others, raw materials, machine tools, repair, marketing and consultancy services. Thus, small-firm industrial districts not only become "nearly as spatially concentrated as a big integrated plant" (Bellandi, 1989, p.139) but are also capable of collectively exploiting external economies of scale and scope.

While industrial districts are known for inter-firm cooperation, there is also substantial competition between firms. Given the fine balance between competition and cooperation, and the fear of free riders, institutions and mechanisms are required that regulate relations among firms, minimize transactions costs within inter-firm relations, and provide the foundation for inter-firm cooperation. Consensual relations of trust and reciprocity between firms within the cluster have to be rooted in categories that go beyond impersonalized market transactions and into the community. Hence, inter-firm production networks are strongly supported by social and cultural categories (of, for example, kinship, religion, ethnicity, caste, education, history, political and corporate identities) that define the community and its institutions of governance. Industrial districts have been interpreted as "both a community of people and a population of firms in one naturally and historically bounded area. In the district, unlike in other environments, community and firms tend to merge [leading to a] thickening of industrial and social interdependencies" (Becattini 1990, p.38). The successful industrial district is marked by an extensive and intermeshed net of personal interactions between entrepreneurs, supported by the local "social milieu" which provides it with a set of "agglomeration economies" (Asheim 1992).

The social milieu also strongly influences, and is itself influenced by, patterns of technological change, innovation and diffusion. Technology is thus seen as an endogenous category directly related to the social fabric in which it is located. This has two important implications. First, that clusters of small firms carry with them an element of "tacit knowledge" regarding technology, skills, products and processes, often specific to that community, usually accumulated over an extended historical period and socially codified (Kozul 1992). Secondly, that innovation and technical progress is an evolving, incremental and systemic (as opposed to atomistic) process which builds upon tacit knowledge through the dynamics of interactions between users and producers (Lundvall 1988).

An interactive method of incremental "learning-by-doing/ learning-by-using" is of mutual benefit to both users and producers, particularly within vertical chains of sub-contractual and process specialized production. Informational exchanges in both individual user-producer interactions, and importantly within multilateral sets of interactions, allow for improvements in both product (i.e. design, price, marketing, etc.) and process (more efficient systems of production organization, improved use of technologies and adaptation of technology and skills). Such interactive "cooperation during the process of innovation" requires commonly accepted "codes of behaviour", "channels of information" and "mutual trust", all of which are anchored in the contextual social milieu of industrial districts where such interactions take place (Lundvall 1988, pp.352-354).

In addition to the production networks and the over-arching social codes that regulate production interrelations between small firms within industrial districts, the State (especially at the municipal and regional levels) and sectoral associations can play an important role in providing institutional support to industrial districts. At the national level, the State can influence the workings of industrial districts through the overall macroeconomic policy framework, particularly via fiscal, trade, industrial, sectoral and regional development policies, as well as through infrastructural development programmes (especially in the areas of transport, education, technology and vocational training).

At the cluster level, more devolved tiers of the State (municipal, local and regional governments) assist via urban development, locational and housing policies (Best 1990). Local governments, in tandem with sectoral associations, are also instrumental in the provision of credit, technical advice, vocational training and various "real services" (Brusco 1992). These include financial, managerial, accounting, quality control, research and information services. Such services are often either unavailable to small firms or are priced beyond their reach. Sector- specific real service centres have an important function in making information accessible to firms within the cluster. Such knowledge includes, among other elements, market information regarding consumer preferences, fashion trends, prices, input sources, as well as technological developments, technical standards, legal stipulations, import and export regulations, design and quality standards. Real service institutions can also play a significant part in facilitating the formation of financial and credit consortia and marketing cooperatives (Best 1990).

An important consideration for the successful functioning of real service institutions observed across a range of European cases is the active involvement, in both policy and management functions, of those very parties to whom such services are aimed (Schmitz 1992a, Asheim 1992, Best 1990, Brusco 1992). This requires the institutionalization of collective and representative sectoral associations and trade bodies within the cluster; and, the formation of cohesive and organic links at the local level between the cluster, the State and political organizations within civil society.

It is worth remembering that the ideal type image of industrial districts has been outlined in this section. The European experience does not always live up to this picture and there is a marked degree of heterogeneity. Furthermore, in spite of the "excitement" generated by the industrial district concept, there remain a number of concerns regarding the replicability in less developed countries of what is largely a developed European experience. As it is, there are doubts about whether the social milieu and territorially rooted trust relations embedded within an industrial district can be simulated through planned intervention from above even in industrially advanced economies (Asheim 1992).

In a developing-country environment, it is suggested that "sweating" labour is often the primary route for reducing production costs in a manufacturing system that lacks an innovatory spirit (Piore & Sabel 1984). Labour surplus conditions dull the prospects for innovation and it is feared that "the sheer unlimited size of the labour surplus makes a break out of [the] low-technology low-wage syndrome unlikely" (Schmitz, 1989, p.32). This has led to the argument that small-firm clusters may well face two contrasting growth paths (Sengenberger & Pyke 1991, Storper & Walker 1989). At one level, there is the "high road" or "strong competition", characteristic of the successful industrial districts, and synonymous with innovation, high quality, good working conditions, and technological progress. Alternatively, there is the "low road" or "weak competition", with low quality products, cheap labour, standardized production, and numerical labour flexibility.

It is debatable, however, whether small-firm clusters in developing countries face such starkly dualistic options. More probable is the notion of a continuum between the high and the low roads on which, for example, aspects of innovatory behaviour coexist with poor labour conditions. Such hybrid paths also strengthen the argument that the image of an ideal type industrial district applicable to all diverse experiences of developing countries is unhelpful. What is more useful is understanding the industrial district as a dynamic entity and analyzing the propulsion of its underlying growth trend.

II. SMALL-FIRM INDUSTRIAL DISTRICTS
IN DEVELOPING COUNTRIES

As mentioned earlier, the literature on small-firm industrial districts in developing countries is sparse and patchy. What information exists is largely incomplete and often based upon observations derived from data on the informal sector or small scale manufacturing studies which do not necessarily fit the broad parameters of the industrial district framework. Although useful insights can be drawn from such work, they fall short of holistic picture provided by a more focused approach. Consequently, the review will concentrate solely on those case studies which offer more convincing evidence of the existence of potential industrial districts or at the very least of small-firm clusters. On the basis of this material, we attempt to link observations on the themes indicated above and consider how they affect the process of technological development. These are: first, the nature of inter-firm relations; secondly, the issue of the social milieu; thirdly, the role of the State, particularly at the local level, and of sectoral associations, in supporting small-firm clusters; and, fourthly, the effects of labour surplus on the overall growth prospects of such clusters.

Case studies of small-firm clusters and "potential" industrial districts are found in countries with extremely divergent levels of economic and industrial development (including Burkina Faso, Cyprus, Ghana, India, Indonesia, Kenya, Mexico, Pakistan, Peru, Republic of Korea, Slovenia, Sudan, United Republic of Tanzania and Zimbabwe). Naturally, with differing industrial and trade regimes, this results in mixed experience regarding technology patterns and systems of production organization and implies that generalizations ought to be treated carefully. Broadly speaking, however, certain common patterns of inter-firm relations, social milieu, institutional intervention and technological developments can be discerned. Before turning to the discussion of each of these specific themes, an overview of small-firm clustering in developing countries is necessary.

A. The phenomena of small-firm clustering

As stated earlier, an essential building-block for potential industrial districts is spatial clustering of enterprises. Sector-specific and geographically bounded clusters seem to be a common phenomenon for small-scale manufacturing in developing countries. This has resulted in regions becoming known for specific sectors and activities. Firms are specialized within an industry; specialized and sector-specific factor markets as well as an assortment of ancillary services are found within the region. In many cases, such small-firm clusters enjoy a historical tradition in the area with local expertise in craft or artisanal workings of certain products alongside a custom of self-employment and entrepreneurship. Among manufacturing sectors commonly observed in a number of case studies of small-firm clusters in developing countries, four stand out. These are textiles and garments, footwear, carpentry and furniture, and metal products. Each activity has historical antecedents with the agrarian economy either in fashioning agricultural products or providing inputs to the local agricultural sector. Over time, such clusters of artisanal manufacturers have become increasingly specialized, having improved their technological capacity and acquired attributes of "modern" industry.

In India there have traditionally been "a large number of spatial clusters of small firms engaged in specialised industries - locks at Aligarh, leather footwear at Agra and Kanpur, cotton hosiery at Calcutta and Delhi; power looms at Bhiwandi, roofing tiles at Morvi; diesel engines at Rajkot and Coimbatore; brass parts at Jamnagar" and diamond polishing in Surat, Gujrat (Kashyap 1992, p.37). Such "space-bound dense clusters of small firms...related to a specialized industry" are even more pronounced in the Indian Punjab with "woollen garments, bicycles and bicycle parts, sewing machine parts [and] machine tools in Ludhiana; printing and printing goods, water pipes and bathroom fixtures, sports goods in Jullander; foundries in Batala; [and] agricultural machinery at Goraya" (Kashyap 1992, p.35).[6] Similar clusters may also be observed in various small and medium sized towns in the central and north-eastern region of the Pakistani Punjab. "Sialkot is famous for its sports goods and surgical equipment industries both of which are almost wholly export oriented. Gujrat is noted for the manufacture of electrical fans. Faisalabad is known for textiles and electrical products. Daska for farm machinery, Wazirabad for stainless steel cutlery and Gujranwala for producing textiles, metal products, electrical appliances, steel utensils and machine tools" (Nadvi, 1992, p.15).

Patterns of small-firm clustering have also been reported in Latin America. Mexico's footwear industry, with "86.5% of firms employing less than 50 employees", consists of small-firm clusters "concentrated in three different areas": Leon, Mexico City and Guadalajara. Each location is "specialized in a particular segment of the market: Leon mainly produces men's and children's shoes, Guadalajara women's shoes and Mexico City athletic shoes" (Rabellotti, 1992, p.4). The export-oriented footwear sector in Brazil is also regionally concentrated in two distinct centres, one specialising in men's shoes (Franca) and the other in women's shoes (Sinos Valley). Similarly, a significant component of the Peruvian shoe industry consists of a cluster of approximately 1,000 small firms located in the city of Trujillo (Villarán 1992).

Spatial clustering of manufacturing units along industry-specific lines is pronounced in the Republic of Korea. The footwear sector is largely found in Pusan (Levy 1991), the textiles industry in Daegu (known as the "textiles city"), automobile manufacturing in Ulsan and the high-tech microelectronics and semiconductor sector in the Seoul metropolitan region (Cho 1992). What distinguishes this country's industrial clusters is the manner in which small- and medium-scale firms are hierarchically networked and spatially clustered around large enterprises and industrial conglomerates ("chaebols"), and the way in which they are uniformly export-oriented and technologically differentiated within and between clusters.

At a more disaggregated level and in a less pronounced fashion, clusters of small firms are observed in sub-localities of urban centres in much of the developing world. In Lima, there is the "Gamarra Complex" consisting of "between 4,000 and 6,000 shops and workshops" manufacturing and marketing garments and fashionwear; and, the Tacora district with "between 500 and 700 metallurgical workshops and small foundries...located in a 15 acre area [operating in] crowded conditions...[in]...a somewhat marginalised district unlike any other area in Lima" (Villarán, 1992, pp.32 and 47). Suame, the "industrial shanty suburb of Kumasi", in Ghana is renowned for its small-firm clusters in the carpentry, vehicle repair, blacksmithing and engineering sectors with "around 40,000 craftsmen operating out of about 5,000 workshops" (Dawson 1992, p.35). Nadvi (1990) has observed clusters of small firms in a range of manufacturing sectors (woollen carpets, textile-weaving, footwear, furniture-making, and metal-working) located in different and distinct low-income areas of

Karachi and Gujranwala in Pakistan. Comparatively less spatially and sectorally distinctive patterns of clustering have been noted among urban small-scale manufacturing units in Nyala, Sudan (Hansohm 1992); for small woodworking units in intermediate towns in Kenya, United Republic of Tanzania and Zimbabwe (Sverrisson 1992b, Aeroe 1992); and in the informal sector of Ouagadougou, Burkina Faso (Van Dijk 1992).

Small-firm clusters are also found in rural areas. In Indonesia, it is said that rural cottage industries "tend to operate in clusters" and that "craft clustering may even lead to specialisation of entire villages" (Weijland 1992, p.4). An example of this is the Javanese village of Tegalwangi and its surrounding area which is the centre of Indonesia's increasingly export-oriented rattan furniture industry with nearly 400 (almost all small-scale) enterprises (Smyth 1991). Wilson (1992) has reported that small-firm clusters, many of which are exporting to the United States market, are found in "some 50 to 60 small [rural] towns which have specialized in a particular 'modern' industrial sector [especially garments] in the western central region" of Mexico (Wilson, 1992, p.58).

B. Industrial districts and inter-firm relations

Despite the efficiency gains associated with production subcontractual relations and information exchanges, clustering does not necessarily lead to inter-firm collaboration. The diamond-polishing cluster of Surat (India), marked by high growth in export earnings and employment levels and bearing a strong element of trust relations was characterized by "competitive individualism" not inter-firm cooperation (Kashyap 1992). Within the Slovenian furniture industry "enterprises neither compete nor cooperate but are forced into vertical integration, self sufficiency and economic autarchy" (Kozul 1992). In the small-firm construction sector in Zimbabwe, although a number of units were specialized in various trades and worked on a subcontracting basis, there was "no evidence of enterprise cooperation in terms of production innovation" and extremely low levels of technical division of labour (Rasmussen 1992).

In the Mexican footwear cluster, Rabellotti (1992) found little sign of small firms engaging in subcontractual arrangements. Among the few that did (usually larger concerns), there appeared to be a positive correlation between profit levels and subcontracting. Wilson (1992), from her study of the rural knitwear cluster in Mexico, observed that earlier patterns of inter-firm cooperation, such as emergency assistance, information-exchange and horizontal capacity-sharing during peak periods, had over time been eroded with the increasing differentiation within the cluster and the weakening of former interpersonal social networks.

By the same token, inter-firm production network arrangements associated with industrial districts can occasionally occur in the absence of clustering. The Consortium for Capital Goods Industry Development (CBK) in Lima brought together 30 small- and medium-scale enterprises in the metallurgy sector into various subcontractual production and innovation relations with each other yet without being located in the same area (Villarán 1992). Similarly, Hansohm's (1992) study of Nyala (Sudan) shows that relatively dispersed small carpentry workshops were far more integrated in terms of production networking and more innovative than spatially concentrated metal workshops.

Nevertheless, geographical proximity and sectoral specialization represented in clustering facilitate inter-firm networking. Inter-firm relations, or production networks, lie at the core of the industrial district concept. At the very least, inter-firm networking can ease the exchange of information within the cluster. A more "advanced" form of inter-firm production network is that of subcontracting arrangements within the cluster which lead to process specialization; enable an "evolutionary" process of incremental technological innovation through multiple levels of user-producer interactions; and, cumulatively bring about "collective efficiency".

Forms of inter-firm relations

(a) *Information-sharing*

Information-sharing appears to be a common feature of small-firm clusters, even in the absence of direct production interrelations between firms within the cluster. Informal exchange of information can be deconstructed into two components of "generalized" and "particular" information (Granovetter 1973, Werbner 1990). The former consists of information regarding production, marketing, input and factor markets considered as being available to all within the cluster. The possession of such information is not likely to provide a firm with a significant competitive edge over firms that do not hold such knowledge. Particular information, however, is highly valued, closely guarded and shared only with those with whom an entrepreneur retains "strong ties".

Even if firms within the cluster remain secretive about particular information, sharing of general information can lead to collective gains in that it helps to reduce information-related transaction costs within the cluster, while improving the skill and technological capacity of the cluster and the ability of the cluster to respond collectively to shifts in markets. Such tendencies of sharing knowledge of product developments, labour- market information and interpersonal knowledge of skill and reliability of other producers and suppliers within the cluster was a feature of most clusters where inter-firm production networking existed. Even in some clusters where inter-firm networking was weak or had begun to break down, such as small/informal enterprises in Burkina Faso (Van Dijk 1992), and among the footwear and rural-based sweater manufacturing clusters in Mexico (Rabellotti 1992, Wilson 1992), information-exchange continued.

The exchange of particular information, notably regarding specific technologies, product and process innovations was generally restricted to those clusters where more extensive production networking and interactive relations were found. This, for example, could be seen within the Peruvian CBK consortium where firms were collectively engaged in product development; among the export groups set up by the Peruvian Association of Apparel Industry (APIC) (Villarán 1992); between the large firms and technologically skilled subcontractors within the Korean techno-spatial clusters (Cho 1992); and, to some extent, within the Kumasi cluster (Schmitz 1989, Dawson 1992).

(b)   *Large-small firm production relations*

Production networks within industrial districts that bring together large and small enterprises appear to be less frequent than networks between small firms. In some cases, large- and small-firm sectors operate in total autonomy from each other, producing distinct products, or catering for discrete market segments.[7] The Republic of Korea, however, stands out in that inter-firm linkages among its "techno-spatial" clusters are almost solely within a large-enterprise small-firm nexus. These consist of extensive subcontracting chains and supplier/vendor arrangements organized from above by large lead firms. This pattern, which is similar in many respects with the Japanese model of "relational" industrial subcontracting (Dore 1987, Best 1990), reflects the overall dominance of large-scale enterprises and industrial conglomerates (chaebols) in The Republic of Korea's industrial manufacturing structure (Cho 1992).

Within the array of production networks seen in the Republic of Korea, two distinct types of linkages may be discerned. At one level, subcontractual arrangements are governed by "technical mutuality on a functional division of labour" between large and small firms. This implies a relatively non-hierarchical, often personalized, association marked by a sharing of technical knowledge and skills between interacting parties of large and small firms and cooperative forms of technological innovation and diffusion. An element of consistency and reliability derived from previous experience of cooperatively working together and founded on mutual trust and respect is built into this relationship (Cho 1992). Production objectives of both parties are common and intertwined. Technological cooperation is motivated on the part of the lead firm to ensure that the subcontracting unit maintains required delivery schedules (to conform with "just-in-time" techniques) and quality standards, and importantly in accessing the specialized pool of knowledge and technological capabilities of the subcontracting unit which is critical to the process of innovation within the lead firm. The subcontracting unit, in dedicating itself to the lead firm, gains consistent financial and technical support and minimizes the degree of uncertainty it faces in both product and input markets. The second type of large-small production nexus is driven by cost-reduction motives of large enterprises and benefits of lower wages, less stringent labour standards and poorer working conditions of small firms. Subcontracting units within such arrangements are dependent upon large enterprises, face minimum quality stipulations and gain little in the form of direct cooperation that results in improvements in technological capabilities and skills. Nor do such arrangements reduce the degree of uncertainty that such small subcontractors face in product and factor markets. In contrast to the former, this relationship is hierarchical, vertically differentiated, transient and impersonal in character (Cho 1992).

In the automobile sector in Ulsan (Republic of Korea), there were reportedly 1,940 subcontracting enterprises in 1990 of which 540 were technically specialized units within the framework of the first form of interlinkage (Cho 1992). The remainder capitalized on their ability to keep wage costs low. Similar forms of production disaggregation were found in the microelectronics industry. A "few innovative technological nuclei" lead firms were spatially surrounded by a cluster of small subcontracting firms providing "highly specialized materials, parts and know-how", while a plethora of geographically dispersed household units undertook low-value labour-intensive piecework at the lowest level of a hierarchical chain of subcontracting in the microelectronics industry (Cho 1992). In the textiles cluster in Daegu, subcontracting was motivated by production cost minimization. In response to increasing labour management problems, large enterprises in the textiles industry raised production flexibility through the "Little Owner System (LOS)". Under this scheme the less skilled and most labour intensive aspects of textile production in the Republic of Korea were farmed out as semi-autonomous small units, initially on rent and eventually on an ownership basis, to technically skilled former employees of the large firm. This practice reduced risks and labour costs for large firms. The LOS units' extensively self-exploited family labour bore the primary brunt of shifts in product demands and input supplies and allowed the core firm to concentrate on the technically intensive aspects of production, using high- tech equipment, and on design and product development.

In contrast to arrangements with low-wage suppliers, relations between lead firms and technically specialized subcontractors was "more associational and collaborative in nature, although remaining partly hierarchical and vertical", with the former providing the latter with technical and financial assistance to improve the subcontracting firm's technological abilities (Cho 1992, pp.9-10). "Through these [inter-firm] networks, innovative technology diffuses from the upper to the lower tier of technological firms, individual creativity is translated into collective innovation, interaction among actors supplements each other's shortcomings...[and]...is conducive to the realisation of innovation via collective effort" (Cho 1992, p.11). An example of innovation through collective technical cooperation between lead and subcontracting firms cited by Cho is the development of new auto engines in Ulsan.

Although the above case may appear to be the exception (given the magnitude of the large-scale sector), aspects of the two types of large-small firm interlinkages seen in the Republic of Korea may be observed in other case studies.[8] In the small-firm footwear clusters of Trujillo (Peru) and Agra (India) there are signs of large-small firm production networking primarily to reduce large firms' wage costs but also involving a degree of technological collaboration to ensure product quality (Villarán 1992, Knorringa 1992). In both locations, the comparatively more advanced and reliable small firms within the footwear clusters undertook subcontractual production for large national shoe manufacturers (including Bata in both countries). Such arrangements provided the small firms with access to the specialized "know-how, distribution networks and brand-name" of the large producers as well as knowledge of the "latest technological and marketing developments" (Knorringa 1992). While the provision of technical support to small subcontracting units was necessary on the part of the large enterprise in order to ensure a consistent level of quality synonymous with their brand name, such arrangements also offered extensive production flexibility by lowering wage and labour management costs and reducing risks inherent in market fluctuations.

(c)   *Small-small firm vertical production relations*

A more frequently reported form of inter-firm networking in small-firm industrial districts are those among small firms within the cluster. At a rudimentary level, this involves an exchange between firms of generalized information regarding technology and product development and factor and product market conditions. This is followed by informal arrangements of sharing of tools and labour, as well as dividing large orders, both vertically and horizontally, among firms. The most sophisticated forms of inter-firm linkages are of a vertical nature, involving process and/or product specialized firms not in direct competition with each other and encompassing substantial consultation and interaction between firms regarding technical and design specifications and product and process development.

In some cases, inter-firm production networks involving process specialization is at an early stage, involving at best the provision of specialized services by a few individual units to others in the cluster. This, for example, has been observed in the woodworking and carpentry clusters in the United Republic of Tanzania (Aeroe 1992), Sudan (Hansohm 1992), Kenya and Zimbabwe (Sverrisson 1992b). In others, such patterns of inter-firm relations have been the dominant form of production organization. A "proliferation of [vertical] subcontracting relations" in industries as diverse as machine tools (Amsden 1985) and footwear (Levy 1991) overwhelmingly marked the small-firm manufacturing sector of Taiwan Province of China. For footwear, process-specialization has resulted in a situation where "it is rare for a Taiwanese footwear firm to perform in-house more than at most two of the various subprocesses" of footwear production. Furthermore, "subcontractors tend not to work exclusively with individual firms, but to maintain supply relationships with multiple independent affiliates" (Levy 1991, p.56). Although Levy offers no evidence of the implication of such inter-firm relations for innovation, technological improvement and overall growth of the economy's footwear sector, part of its export success lay in its ability to improve collectively production techniques and develop new products through user-producer interactions at various stages of production.[9]

At a qualitatively different level of technological development, subcontracting arrangements in the small-firm rattan furniture cluster of Tegalwangi, Indonesia, are also said to be a traditional and widespread entity. Three types of subcontracting arrangements have been identified, each one geared to distinct and discrete quality segments of the product market (Smyth 1991, Boomgard *et al.*, 1992): household-based units producing low-quality finished products for sale in local markets; medium-quality products, manufactured for the domestic market, frequently handled through the producers' own retail outlets and often with specific activities subcontracted to other small household-based units. At the high-quality (export) end, subcontracting was usually initiated by large exporting firms, and resulted in individual units becoming specialized in the manufacture of specific components, and particular aspects of the production process or in the making of semi-finished goods (Smyth 1991). Time schedules, quality standards and contractual terms and obligations were determined and enforced by the lead (usually exporting) firm. Frequently the lead firm was only directly engaged in either assembling, finishing, packaging or marketing tasks. Even here, subcontractual practices could be of a hierarchical nature with small- and medium-scale units putting out the most labour-intensive aspects of production - weaving and tying of rattan - to home-based women workers. "In some instances chains of sub-contracting are formed, from large exporter, to medium- or small-scale enterprise, to home worker" (Smyth 1991, p.266).

The direct technological development implications arising from inter-firm relations within the rattan furniture sector are unclear. Smyth mentions benefits of clustering and subcontracting in the form of low transport costs, reduction in storage and space costs, numerical flexibility offered by large pools of family labour undertaking work on piece-rated terms, the availability of better quality raw materials, access to working capital in the form of credit provision by lead firms for the purchase of raw materials as well as behavioural advantages of self-employment. Many of these indicate that clustering serves as an institutional framework which reduces transaction costs of individual producers. There are also some signs of sharing of tools, access to specialized machinery, and the development of units specialized in specific production activities that indicate potential for technological progress. The fact that the share of finished and semi-finished goods within total rattan exports in Indonesia rose rapidly during the 1980s (from 16 per cent in 1979 to 99.5 per cent in 1987) suggests that collectively the cluster has undergone a substantive degree of technological upgrading in terms of producing more sophisticated and higher value-added products. However, it is also apparent that the success of the cluster in penetrating export markets lies not in technological improvements, but rather in the strength of its low-cost skilled labour and high-quality inputs.

Patterns of extensive vertical subcontracting and specialized division of labour are observed in small-firm clusters in India's garment industry and across a number of manufacturing activities in Indian Punjab (Kashyap 1992, Tiwari 1990), as well as in Pakistan's textile weaving, electrical appliances, furniture, footwear and steel utensils sectors (Nadvi 1992). Within the Pakistani small-firm clusters, "the finished commodities of a number of industries sampled were produced through production processes which were easily disaggregated into distinct activities or sub-processes...[with] independent units [which] were considered to be autonomous artisanal workshops skilled in specific tasks each of which required a distinct set of tools and equipment. Each process specific unit took on work from a number of other firms and was not tied or dependent within the division of labour to one particular concern" (Nadvi 1992, p.16). Tools were often shared, units were becoming further process-specialized, and the cluster as a whole was able to acquire previously unavailable specialized machinery. There were some signs of user-producer interaction within the metal-working sectors. There were also indications that the acquisition of new technologies (such as CAD, NC machine tools and high-temperature furnaces) by individual units could result in the breakdown of cooperative production arrangements and lead to increasingly vertically integrated manufacturing. In these cases, "new technology was considered a guarded secret whose benefits could only be optimized if such firms [those which acquired new technologies] retained a monopoly over its availability" (Nadvi 1992, p.22).

Concrete cases of technological upgrading directly emerging from inter-firm collaboration have been found in Peru. Extensive process- specialized subcontracting has been cited as a feature of the garment producers cluster in Lima's Gamarra district: among the (approximately 4,000) firms that constituted the Peruvian Association of Small-Scale Garments Manufacturers (APIC), and within the capital goods industry consortium (CBK) (Villarán 1992). The export consortia set up or encouraged by APIC led to inter-firm cooperation with "collective efficiency [being] achieved through the division of labour. Some firms concentrate exclusively on circular weaving, others on dyeing, making-up or printing. There is a flurry of subcontracting among the group's members, occasional transfers of liquidity and an increase in worker specialization" (Villarán 1992, p.46). The CBK stands out for the manner in which collaboration among members, via both a division of labour and a sharing of technical information, has resulted in a number of technological innovations and adaptation of machine tools used in a range of Peruvian small-scale industries. In the footwear cluster of Trujillo, in addition to collaboration among manufacturers, vertical cooperation has developed between footwear producers and leather tanners, resulting in some improvement in the quality of raw materials used (Villarán 1992).

Kumasi's Suame district also shows signs of extensive cooperation between firms both at vertical and horizontal levels with a positive impact upon technology adaptation and innovation. Enterprises have developed specialized expertise, produced specific parts or acquired exclusive technological capabilities. "A significant degree of cooperation in the production process has developed. This has enabled small workshops with only limited equipment and staff to take on substantial pieces of work, parts of which are shared or subcontracted out to neighbouring enterprises" (Dawson, 1992, p.37). As a result, the indigenous technological innovative and adaptive capacity of the Suame cluster has become renowned in the region. Cooperative interaction and technical information-sharing has aided incremental technological progress. In response to the overall crisis in the Ghanaian economy, Suame's "industry is beginning to build its own equipment" (Schmitz 1989, p.28); and has developed ability, reinforced through extensive user-producer interactions, in designing, manufacturing and maintaining machine tools for other enterprises and sectors within the locality (Dawson 1992).

As in the Peruvian CBK case, technological improvement, adaptation and development of machine tools in Suame has a dual multiplier effect. First, it significantly aids production capacities of sectors that use such technologies; and secondly, it promotes an interactive, integrated and continuing "learning nexus" where joint technical learning by users and producers involves the acquisition and understanding of both technological "know-how" and "know-why" (James 1991).

(d)   *Small-small firm horizontal production relations*

Horizontal production linkages between potentially competing units are often considered to be a survival or coping strategy for meeting large and critical production orders through collectively raising capacity. "Capacity contracting" was cited as the grounds for horizontal patterns of inter-firm linkages in Suame (Dawson 1992); within the traditional blacksmithing sector in Nyala (Hansohm 1992); in the Agra footwear cluster (Knorringa 1992); among the footwear and steel utensil manufacturing clusters in the cities of Karachi and Gujranwala in Pakistan (Nadvi 1992); within the Indian small-firm garment-making clusters of Delhi, Bombay and Madras (Kashyap 1992); among small carpentry workshops in Kenya and Zimbabwe (Sverrison 1992a, 1992b); and by the roof tiles sector in Indonesia, where larger enterprises used kilns and drying space of somewhat smaller/weaker units in their neighbourhood (Sandee 1992). Given the nature of horizontal competition, such interlinkages would seem unlikely to lead to inter-firm cooperation conducive with technological innovation.

The Indonesian rural roof tiles sector, however, provides an illustration of how horizontal linkages can assist in technological upgrading. Relatively egalitarian horizontal cooperation among economically stronger units was instrumental in the cluster acquiring and using new production techniques based upon more sophisticated, costlier and indivisible mixers. At the initial stages of the adoption of this new technology, "sub-clusters" developed around the new mixers in order to share costs and economically exploit scale economies. As ownership of mixers spread, however, such sub-clusters reshaped around the traditional patterns of subordinate linkages (of capacity contracting) that existed between dynamic units and their less dynamic neighbours (Sandee 1992). This finding supports the view that horizontal systems of inter-firm cooperation are not solely survival mechanisms, but can have important implications for technical development. Furthermore, the foundation for sectoral associations (including in some cases process-specific associations) is effectively based upon horizontal cooperation in which such collaboration is clearly perceived as leading to collective benefits.

(e)   *Producer-trader interrelations*

Knorringa's study of the Agra footwear cluster underscores an important aspect of interlinkage. It also holds significance for a number of other cases (including the Indonesian rattan furniture cluster, the footwear sector in Taiwan Province of China, the diamond-polishing cluster of Surat and some of the Pakistani clusters), namely that between marketing agents and producers. The characteristic features of such linkages, which Lazerson (1990) terms "commercial sub-contracting", are determined by the market segment to which the product is targeted. At the predominantly low-quality low-price end of the market (domestic and foreign), in which the bulk of the cluster is found, such interrelations between producers and market agents are generally impersonal, hierarchical and involve little exchange of knowledge or information between them. Rather than being of a genuinely cooperative nature, relations between "makers" and "sellers" are often opportunistic and further polarized when the two groups have distinct social lineages and associated tacit knowledge. Thus "the traders have no eye for changes in the production process, while the artisans have no eye for changes in product specifications. Both groups are highly adaptable within their own environment, but the two worlds do not meet to combine their knowledge." (Knorringa 1992, p.13)

Where quality as opposed to solely price is a determining aspect in a finished product's marketing strategy, the relationship between producers and traders becomes more collaborative, personalized and involves elements of trust and stability. "Consistency and trust" are core features of the relationship between modern direct exporting firms in the Agra footwear cluster and foreign buyers, although "the linkage is not free from hierarchical feelings" (Knorringa 1992). Such relatively non-antagonistic and complementary bonds can assist product innovation and technological development. This, for example, is an important element of production arrangements in the export footwear sector of Taiwan Province of China and the Republic of Korea, where a number of firms produce directly for major international brand names (Nike, Reebok) or for foreign and domestic traders (Levy 1991).

C. The social milieu

The social milieu is a core aspect of industrial districts in that it provides the basis for trust relations which consolidate interpersonal and collaborative inter-firm production linkages within the cluster. In certain cases, the social milieu consists of an abstract and generalized social character which aids inter-firm relations, innovation and entrepreneurship. In others, it includes concrete and particular social institutions and social norms which effectively minimize transaction costs within the cluster by regulating its functioning, mediating between potentially divisive aspects of competition and cooperation, and enforcing sanctions upon those who contravene socially-defined "rules" of behaviour. The ultimate sanction, that of exclusion from the social and economic space of the community, can be a sufficient deterrent to breaking trust relations if this results in what Rasmussen (1992) refers to as Hirschman's idea of high "exit costs".

Finally, the social milieu carries within it aspects of "agglomerative economies" which are specific to that community. Included in this is a bank of tacit knowledge related to the manufacturing activity of the community, and often specific to that cluster. The codification of such knowledge and its transmission, particularly the dynamics of learning, takes place within the social space of the cluster. The process of acquiring skills usually occurs through informal socially- defined institutions (particularly via skilled craftsmen and the apprenticeship system) and on-the-job learning, thus ensuring the collective reproduction of the community and the enterprise.

Many social functions and community attributes are intangible, abstract, informal or subterranean, and thus not directly observable. Frequently members of the community internalize social identities, and their associated properties, without being consciously aware of it. Hence, what constitutes the social milieu and how it functions is usually more difficult to discern than the relatively perceptible patterns of inter-firm production relations.

At the abstract level, the social milieu can take various forms. It has been suggested that an "entrepreneurial tradition" of self-employment as a broad social characteristic is more pronounced in parts of West Africa than in East Africa, resulting in more cogent forms of "enterprise development and inter firm division of labour" in, for example, Ghana, as compared to the United Republic of Tanzania (Aeroe 1992). Likewise, small firms in Taiwan Province of China are said to be heavily influenced by the Chinese (or Confucian) spirit of entrepreneurship and by social codes of family, operating under strong patriarchal family structures which regulate and influence both the social space and the economic activities of the unit (Lauridsen 1992). The comparative success of the small-firm sector in Cyprus is said to be strengthened by "strong civic and national cohesion". This is related to the current difficulties with Turkey and provides the basis for strong national identity and consensual politics. Furthermore, the high social worth attached to education, the acquisition of technology and the overall cosmopolitan nature of the Cypriot culture all go to shape a society which sees development as a collective goal (Murray 1992). In a similarly abstract fashion, the rural knitwear cluster of Mexico is characterized by a strong *mestizo* identity, rooted in shared values of family, God, work, and conservative and patriarchal moral codes, which impact upon work practices within the cluster (Wilson 1992).[10]

Less abstract and more concrete social identities and institutions can be particularly influential in regulating small-firm clusters in a number of developing countries. Social networks, and their associated identities, are usually derived from some notion of common kinship. Thus, the trust-based interaction between lead firms and technologically specialized subcontractors within technospatial clusters in the Republic of Korea were often reinforced by interpersonal networks of acquaintanceship derived from common schooling, regional and family backgrounds (Cho 1992). With stable economic and social relationships over time such interpersonal networks have taken on a shared corporate identity and loyalty.

In the Trujillo footwear cluster of Peru, a common regional and historical background, whereby entrepreneurs within the cluster have predominantly originated from a poor, densely populated and economically backward region, has formed the basis of kinship identity (Villarán 1992). For the rattan furniture cluster of Tegalwangi (Indonesia), where enterprises are concentrated in one small rural region, there are social networks in which "neighbours are related by ties of kinship" (Smyth 1991). In Burkina Faso, "personal relations (based upon family, kin, tribe, religious grouping) are important to survive in the informal sector" (Van Dijk, 1992, p.48). Small-firm clusters in rural Mexico are said to be characterized by social networks of male return migrants (who worked in the United States) (Wilson 1992). The common experiences of migrant life and migrant employment provided the basis for strong social bonding which was noted as being particularly important when the industrial cluster was beginning to take shape. Such relatively "egalitarian" male migrant networks provided informal mechanisms for emergency assistance, information pooling and capacity sharing within the cluster as well as "facilitating access to loans and credit, labour, information and contacts" (Wilson 1992, p.60).[11]

In South Asia, caste identities are the leading criteria in delineating social groups within small-firm clusters. In the diamond-polishing industry of Surat, workers and entrepreneurs belong to the same caste (Patels); job search is carried out through kinship networks (Kashyap 1992). A significant proportion of the Ludhiana's highly successful regional small-firm economy consists of those who are from the artisanal caste of *ramgarhias* known for their collective ability to fashion and adapt machinery (Kashyap 1992, Tiwari 1990). Among small-firm clusters observed in Pakistan, almost 90 per cent of entrepreneurs sampled in the cotton-weaving sector and a significant proportion of entrepreneurs and workers in other textile-related industries were *ansaris*, the traditional Muslim rural artisanal caste (more appropriately *biradari* or fraternity) of weavers. Similarly, *lohars*, the ironsmiths' *biradari*, accounted for a substantial number of those in the metal-working sectors (Nadvi 1992). Although job search was not explicitly tied to *biradari*-based kinship networks, *biradari* ties within the cluster were effectively reproduced through informal training and skill-acquisition being imparted through inter-generational skill transfers and via traditional skilled craftsmen.[12] This was usually restricted to those who carried some tacit knowledge of that cluster or its skills. Kinship networks in production were further buttressed by the convergence of residential and economic space within the cluster. Each locality was simultaneously known for being the home of a specific community and for the manufacturing activity associated with that community. Skills and knowledge within the cluster were passed on by a "process of osmosis" as much as through direct learning (Nadvi 1990). Similar patterns of social interpersonal linkages, involving associative relations, informal skill-acquisition and shared common knowledge and emerging from a communal space where the domestic/residential and productive arenas are intermixed, were features of the low-income shanty/small-enterprise cluster in Suame, Kumasi, and in the Tacora metalwork district/ marginalized neighbourhood of Lima.

The degree to which common social identities directly serve to reinforce inter-firm cooperation has been, however, unclear. Rabellotti has observed that within the footwear clusters in Mexico the existing limited "technological and commercial cooperation [there is] between firms is often linked by family ties which exchange technological information and machines and sell products jointly" (Rabellotti 1992, p.11). Alternatively, within the rural knitwear cluster of Mexico a "process of differentiation [has set in which] appear[s] to have undermined rather than strengthened" existing social networks. As a result, "business relations [between firms within the cluster] are marked by competition and secrecy" (Wilson 1992, p.62). Similarly, within the diamond-polishing cluster of Surat (India), despite strong caste and social kinship ties, "firms appeared more competitive than complementary" (Kashyap 1992, p.31). The divisions within the Agra (India) footwear cluster between producers and traders were further heightened by the distinct social castes to which producers and traders belonged. While the former were largely backward caste Hindus (*jatavs*) and poor Muslims, the latter were forward caste Hindus (*banias*) and rich Muslims. The antagonistic exchange relationship between producers and traders was reinforced by the distrust and social contempt that the two caste groups had for each other, thereby weakening the prospects for cooperation and collective innovation (Knorringa 1992). Similarly, the lack of locally embedded social networks which foster over-arching social cohesion is cited as a primary factor for the failure of small enterprises in Zimbabwe's construction sector in entering into trust-based cooperative production networks or even extensive information-exchange relations. In contrast, the Asian and European business sectors had access to very powerful respective social networks and institutions which facilitated their business strategies (Rasmussen 1992).

This underlines the contrasting characteristic of the social milieu. In some cases, social identities carry within them some innate abilities of an entrepreneurial spirit (the Chinese/Confucian business ethos in Taiwan Province of China, for example) and/or technological and innovative vibrancy (such as the Punjabi *ramgarhias*) which assist the dynamism of small-firm clusters. In many others, they serve the relatively more modest function of providing a commonly accepted set of codified knowledge and interpersonal trust relations, on which production arrangements are based, and through which information exchanged, skills transferred and capital allocated. This is often necessary, albeit not sufficient, for a collaborative process of technological upgrading to be set in motion. In all cases, however, while social identities may remain constant, the social networks that they engender are not static, but can, and frequently do, change dynamically with time. This is clearly observed from Wilson's (1992) study of the rural Mexican cluster. Similarly, the process of differentiation observed to varying degrees within the small-firm clusters of rattan furniture-makers in Tegalwangi (Smyth 1991), among the Suame workshops (Dawson 1992) and within small-firm clusters in urban Punjab (Nadvi 1992) calls into question the ability of existing social networks not only to regulate the functioning of social norms of behaviour, but effectively to survive changes in the cluster's economic structure.

D.   The role of State and sectoral institutions

A common feature of many successful European industrial districts is that of an active strategy of state support and intervention, usually at the sectoral level. This has significantly aided the working of small-firm clusters. Such support has included locational programmes that have facilitated the formation of sector-specific industrial sites, credit schemes and vocational training centres (Best 1990) as well as marketing, research and development assistance through the formation of specialized technical support agencies (Brusco 1992, Schmitz 1992a, Asheim 1992). Many of these programmes have been run in conjunction with sectoral associations and have usually been articulated by local (as opposed to central) levels of government.

What emerges from this experience is that, while State intervention does not actually create industrial districts, such assistance, particularly in the form of "real services", can be critical in ensuring the overall success of small-firm clusters which otherwise lack the capacity to generate internally support infrastructure. Secondly, such programmes are likely to be more effective if formulated by levels of government which are politically rooted in the community, in much the same way that the industrial cluster is socially embedded;   moreover, they must actively involve the participation of those to whom they are directed through representative sectoral associations.

Support for small-scale manufacturing in developing countries, albeit rarely effective, has certainly been an important platform for State industrial and technology policies in many developing countries.[13] Usually small-enterprise development schemes have taken the shape of credit provision, marketing support and vocational training. This has involved the creation of sector-specific technical support centres and small-enterprise estates. The implementation of such programmes has tended to be the responsibility of centralized levels of government, although, in some cases, local governments have played a significant role. Targeted support strategies aimed at small-firm industrial districts, which include active participation by sectoral associations, are comparatively less pronounced.

Although the overall macroeconomic framework clearly has a significant impact on the performance of small-firm clusters, the focus here will be on the more microeconomic-level programmes[14,] particularly those which fall within the ambit of provision of "real services". Some of these schemes are operated by the State, both at national and local levels, while others have emerged from sectoral and business associations, often in collaboration with government agencies.

(a)   *State support institutions*

A number of State institutions, although not overtly geared to small-firm clusters, are supposed to provide "real service"-type facilities to small manufacturing enterprises in developing countries. While evaluations of the impact of such institutions are rare, suspicion exists that such policy initiatives are bureaucratically inefficient, ineffective and fail to target appropriately truly small firms. Some examples of State-initiated institutional support schemes for small firms in developing countries are given below.

The regional level Small Business Advisory Centres (SBAC) in the Philippines are reported to be active in furnishing a range of support services to small enterprises. These include consultancy, research, product and process development, management and vocational training, feasibility studies, financial planning, marketing assistance and the dissemination of information on products, technologies, legal and trade stipulations (Tan 1991). The SBAC is also said to have been instrumental in forming regional industrial associations and sectoral bodies designed to provide a forum allowing small firms within a given sector to interact, discuss common problems and collectively seek technical solutions.

In Malaysia, the Subcontractor Exchange Programme (SCX) is supposed to encourage inter-firm subcontractual linkages by maintaining a detailed database of potential vendors and subcontractors in the heavy and light engineering, electrical products, rubber and plastic and automobiles sectors. In addition, the programme is supposed to provide subcontracting firms advisory and information services regarding product, process, technology and market developments (Jamil & Said 1991).

The Small- and Medium-Sized Promotion Corporation in the Republic of Korea is said to supply advisory, information and extension services along with financial assistance to encourage small firms to raise technological standards and improve production organization systems. Such services are often developed in tandem with the existing support given by large lead firms to subcontracting units. The Korean Institute of Economics and Technology (KIET) offers detailed technical information to small firms through an extensive library of scientific material and via access to leading local and international computer-based data banks (Lee 1991).

In India, State support for small-scale manufacturing, particularly at the regional level, has historically been an important area of policy for both economic and ideological reasons. Such support has included trade protection, fiscal incentives, technical and marketing assistance, credit provision and specialized small-firm industrial estates.[15] Regional-level Small Industries Service Institutes (SISI) are supposed to give technological and market information, managerial advice and provide testing services, workshop facilities and vocational training programmes for small enterprises. The impact of such policies and institutions has, however, been extremely mixed (Kashyap 1990). Kashyap (1992) argues that in keeping with the general aversion of small firms to being brought under State regulation, the Punjab Government's strategy of being a "facilitator from a distance" has proven relatively successful compared with more interventionist approaches adopted by other State Governments in India.

In Pakistan, it appears that while a number of sector specific technology support centres and small-industry estates have been formed by the provincial Governments (particularly that of Punjab), their overall impact in improving the technological capacity of the respective clusters to which they are directed has been generally paltry (Nadvi 1992). Part of this failure lies in the lack of technical and organizational linkages between such centres and the cluster. Sectoral representation in the running of such centres, in the identification of required needs of the cluster to which the centre should be directed, and in the effective operationalization of technological developments of the centre with target firms within the cluster is almost non-existent. An exception to this general trend is the Metal Industries Development Centre (MIDC) in Sialkot which caters to the export-oriented surgical equipment industry of that city; it has received substantial foreign technical assistance. Although the sectoral association within the surgical equipment industry is not formally incorporated in the running of the MIDC, the economic and political strength and lobbying power of the association at both local and provincial levels has had a positive impact on promoting the MIDC and linking its activities directly with the cluster. "Since 1985 [the MIDC] has introduced vacuum based heat treatment, spark erosion die making, CNC wire cut machines and short blasting techniques. It also provides a materials testing laboratory. The effectiveness of the MIDC in terms of technology extension services can be partially gauged from the fact that there are a reported 15 spark erosion machines in use in the Sialkot surgical equipment industry compared to only 2 machines in use five years previously" (Nadvi 1992, p.20). In contrast, most other technology support centres in Pakistan operate in greater isolation from their target groups and "have been singularly unable to provide technological leadership".

Within the Indonesian rattan furniture sector, vocational training and technological upgrading have been the leading objectives of two support programmes directly aimed at the cluster. One was set up in 1973 by the national Government's Department of Industry, in collaboration with a non-governmental education and social research institute and the Institute of Technology (Smyth 1991, p.259), whereas the other is part of the USAID-funded Central Java

Enterprise Development Project (CJEDP) (Boomgard *et al.*, 1992). Under the aegis of the Department of Industry programme, five training courses of various duration were run between 1979 and 1987 with a focus on "practical training on design, techniques of production and finishing, to discussions on management and export practices" (Smyth 1991, p.259). In addition, the project has been involved in assisting in marketing activities and in running trade exhibitions. Similarly, the CJEDP programme has been aimed at firm-level training geared to improving the ability of trainees to enter export markets (Boomgard *et al.*, 1992, p.207). A Technical Service Unit has been established providing the cluster with access to specialized and technical support. This unit has also entered into collaboration with a private firm within the rattan sector which supplies credit and technical support to a cooperative of producers within the region (Smyth 1991).

(b)   *Local sectoral and business associations*

Sectoral and business associations have often proved more competent than government initiatives in establishing support networks including technology support centres, quality-control standards, credit and marketing consortia, and in lobbying for sectoral interests at various levels of government. Sectoral associations have been reported in a number of the small-firm cluster case studies, although with varying degrees of strength and effectiveness. Sectoral bodies, process associations and traders' organizations were found in most informal manufacturing clusters in Pakistan (Nadvi 1992). In India, they have been associated with small-firm estates (Gorter 1992) and as part of larger regional clusters (Tiwari 1990, Kashyap 1992); in the Trujillo (footwear) and Gamarra (garment) clusters of Peru (Villarán 1992); within the Indonesian rattan sector (Smyth 1991); and, even within the low-income enterprise neighbourhoods of Suame (Ghana) and Tacora (Peru). Not all such bodies are particularly efficient, with many becoming the preserve of more powerful elements within the cluster. A few, however, stand out in their provision of "real services".

The Mexican footwear association, *Camara del Calzado*, operates at both national and local levels. It includes most footwear manufacturers within its membership and offers a range of services including "fiscal and labour consultancy, commercial assistance, managerial training, organisation of trade fairs and political lobbying" (Rabellotti 1992, p.12). It has been instrumental in setting up credit unions which arrange joint purchase of machinery and obtain credit for members at below market rates. It was also active in starting a technical institute in Guadalajara concentrating on technological research and training along with a technology support centre in Leon geared to quality-control and technical assistance services (Rabellotti 1992). The *Camara* also encourages informal cooperation in the form of production interaction and information-exchanges. As such activities are fairly recent, it is thus too early to gauge the *Camara*'s impact in stimulating collaboration within the Mexican footwear clusters.

Villarán (1992) cites a number of sectoral associations in Peru that appear to provide members with a range of services effectively aimed at raising the sector's competitive edge in international markets and in improving technological capabilities. Within the garment sector, the Peruvian Small-Scale Garment Manufacturers' Association (APIC) is involved in forming export consortia, organizing trade fairs and undertaking joint purchasing of machinery. The Peruvian Association of Small-scale Footwear Industry (APEMEFAC), with 500 members and regional branches (in particular for the Trujillo footwear cluster), also organizes trade fairs. It has set up an export consortium and notably has coordinated a process of mutually compatible technological upgrading within the footwear sector as a whole through joint investment, purchasing and information management. In addition, it furnishes members with intelligence gathered on market trends, product designs, input suppliers and their quality and on international trading practices. A number of regional and small business associations and the local Chamber of Commerce are also active within the Trujillo footwear cluster. They bring together tanners and distributors with small and micro-scale enterprise producers.

Murray (1992) indicates that sectoral associations and employers' bodies have been important and cohesive institutions central to the implementation of the flexibly specialized small-firm-oriented Cyprus Industrial Strategy (CIS). Concerted action by sectoral associations has led to an improvement in both input and product qualities, and has strengthened the national corporatist ethos. Specialized joint-production consortia are also seen in Cyprus. A number of Nicosia-based furniture-makers came together with the assistance of the Cyprus Development Bank to form a manufacturing consortium. Emphasis is placed upon quality with each unit being product- and/or process-specialized. Inputs are collectively purchased; joint domestic retail outlets have been initiated alongside shared advertising and joint export-marketing (Murray 1992).

Along with sectoral associations within most industries, and in some cases, process-specific associations, the example from the Republic of Korea is also noted for corporate associations. These provide a formal institution for ensuring cooperative behaviour, resolving contractual conflicts within collaborative linkages and encouraging technical interaction between lead firms and technically qualified subcontractors. Examples of such corporate organizations include the Hyundai Cooperation Association that contains, along with the Hyundai *chaebol*, 250 subcontracting firms in the automobile sector; and, the Seong-Ryuk-Hoe, which acts as the corporate association between the Lucky-Goldstar conglomerate and its technical subcontractors in the microelectronics sector (Cho 1992).

The effectiveness of sectoral associations, in both encouraging cooperative interaction among members and in providing "enabling services" is directly related to the overall development and formalization of business practices. Where manufacturing and industrial activity is at an early stage, the ability of sectoral associations to take shape and to influence the domain in which their members operate, is limited. Thus, in some of the African case studies (such as the small-firm/small-town clusters in Sudan and the United Republic of Tanzania), where cooperative business relations were scant and industrial development at a nascent stage, sectoral associations had not formed. Trade bodies were further weakened in cases where collective perception of common problems was undermined by individualized and atomistic behaviour among firms within the cluster. Sectoral entities are endogenous to the cluster from which they emerge. Where clusters are frail and interrelations ineffectual, sectoral associations are equally poor. Furthermore, whereas sectoral bodies are clearly important in representing the felt needs of a cluster, they also reflect existing power structures within that cluster or industry. In clusters which are heterogeneous and highly differentiated, the collective benefits of sectoral associations can be undermined by disparate interests. Thus, the ability to form effective collective institutions, such as real service centres aimed at technical upgrading and promoting collective economic growth of the cluster, can be diminished.

E. Labour surpluses and the growth prospects for small-firm industrial districts: the high *versus* low roads

Small-firm clusters in developing countries generally operate under labour-surplus conditions and usually in the absence of labour regulations regarding wages, health and safety standards. Consequently, wage rates within small-firm clusters are on the whole lower than those found in the large-scale and comparatively more formal industrial sector. Low wages and the possibility of further reducing wage costs through practices of putting out and via the incorporation of marginalized segments of the labour force (particularly women and children) into production can, and usually does, become the primary avenue for competition among small-scale manufacturers in developing countries. Furthermore, surplus labour can act as a powerful disincentive to process innovation and, along with being synonymous with poor working conditions, is likely to dampen technological progress (Schmitz 1989, Sengenberger and Pyke 1991).

Are small-firm clusters in labour-surplus environments, however, necessarily doomed to a non-innovative and technologically stagnant "low road" growth path, or is there a possibility of innovative behaviour within the cluster despite the existence of a labour surplus? In contrast to the stark duality in potential growth paths for industrial districts suggested by Sengenberger and Pyke (1991), in the developing environment, a continuum of possible paths lying between the two extremes of high or low road may well be more plausible. If that is the case, the question still remains under what general conditions are clusters likely to demonstrate a growth trend that is closer to the continuous innovation and technological upgrading associated with the "high road"? A further and allied concern regarding the growth dynamics of industrial districts within the developing context is whether existing patterns of inter-firm relations are strengthened by the process of technical change or begin to erode.

Cyprus appears to be one of the few cases which has the potential for closely assimilating the "ideal-type" attributes seen in the Third Italy industrial districts. Along with an economy dominated by small enterprises, it faces no labour surplus and has been restructuring its manufacturing sector towards high-quality European markets for consumer goods. Under these conditions, an industrial strategy centred around quality-conscious, process-specialized and interlinked small firms operating under the production organization principles of the flexible specialization paradigm not only seems to make sense but suggests positive prospects for growth and technological progress (Murray 1992).

The Republic of Korea, with starkly different characteristics, also emerges as a case where the prospects for small-firm clusters favour technological progress following a path, if not akin to that of Emilia-Romagna, then certainly congruent with aspects of the Japanese system of industrial manufacturing and small-firm subcontracting. In part, the qualitative shift observed within the country's industrial economy during the 1980s, from low-technology labour-intensive exports to increasingly high-technology manufactures, is in line with structural changes within the country's labour market following the period of industrial strife during the mid-1980s which resulted in substantial wage increases. The corporate and national emphasis on moving away from a labour-intensive manufacturing export strategy to acquisition of new product- and process-technologies, along with innovation and design, has placed a premium upon increasingly skilled labour and led to an improvement in working conditions and human resource management and organization. There are also very clear signs of dualistic structures within technospatial clusters in the Republic of Korea, demarcated on levels of technology between core and peripheral enterprises. The latter, including units engaged in work at home, have a high propensity to employ lower-waged women, often operating under poor working conditions. Such enterprises nearly always profit from their ability to keep wage costs low (Cho 1992). The case of the Republic of Korea suggests, therefore, both a high- and low-road potential for technologically distinct elements within small-firm clusters and between sectors differentiated by disparate levels of embodied technologies; nevertheless, for the cluster as a whole, an overall climate of technological progress appears dominant.

In contrast to the distinct experiences of the Republic of Korea and Cyprus, small-firm clusters observed in developing countries present a relatively mixed picture regarding growth prospects. Broadly speaking, the following generalizations can be tentatively made. Those clusters which are either engaged in manufacturing for specific product-niches, or have incorporated some degree of technological upgrading at the level of the cluster, or have active representative and participatory sectoral associations, or avail themselves of benefits from technology-support centres and real service institutes have tended to fare better and display some degree of positive growth potential. Alternatively, clusters engaged in non-niche markets, which lack extensive inter-firm cooperation and have weak sectoral bodies, are in a more difficult situation. In certain clusters, both patterns are discernible.

Although the Suame cluster in Kumasi (Ghana) has proved resilient in the face of severe economic restructuring, depressed conditions and shrinking employment opportunities have led to substantial increases in the number of enterprises "resulting in cut-throat competition and falling returns" and sharply rising levels of firm mortality (Dawson 1992, p.38). Workshops in the carpentry and blacksmithing sectors were particularly badly affected, whereas those engaged in specialized engineering niches and able to undergo a sustained process of technological enhancement fared far better. The fact that Dawson identified only 31 "hard core innovating engineering workshops" from a total sample of 672 firms suggests that the continued growth and technological prospects for the Suame cluster must be treated cautiously.

Rabellotti's survey of the Mexican footwear cluster also highlights a mixed experience. A clear dualism exists in so far as "most innovative firms are large ones, while 82% of small firms have introduced small innovations or do not innovate at all" (Rabellotti 1992, p.9). Although inter-firm collaboration did not appear extensive, the operations of the Footwear Sector Association (Camara del Calzado) suggests comparatively better prospects for larger and technically more advanced enterprises. Similar patterns of differentiation are seen in the Mexican rural knitwear cluster between larger export-oriented firms producing goods with the aid of relatively modern technologies and smaller units using older machinery and producing lower-quality products. The number of firms had increased while inter-firm production cooperation had broken down to such an extent that geographical clustering "is no longer seen as giving a clear advantage" to the more successful units within the cluster (Wilson 1992, p.62).

The rattan furniture industry of Tegalwangi (Indonesia) is another case of a cluster marked by a process of growing economic and social differentiation between export-oriented enterprises and those that cater to the local and domestic markets. The former set of firms has tended to be more process-specialized, has better technological capacities and product quality, and generally offers higher wages and better working conditions compared to other firms within the cluster. Again, a dualism between core and periphery units (particularly workers at home) is emerging. Whereas one component of the cluster has been systematically progressing along a quality-based, technically evolving growth path, the other remains very clearly on a low-skill, low-wage trajectory. The success of the cluster as a whole requires the combined and integrated efforts of both components. To date, this has been brought about through sustained polarization and segmentation between the core and periphery elements. From this, Smyth (1991) concludes that, despite displaying collective efficiency, the cluster appears to have followed the low road.

Heterogeneity is also a feature of the Agra footwear district. For the vast majority of the approximately 5,000 enterprises involved in different aspects of footwear manufacture within the cluster, competition is based upon a stock of cheap, skilled and abundant labour and low- quality imitations of successful shoe designs. Cost-competitive behaviour has resulted in a spiral of lower wages and lower prices with little sign of either process- or product-innovation. The cluster is resilient and is certainly expanding in terms of numbers of enterprises and employment levels, yet displaying the characteristic features of the low road. Two distinct elements stand out from this general picture. The somewhat larger, technically more advanced, quality-conscious, reliable enterprises are engaged in producing for direct export markets products at the high- quality end of the spectrum or for the leading domestic brand-name shoe manufacturers. Although the competitive edge of such units for the markets to which they cater lies in lower wage costs, there is sufficient emphasis upon quality and design to ensure a degree of technical upgrading. Such upgrading is further augmented by the nature of their interactive relationships with their trading partners.

Labour surpluses and ease of entry of new units into the sector has meant that working conditions, wage rates, product quality and nature of technologies used within the Indian ready-made garments and diamond-polishing clusters are uniformly low with little indication of innovatory behaviour (Kashyap 1992). Nevertheless, in both sectors, employment levels have been systematically rising and there are signs of upward social and economic mobility as waged workers and apprentices become self-employed small entrepreneurs. More positive signs of innovatory behaviour supported via extensive inter-firm networking, underscored by strong sets of social identities and promoted through sectoral and State support institutions, may be seen within the Ludhiana industrial cluster (Tiwari 1990, Kashyap 1992).

The clusters, or "efficiency groups", cited by Villarán for Peru suggest that a process of incremental technical advancement within small-firm clusters, usually aided by sectoral associations, is possible alongside conditions of labour surplus. One of the most striking cases is that of the CBK which has, in spite of not being physically located in the same area, acquired through inter-firm collaboration a collective innovative and design capability the impact of which is potentially far-reaching. In a matter of four years, the membership of this capital goods production consortium has increased from 6 to 30 small firms with 14 separate technological development projects being undertaken. The consortium has acquired specialized technical consulting services to assist it in product development; it has participated in major trade fairs and plans to acquire numerically-controlled (NC) machine tools for use by members, as well as to set up a quality-control centre and retail outlet. The success of this collaborative network lies in part in the fact that it remains small and operates in essentially a niche-market. The existence of active and participatory sectoral associations in the Peruvian footwear and garment industry has also consolidated small-firm clusters within these sectors and ensured that a degree of technical upgrading is taking place in spite of an increase in the number of enterprises and overall depressed economic conditions.

The case studies of small-firm clusters in some of the least developed countries of Africa indicate a more precarious picture. Cluster patterns, involving some information-related and process-based interactions are emerging in certain sectors (particularly woodworking) in medium- and intermediate-sized towns in Kenya, Sudan, the United Republic of Tanzania and Zimbabwe. These have had some impact on improving technological standards. On the whole, however, most such clusters are marked by a lack of inter-firm cooperation despite the fact that in some cases enterprises have acquired relatively advanced machinery.[16] The sharp duality in technology and production conditions between small-scale/informal manufacturing units and relatively more modern formal and large-scale manufacturing sector in Africa has given rise to the argument that production systems somewhat akin to the flexible specialization paradigm are more likely to be apparent in the latter case (Van Dijk 1992b).

CONCLUSION

This somewhat sketchy overview of potential industrial district patterns in developing countries casts up more questions than answers. This reflects both the inadequate nature of the empirical information currently available from developing countries and underlines the need for further, more targeted case studies. It also reveals that much conceptual thinking still needs to be done on discerning the tangible and concrete links between technological innovation and sustainable growth dynamism of potential industrial districts in developing countries, on the one hand, and inter-firm linkages, the social milieu, State and sectoral support and regulatory institutions, on the other. Before turning to the questions that need to be addressed and the policy implications, it would be worthwhile to extract what is known and broadly generalizable from the evidence that has been marshalled.

First, clustering as a phenomenon is clearly of significance to small-scale manufacturing in developing countries. In some cases, clustering has evolved into territorially-specific regional industrial spaces often associated with specific levels of technological development. Among these are the "technospatial clusters" of the Republic of Korea, the industrial economy of parts of the Punjab, small-firm sectoral clusters in Agra and Surat (India), in Trujillo (Peru) and in the rural environment of Tegalwangi (Indonesia). In others, clustering is less pronounced in terms of its regional specificity but nevertheless involves dense agglomerations of small enterprises in various sub-localities and in various industries. In this are included the Suame cluster (Kumasi), the Tacora district (Lima), and the footwear clusters of Mexico, at one end, to the more disaggregated spatial clusters cited in Kenya, Sudan, the United Republic of Tanzania, Zimbabwe and rural Mexico.

Secondly, in most of the case studies, clustering has not been the outcome of a planned intervention by the State (the Republic of Korea being a marked exception where State intervention has been critical), but has emerged from within. What this implies is that, as in the European industrial districts, such spatial patterns that bring together, and are based upon, the economic and social activities of a community can rarely be created from above, and develop only under particular and contextual settings.

Thirdly, clustering has resulted in varying degrees of inter-firm relations. These range from examples where inter-firm cooperation is non-existent to those where extensive collaborative arrangements in the form of production networks have emerged. In most cases, small-firm clusters have led to information-exchanges, informal sharing of tools and equipment between firms, collective notions of informal training and well-functioning local specialized labour markets. In this fashion, the cluster has generated a number of external economies both of scale and of scope for member firms. This has effectively improved the working of individual firms and the efficiency of the cluster as a whole.

More sophisticated forms of inter-firm relations, involving extensive vertical production subcontractual chains and arrangements both between large and small enterprises, and among process-specialized small units, have led to collective efficiency with improvements of technological standards and skill levels. In very few cases, however, has such an arrangement brought about significant innovations or product development (the Republic of Korea's technospatial clusters in the auto industry and the CBK consortium in Peru being prime exceptions). More frequently, it has led to incremental forms of process and technological innovation (the Punjab clusters, the Peruvian small-scale garment sector). Horizontal cooperation has also been effective in raising a cluster's technological capacity through the shared introduction and use of new machinery (the Indonesian rural roof-tiles sector).

Fourthly, clusters have tended to be associated with some type of social identity or kinship-based social networks. These have been important in providing the basis for interpersonal relations, for notions of trust and reciprocity and for providing social sanctions that effectively limit the boundaries of accepted competitive behaviour. In some cases where over-arching social networks are weak, inter-firm cooperation is limited (e.g. Zimbabwe's construction sector). Social identities also appear to influence patterns of informal acquisition of skill through the institution of apprenticeship and via the body of tacit knowledge that is intrinsic to members of a community. Thus, the reproduction of the cluster in many cases runs in tandem with the social reproduction of the community.

Fifthly, existing State support programmes and the working of State institutions geared to small-firm clusters, while being on paper quite commendable, in practice seem largely ineffective. In part, this failure lies in the lack of organic links between bureaucratic State institutions and the target communities which they are geared to serve. In contrast, most small-firm clusters have achieved existing levels of development in the absence of direct state support. In several cases, sectoral associations have been particularly influential in shaping collaborative alliances, production, marketing and credit consortia. More dynamic sectoral associations in a few clusters have formed fledgling "real service" centres (Peru's garment, footwear and machine-tools sectors and Mexico's footwear industry) to provide critical information and technical support.

Sixthly, the growth patterns of small-firm clusters and potential industrial districts in developing countries reflect a more heterogeneous picture than that seen in Europe. In particular, several case studies have emphasized the process of internal social and economic differentiation associated with the economic growth of the cluster (the Tegalwangi rattan cluster, the Mexican and Indian footwear clusters). In a few examples, such differentiation between units having access to capital has raised their technical capabilities, and they are increasingly competing in quality-conscious market segments; for others, that have stagnated technically, it has resulted in the breakdown of the cluster as a spatial entity (the rural Mexican knitwear clusters) or has led to increasingly subordinatory linkages between core and peripheral elements within the cluster (the rattan sector of Tegalwangi).

Seventhly, in most of the developing-country cases (with the partial exception of the technospatial clusters in Cyprus and the Republic of Korea, both of which are effectively industrialized economies), the competitive advantage of small-firm clusters lies in their low labour costs and numerical labour flexibility. While, in most examples, labour surpluses have resulted in poor working conditions and low levels of process-innovation, they have not necessarily precluded small-firm clusters from technologically upgrading themselves. In a number of clusters, there are signs of technical improvements alongside increasing labour surpluses (the Suame cluster, for example). These factors emphasize the various hybrid growth paths, that lie between the high and the low roads, which can be found.

Eighthly, broadly speaking a number of the developing- country case studies of potential industrial districts conform to Brusco's (1990) notion of stages of development. In Brusco's view, the Mark I model of industrial district is the one in which there has been no State intervention and where inter-firm production relations associated with clustering have emerged as a result of local and contextual socially-embedded factors. The Mark II model carries the development of a Mark I industrial district further, through targeted intervention and support by the State and local government.

As Pecqueur and Silva (1992) state, a necessary condition for successful industrial districts attaining what they term "territorial solidarity" is that such districts should have a "minimal density and critical duration". This implies a sufficient number of collaborating and process-specialized enterprises within the cluster and a period of time during which extensive patterns of production, social and business networking have formed as a base for institutional support programmes. The example of the CBK consortium suggests, however, that it is not so much an issue of minimal numbers (or density) of firms that is critical, but rather of what can be termed "strategic density", whereby "strategic relations" emerge between firms and other agencies (including community groups, non-governmental organizations and the State) that result in the ability of a cluster to develop a growth potential.

Where such conditions are met, in that strategic patterns of inter-firm collaboration have been initiated, social and production interrelations have over time become embedded, and specific forms of social regulatory institutions function favourably within the cluster. In such cases, targeted intervention in support of the cluster can have an important impact. However, institutions geared to supporting the cluster (the Mark II industrial district) and raising its technological capabilities must have local roots; they have to develop associational and organizational linkages with the cluster and its sectoral bodies and be embedded in the social fabric of the society in order to be effective. This implies that State institutions created from above and supplanted on small-firm clusters are likely to be far less effective than those founded on participatory linkages within the cluster, and which augment sectoral associations that may exist and develop slowly from below. In this regard, the effectiveness of non-governmental support through participatory non-governmental organizations in urban and rural development and in specific credit, vocational training and enterprise-development programmes may offer some fruitful lessons for the conception of local government strategies.

Furthermore, intervention strategies should consciously attempt to complement, or encourage, cooperative interrelations within the cluster, but not further individualistic competitive tendencies. This requires a careful assessment of the types of knowledge (and technologies) which firms within the cluster are willing to share with each other or perceive as being of a common property nature, offering gains to all members, while at the same time improving the competitive advantage of the cluster as a whole.

Finally, a number of further questions arise that need to be addressed. Beyond broad comments on the traditional and historical links between small-firm clusters and the agrarian economy, little has been said about the way in which the developing-country small-firm clusters have emerged. This requires substantial historical analysis. This task remains to be done, but it is essential if one is to understand the way in which new clusters are likely to appear and existing ones to evolve. Neither have we commented on the specific constraints faced by small-firm clusters. The existing literature on small-firm manufacturing, both overall and at the sectoral level, and the work on the informal sector have abundantly documented the fact that small enterprises face severe capital constraints, entrepreneurial and managerial limitations, poor skill and technological standards and limited access to factor and input markets (Schmitz 1982). Does the system of production organization based upon the industrial district concept effectively ease such constraints? The results from the case studies reviewed in this paper indicate that, as an institutional system, industrial districts can, at the very least, reduce transaction costs faced by small firms in accessing imperfectly functioning factor and input markets. In addition, social networks can effectively assist in easing some of the constraints that small firms traditionally face over credit, skills and technical developments.

A number of questions are pertinent to the overall issue of technological progress. The review suggests that the industrial district framework, and especially the concept of user-producer interactions associated with it, is particularly helpful in encouraging incremental technological development. However, only limited evidence exists of substantial technological dynamism (in either product or process) that goes beyond an incremental nature. Very little is known about the role played by technology transfers, particularly from foreign sources, in the technical upgrading of small-firm industrial districts in developing countries.

In order to develop effective technical assistance programmes, we need to know more, through detailed case studies, about the actual mechanisms whereby inter-firm collaboration leads to technical upgrading, product- and process-innovation and adaptation. How is knowledge passed on and built upon? What are the venues and medium in which such interactions take place? What kind of information is shared? What is kept secret? What types of interrelations exist in backward and forward technical linkages and what forms of hierarchical and power arrangements ensue from this? Similarly, we need to identify explicitly the links between the social milieu and technology diffusion. In what ways are technologies socially-embedded? How is tacit knowledge built upon? What are the social roots of user-producer interactions?

To conclude, although the review of potential industrial districts in the developing world has given rise to many queries, we are at least closer to more precise questions on which targeted information can be sought through detailed empirical case studies across a range of countries. Not only do industrial manufacturing systems akin to small-firm industrial districts occur in developing countries, but observations indicate that the institutional and organizational framework of the industrial district concept has great relevance to small-enterprise development under incipient industrialization. This in itself is substantial progress from the existing body of knowledge on the subject.

REFERENCES

Aeroe, A., 1992, "New pathways to industrialisation in Tanzania: theoretical and strategic considerations", *IDS Bulletin*, vol.23, no.3.

Alcorta, L., 1992, "The impact of new technologies on scale in manufacturing industry: issues and evidence", INTECH, Maastricht (mimeo).

Amin, A., 1989, "A model of the small firm in Italy", in Goodman *et al.*, eds., 1989.

Amin, A. and K. Robins, 1990, "Industrial districts and regional development: limits and possibilities", in Pyke *et al.*, eds., 1990.

Amsden, A., 1985, "The division of labour is limited by the rate of growth of the market: the Taiwan machine tool industry in the 1980s", *Cambridge Journal of Economics*

Amsden, A., 1991, "Big business and urban congestion in Taiwan: the origins of small enterprise and regionally decentralised industry (respectively)", *World Development*, vol.19, no.9.

Anderson, D., 1982, "Small industry in developing countries: a discussion of issues", *World Development*, vol.10, no.11

Asheim, B., 1992, "Flexible specialisation, industrial districts and small firms: a critical appraisal", in Ernste & Meier, eds., 1992.

Becattini, G., 1990, "The Marshallian industrial district as a socio-economic notion", in Pyke *et al.*, eds., 1990.

Bellandi, M., 1989, "The industrial district in Marshall", in Goodman *et al.*, eds., 1989.

Best, M., 1990, *The New Competition: Institutions of Industrial Restructuring*, Polity Press, Cambridge.

Bhalla, A.S., ed., 1991, *Small and Medium Enterprises: Technology Policies and Options*, Greenwood Press, New York.

Boomgard, J., S. Davies, S. Haggblade, and D. Mead, 1992, "A subsector approach to small enterprise promotion and research", *World Development*, vol.20, no.2.

Bromley R. (ed.), 1978, *The Urban Informal Sector*, Pergamon Press, Oxford.

Brusco, S., 1982, "The Emilian model: productive decentralisation and social integration", *Cambridge Journal of Economics*, vol.6.

Brusco, S., 1990, "The idea of the industrial district: its genesis", in Pyke *et al.*, eds, 1990.

Brusco, S., 1992, "Small firms and the provision of real services", in Pyke and Sengenberger, eds., 1992

Carr, M., ed., 1985, *The AT Reader: Theory and Practice in Appropriate Technology*, London, Oxford University Press.

Cho, Myung-Rae, 1992, "Weaving flexibility: large-small firm relations, flexibility and regional clusters in South Korea", paper presented at EADI Workshop on 'New Approaches to Industrialisation: Flexible Production and Innovation Networks in the South', Lund, June 1992.

Dawson, J., 1992, "The relevance of the flexible specialisation paradigm for small-scale industrial restructuring in Ghana", *IDS Bulletin*, vol.23, no.3, July.

Dijk van, M.P., 1992a, "How relevant is flexible specialisation in Burkina Faso's informal sector and the formal manufacturing sector?", *IDS Bulletin*, vol.23, no.3, July.

Dijk van, M.P., 1992b, "The importance of flexible specialisation, new competition and industrial districts for the modern industrial sector in Burkina", paper presented at EADI Workshop on 'New Approaches to Industrialisation: Flexible Production and Innovation Networks in the South', Lund, June 1992.

Dore, R., 1987, *Taking Japan Seriously*, Stanford University Press, Stanford, Ca.

Ernste, H. and V. Meier, eds., 1992, *Regional Development and Contemporary Industrial Response: Extending Flexible Specialisation*, Belhaven Press, London.

Garofoli, G., ed., 1992, *Endogenous Development and Southern Europe*, Avebury, Aldershot.

Goodman, G., J. Bamford, and P. Saynor, eds., 1989, *Small Firms and Industrial Districts in Italy*, Routledge, London.

Gorter, P., 1992, "Vapi: From formalisation to collective efficiency?", paper presented at EADI Workshop on 'New Approaches to Industrialisation: Flexible Production and Innovation Networks in the South', Lund, June 1992.

Hackansson, H., ed., 1987, *Industrial Technological Development: A Network Approach*, Croom Helm, London

Hirschman, A.O., 1970, *Exit, Voice and Loyalty*, Harvard University Press, Cambridge, Mass.

Hirst, P. and J. Zeitlin, eds., *Reversing Industrial Decline? Industrial Structure and Policy in Britain and her Competitors*, Berg, Oxford.

James, D., 1991, "Capital goods production and technological learning: the case of Mexico", *Journal of Economic Issues*, vol.25, no.4.

James, J. and A. Bhalla, 1991, "Microelectronics, flexible specialisation and small scale industrialisation", *ILO World Employment Programme Working Paper*, no. 220, Geneva.

Jamil, A. and R. Said, 1991, "Management and technological capabilities of Malaysian small and medium enterprises: constraints and options", in Bhalla, ed., 1991.

Johanson, J. and L.-G. Mattsson, 1987, "Inter-organisational relations in industrial systems: a network approach compared with the transaction-cost approach", *International Studies of Management and Organisation*, vol.17, no.1.

Kaplinsky, R., 1989, "Technological revolution and the international division of labour in manufacturing: a place for the third world?", in Raphael Kaplinsky and Charles Cooper, ed., 1989, *Technology and Development in the Third Industrial Revolution*, Frank Cass, London.

Kaplinsky, R., 1990, *The Economics of Small: Appropriate Technology in a Changing World*, London, IT Publications.

Kaplinsky, R., 1991, "From mass production to flexible specialisation: a case study from a semi-industrialised economy", *IDS Discussion Paper*, no. 295.

Kashyap, S.P., 1988, "Growth of small size enterprises in India: its nature and content", *World Development*, vol.16, no.6.

Kashyap, S.P., 1992, "Recent developments in the small enterprises sector in India: economic and social aspects", International Institute of Labour Studies, *ILO Discussion Paper*, no. 48, Geneva.

Knorringa, P., 1992, "Adaptive capabilities in the Agra footwear cluster", paper presented at EADI Workshop on 'New Approaches to Industrialisation: Flexible Production and Innovation Networks in the South', Lund, June 1992.

Kozul-Wright, Z., 1992, "Organising flexibility: a comparison of the Italian and Yugoslav furniture industries", paper presented at the Eastern Economic Association Conference, New York, March 1992.

Lazerson, M., 1988, "Organisational growth of small firms: an outcome of markets and hierarchies", *American Sociological Review*, vol.53.

Lazerson, M., 1990, "Subcontracting as an alternative organisational form to vertically integrated production", International Institute for Labour Studies, *ILO Discussion Paper*, no. 20, Geneva.

Lee, Kyung Tae, 1991, "Technical and managerial extension services for Korean small and medium enterprises", in Bhalla, ed., 1991.

Levy, B., 1991, "Transaction costs, the size of firms and industrial policy: lessons from a comparative case study of the footwear industry in Korea and Taiwan", *Journal of Development Economics*, vol.34, nos. 1/2.

Lundvall, B.-A., 1988, "Innovation as an interactive process: from user producer interaction to the national system of innovation", in Giovanni Dosi *et al.*, eds., 1988, *Technical Change and Economic Theory*, Pinter, London.

Maldonado, C. and S.V. Sethuraman, 1992, *Technological Capability in the Informal Sector: Metal Manufacturing in Developing Countries*, ILO, Geneva.

Marshall, A., 1890, *Principles of Economics*, 8th edn. (1986), Macmillan, London.

Mead, D., 1984, "Of contracts and subcontracts: small firms in vertically disintegrated production/distribution systems in LDCs", *World Development*, vol. 12, nos. 11/12.

Murray, F., 1987, "Flexible specialisation in the Third Italy", *Capital and Class*, no. 33.

Murray, R., 1992, "Flexible specialisation in small island economies: the case of Cyprus", in Pyke and Sengenberger, eds., 1992.

Nabi, I., 1988, *Entrepreneurs & Markets in Early Industrialisation: A Case Study From Pakistan*, International Center for Economic Growth, San Francisco.

Nadvi, K., 1990, *Employment Creation in Urban Informal Microenterprises in the Manufacturing Sector in Pakistan*, ILO-ARTEP, New Delhi.

Nadvi, K., 1992, "Flexible specialisation, industrial districts and employment in Pakistan", *ILO World Employment Programme Working Paper*, no. 232, Geneva, June.

Pecqueur B. and M.R. Silva, 1992, "Territory and economic development: the example of diffuse industrialisation", in Garofoli, ed., 1992.

Piore M. and C. Sabel, 1984, *The Second Industrial Divide: Possibilities for Prosperity*, Basic Books, New York.

Piore, M., 1990, "Work, labour and action: work experience in a system of flexible production", in Pyke *et al.*, eds, 1990.

Portes A., Castells M. and L. Benton, 1989, *The Informal Sector: Studies in Advanced and Less Developed Countries*, John Hopkins University Press, Baltimore.

Powell, W., 1990, "Neither market nor hierarchy: network forms of organisation", in Barry Straw & L.L. Cummings (eds.), *Research in Organisational Behaviour*, vol.12, JAI Press.

Pyke, F., Becattini G. and W. Sengenberger, eds., 1990, *Industrial districts and inter-firm co-operation in Italy*, International Institute for Labour Studies, ILO, Geneva.

Pyke, F. and W. Sengenberger, eds., 1992, *Industrial Districts and Local Economic Regeneration*, International Institute for Labour Studies, ILO, Geneva.

Rabellotti, R., 1992, "Industrial districts in Mexico: the case of the footwear industry in Guadalajara and Leon", paper presented at EADI Workshop on 'New Approaches to Industrialisation: Flexible Production and Innovation Networks in the South', Lund, June 1992.

Rasmussen, J., 1991, *The Local Entrepreneurial Milieu: Linkages and specialisation among small town enterprises in Zimbabwe*, Research Report no. 79, Dept. of Geography, Roskilde University with Center for Development Research, Copenhagen.

Rasmussen, J., 1992, "The small enterprise environment in Zimbabwe: growing in the shadow of large enterprise", *IDS Bulletin*, vol.23, no.3, July.

Sandee, H., 1992, "The impact of technological change on inter-firm linkages: a case study of clustered rural small scale roof tile enterprises in central Java", paper presented at EADI Workshop on 'New Approaches to Industrialisation: Flexible Production and Innovation Networks in the South', Lund, June 1992.

Schmitz, H., 1982, "Growth constraints on small scale manufacturing in developing countries: a critical review", *World Development*, vol.10, no.6.

Schmitz, H., 1989, "Flexible specialisation: a new paradigm of small scale industrialisation", *IDS Discussion Paper*, no. 261, Sussex.

Schmitz, H., 1990, "Small firms and flexible specialisation in developing countries", *Labour and Society*, vol.15, no.3.

Schmitz, H., 1992a, "Industrial districts: model and reality in Baden-Württemberg", in Pyke & Sengenberger, eds., 1992.

Schmitz, H., 1992b, "On the clustering of small firms", *IDS Bulletin*, vol.23, no.3, July.

Scott, A. and M. Storper, 1992, "Regional development reconsidered", in Ernste & Meier, eds., 1992.

Sengenberger, W., 1988, "Economic and social perspectives of small enterprises", *Labour and Society*, vol.13, no.3.

Sengenberger W. and F. Pyke, 1991, "Small firm industrial districts and local economic regeneration: research and policy issues", *Labour and Society*, vol.16, no.1

Sethuraman S.V. (ed.), 1981, *The Urban Informal Sector in Developing Countries: Employment, Poverty and Environment*, ILO, Geneva.

Sethuraman S.V., 1985, "The informal sector in Indonesia: policies and prospects", *International Labour Review*, vol.124, no.6.

Smyth, I., 1991, "Collective efficiency and selective benefits: the growth of the rattan industry of Tegalwangi (Indonesia)", *Labour and Society*, vol.16, no.3.

Storper, M., 1989, "The transition to flexible specialisation in industry", *Cambridge Journal of Economics*, vol.13, June.

Storper, M. and R. Walker, 1989, *The Capitalist Imperative: Territory, Technology and Industrial Growth*, Blackwell, Oxford.

Storper, M. and B. Harrison, 1990, "Flexibility hierarchy and regional development: the changing structure of industrial production systems and their forms of governance in the 1990s", Carnegie-Mellon University, *Working Paper Series*, WP-90-39, Pittsburgh.

Sverrisson, A., 1992a, "Innovation as a collective enterprise: a case study of carpenters in Nakuru, Kenya", Research Policy Institute, University of Lund, *Discussion Paper*, no.189, Lund, February.

Sverrisson, A., 1992b, "Flexible specialisation and woodworking enterprises in Kenya and Zimbabwe", *IDS Bulletin*, vol.23, no.3, July.

Sverrisson, A., 1992c, "Gradual diffusion of flexible techniques in small and medium size enterprise networks", paper presented at EADI Workshop on 'New Approaches to Industrialisation: Flexible Production and Innovation Networks in the South', Lund, June 1992.

Tan, Q., 1991, "Technology promotion programmes for small enterprises: the Philippine experience", in Bhalla, ed., 1991.

Tiwari, M., 1990, "Understanding the organisation of work: the state, intersectoral linkages, and the historical conditions of accumulation in Ludhiana's industrial regime", Dept. of Urban Studies and Planning, MIT, Cambridge, (mimeo).

Villarán, F., 1992, "Small scale industry efficiency groups in Peru", in B. Späth, ed., *Small Firms and Development in Latin America: The Role of Institutional Environment, Human Resources and Industrial Relations*, International Institute for Labour Studies, ILO, Geneva, forthcoming.

Watanabe, S., 1983, *Technology, Marketing and Industrialisation: Linkages between Large and Small Enterprises*, Macmillan, New Delhi.

Weijland, H., 1992, "Flexible trade networks for small rural enterprises", paper presented at EADI Workshop on 'New Approaches to Industrialisation: Flexible Production and Innovation Networks in the South', Lund, June 1992.

Werbner, P., 1987, "Enclave economies and family firms: Pakistani traders in a British city", in J. Eades, ed., *Migrants, Workers and the Social Order*, ASA Monographs 26, London, Tavistock Publications.

Werbner, P., 1990, "Renewing an industrial past: British Pakistani entrepreneurs in Manchester", *Migration*, vol.8.

Wilson, F., 1992, "Modern workshop industry in Mexico: on its way to collective efficiency?", *IDS Bulletin*, vol.23, no.3, July.

NOTES

1.   See Brusco 1982, Piore & Sabel 1984, Lazerson 1988, Sengenberger 1988, Schmitz 1989, 1990, Best 1990, Sengenberger and Pyke 1991.

2.   See Brusco 1982, Best 1990, and the collection of papers in Pyke, Becattini and Sengenberger, eds., 1990;   Pyke and Sengenberger, eds., 1992; Ernste and Meier, eds., 1992;   and Garofoli, ed., 1992.

3.   Among others, the paper draws upon some of the contributions to the EADI Workshop on "New approaches to industrialisation: flexible production and innovation networks in the south", Lund, June 1992; and the *IDS Bulletin*, vol.23, no.2, July 1992.

4.   See Kaplinsky 1989, James and Bhalla 1991 and Alcorta 1992 for critical overviews of the de-scaling implications of the new microelectronic-based technologies, in general, and their impact on small firms, in particular.

5.   On network approaches to industrial organization, particularly amongst small firms, and their impact on technological development, see Powell 1990, Johanson and Mattsson 1987, Lazerson 1988 and Hackansson, ed., 1987.

6.   In contrast to small firm clusters in "traditional" sectors with long local histories, India's "modern" electronics industry in Bangalore, about which there is very little information, is considered a relatively new and technologically innovative regional industrial cluster.

7.   Zimbabwe's manufacturing sector is cited as a prime example of such dualism, see Rasmussen 1992.

8.   Sethuraman (1985) cites patterns of large-small firms' linkages as a feature of the informal manufacturing sector in Indonesia, although not within the context of small firm clusters.

9.   A crude measure of the benefits of such interactions is that, with identical levels of footwear exports in 1969, total export value of footwear ($2.3 billion) from Taiwan Province of China in 1985 exceeded that of the Republic of Korea (where the sector was dominated by large firms and comparatively integrated production) by over 40 per cent (Levy 1991, p.154).

10.   Wilson (1992) suggests that this also provides the social legitimation for gender exploitation in work, particularly important given that women constitute the bulk of the region's workforce.

11.   Migrant networks are also noted as being particularly powerful in organizing small-firm clusters of British-Pakistani garment manufacturers in the United Kingdom (see Werbner 1990); or the Cuban business community of Miami, United States of America (see Portes et al., eds., 1989).

12.   Traditional apprenticeship systems have also been noted in a number of ILO studies on informal metal-manufacturing sectors in developing countries as being the leading pattern of skill acquisition. See Maldonado and Sethuraman, eds., 1992.

13. See the collection of papers in Bhalla, ed., 1991, for an overview of technology policies aimed at small manufacturing enterprises in developing countries.

14. One cannot, however, discount the impact of macro, sectoral and subsectoral policies. As an example of the latter, the Indonesian Government's decision to ban progressively exports of unprocessed cane (in 1986) and subsequently semi-finished rattan products (in 1989) is cited as having provided the primary boost to the Tegalwangi rattan furniture cluster (Smyth 1991). At a broader level, inter-firm linkage has been an important element of the macro-industrial policy of the Republic of Korea, where State support for large-small firm relations has been explicitly outlined in the Industrial Linkage Promotion Act which stipulates areas of such linkages and the juridical basis for inter-firm cooperation. In addition, targeted strategies aimed at specific sectors (such as automobiles, microelectronics) further underline such inter-firm relations as a desired aspect of business practices. For an example of a recommended Government strategy, the Cyprus Industrial Strategy is explicitly built around flexibly specialized small firms (Murray 1992).

15. Externally created small-firm industrial estates in India, while clearly not industrial districts, appear to have prospered where they were founded on existing cooperative relations, resulting in the emergence of productive and social network arrangements within the estate. The Vapi estate in Gujrat, sectorally concentrated in the chemicals industry, has been cited as such a case (Gorter 1992). Within the estate, there were signs of emerging inter-firm production relations through process-specialized subcontracting, production consortia, and over-arching social (caste) institutions such as the *Panchal mandal*. The latter, in addition to organizing community-based social activities, provided credit to members for working capital needs.

16.   This experience is further borne out by the ILO case studies of the informal metal-working sectors in Mali and Rwanda.   See Maldonado and Sethuraman, eds., 1992.

INDUSTRIAL DISTRICTS AND TECHNOLOGICAL CHANGE: A STUDY OF THE GARMENT INDUSTRY IN DELHI

Ghayur Alam *

INTRODUCTION[1]

The concept of industrial districts (IDs) is far from clear. For example, the characteristics which distinguish them from other clusters of small firms, the role of innovation in their success and their replicability are some of the issues which are yet to be fully understood.

Much of our understanding of IDs is based on studies carried out in developed countries, where IDs are characterized by clusters of small, highly specialized firms using flexible manufacturing techniques. These firms achieve external economies through close vertical linkages achieved through subcontracting. Furthermore, the firms belonging to IDs are found to be largely export-oriented.

The phenomenon of IDs is even less understood in the case of developing countries, where little research on the subject has been carried out. The limited research which is reviewed by Nadvi in his paper suggests that, while clusters of small firms with strong linkages do exist in developing countries, they do not fully conform to the definition of IDs used in the context of developed countries. For example, while the IDs in developed countries often take advantage of new and flexible technologies, this is not so in the case of developing countries. The small-firm clusters in the latter countries

---

* Centre for Technology Studies, New Delhi, India.

are found to exist almost exclusively in low-technology, craft-based industries such as garments, leather-work and pottery. The competitive advantage of the firms operating in these clusters appears to be largely based on low labour costs.

The variety of characteristics of small-firm clusters in developing countries and the paucity of data make generalizations difficult. There is clearly a need to undertake extensive research on the circumstances which contribute to the creation of IDs in developing countries and the factors which provide the firms in these clusters with competitive advantages. Furthermore, the nature of technological capabilities and their diffusion in IDs is required to be investigated in detail. This short paper is an effort in this direction.

The paper is based on a study of Okhla and its surrounding areas in South Delhi which have emerged as major centres of garment production for export in recent years. Four firms, two of which are garment exporters and two fabricators, were studied for the paper. In addition, information was collected from the Okhla Industries Association.[2]

A.   Is Okhla an industrial district?

The Okhla cluster of firms manufacturing and exporting garments meets many of the characteristics attributed to IDs. There is a large concentration of small firms engaged in garment-related business in a small area. About 1,500 of these firms are located within an area of a few kilometres. The cluster is highly export-oriented; only a handful of firms sell locally. Furthermore, there is a great deal of specialization; strong vertical linkages are widespread.

While about 500 firms in this cluster concentrate on designing garments, preparing samples and getting export orders, the rest are specialist fabricators, dyers, etc. Most of these firms are small. This is particularly true in the case of fabricators, many of whom employ between 10 to 25 people. Firms employing more than 100 people are uncommon. Some features of the cluster do not conform to characteristics commonly attributed to IDs in developed countries. The pace of technical change among the firms in the cluster, for example, is very slow; cheap labour is their main source of competitive advantage.

B. How Okhla emerged as a cluster

The export of garments began in Delhi on a small scale in the late 1960s and early 1970s. Most exporters were family firms located in residential areas of south Delhi. As they could not set up manufacturing facilities in these expensive areas, they encouraged small entrepreneurs to set up fabrication units in the neighbouring low-rent areas. South Delhi has a number of old villages which were found to be most suitable for locating these units.

Later, in the mid-1970s, Okhla was designated by the Government as an industrial area. The garment exporters found this to be a particularly attractive area, as it is very near the villages where fabrication units already existed. By the early 1980s, the area was completely dominated by firms engaged in garment export and production-related activities. With the increase in the number of garment exporters in Okhla, the number of fabricators in neighbouring areas continued to increase.

Interestingly, there is a lot of movement of firms within the cluster. This is particularly evident in the case of small fabricators, who are moving to new and lower-rent areas. The rents in areas which are already part of the cluster have increased sharply in the last three years. In order to maintain their competitive advantage, the fabricators are now moving into new areas. For this reason, the cluster is continuously expanding.

C. Advantages of Okhla for the garment manufacturers

Why are garment exporters attracted to Okhla? The following factors made Okhla particularly attractive for these firms:

(a) *Availability of skilled labour in the area*: As garment manufacture is labour-intensive, the availability of skilled workers is very important. As Okhla is known as a centre of the garment industry, it attracts a large number of skilled workers. Also, as the workers live in the same area, it is easy to contact them when they are needed.

(b) *Close proximity of exporters and subcontractors:* This is particularly relevant in the case of fabricators. The exporters like to keep a close watch on the quality and the delivery schedules of the fabricators. In order to assure this, they send their own people to supervise the work at the fabricator's premises. For this reason, the distance between exporters and fabricators is of particular importance. Other facilities, such as dyeing and packaging, are also nearby.

(c) *Availability of materials and other inputs*: Materials such as thread, buttons, zippers and elastic are readily available in the area. Similarly, the packaging and transporting facilities required by exporters are well developed.

(d) *Credit*: As the payment cycle for exports if often long, the exporters require credit facilities. The banks located in the area treat garment exporters as special customers and extend these facilities. They have also set up foreign exchange departments especially to meet the needs of garment exporters. These facilities are not easily available in the banks located in other industrial areas.

D. Linkages

We did not find any evidence of horizontal linkages among the exporters. The business is very competitive and most firms are secretive. The major reason for secrecy is fear that their designs will be copied by their competitors. Designs are considered to be the most important asset of exporters. As they invest a considerable amount of money in obtaining exclusive designs from foreign designers, they are very careful to protect these investments. This factor has eliminated the possibility of cooperation among exporters almost completely. Conversely, cooperation among fabricators is quite common. In most cases, this takes the form of sharing of jobs to carry out large orders.

Vertical linkages between exporters and fabricators are very strong, however. In fact, the success of the firms in exporting competitively from this area is largely owing to these linkages. While the exporters specialize in product-design, the fabricators specialize in low-cost production.

The fabricators manage to keep production costs low by operating sweat-shop-type operations. The workers, most of whom belong to the traditional tailoring caste, come from Uttar Pradesh and Bihar, are employed on a piece-rate basis. On average, a worker works for 14 hours (from 7.00 a.m. to 10 p.m.) and earns about 120 rupees a day (equal to about US$ 3 in 1992).

E. Technology and its diffusion

Most firms in the cluster show little sign of technological change. The main competitive strength of the firms is not their ability to innovate, but the possibility of using low-cost labour. Technical change among the fabricating firms is particularly slight. All the fabricators continue to use the sewing machines introduced in the early 1970s. These are simple machines powered by small motors. Initially, the diffusion of these machines was very slow. The fabricators were not interested in investing in motors. As the workers are paid piece- rate, the owners did not see much advantage in improving machine productivity. (While a new machine costs about 1,000 rupees, a motor costs about 800 rupees. They thus preferred to buy a new machine rather than instal a motor in an old one.) The workers were given the option of installing their own motors, but very few took up the option. It was only when space became expensive and the fabricators could not expand by installing new machines that the use of motors was seen as an acceptable way of expanding production. Now all machines are motorized. No further change in technology has been introduced by fabricators since the late 1970s, when these machines became common.

It is interesting to note that the exporters, who are more exposed to new technology, as they regularly meet foreign buyers, have not greatly stimulated adoption of more productive technologies by the fabricators. The explanation may lie in the fact that the fabricators are useful to the exporter precisely because they use low-tech cheap labour, keeping costs low.

Another important reason for the slow pace of technical change relates to the nature of the garments produced by this cluster. The fabric used in the garments exported by these firms is almost exclusively hand-loom silk. The quality is very uneven and dyeing and weaving faults are common. The use of such fabrics requires that the whole garment be fabricated from the same section of fabric, so that slight differences in shades are not too obvious. This limits the possibility of using more sophisticated machinery, whereby each part of the garment is produced separately and then assembled. At present, the operators using sewing machines prepare the whole garment from the same part of the fabric. This is considered to be the most appropriate production technology for uneven quality fabric. For this reason, advanced fabrication machinery is employed only when fabrics produced in mills are used.

In recent years, increased pressure from the importers to improve quality has led some exporters to introduce advanced fabrication machinery and special machines for sewing buttons and making buttonholes. However, firms in this category are very few. Less than 10 assembly units are reported to be operating in the Okhla area.

There are in-built conditions in the cluster which further limit the possibility of technical change. The structure of the cluster is a reflection of the desire of exporters (who alone have the resources to adopt advanced technology) to minimize the number of workers at any one site by decentralizing production facilities. Most exporters are located in unionized areas. They are keen to limit the power of unions by locating manufacturing facilities (directly or through sub-contractors) in non-unionized areas.[3]

All the subcontractors are located in non-unionized areas. The fabrication unit, as a consequence, is too small to afford advanced technologies.

Furthermore, the system of employing labour working on a piece-rate basis - considered necessary for maintaining low costs and for discouraging workers from joining unions - acts as a disincentive to the introduction of more productive technologies. Like the example of the introduction of motorized sewing machines, the owners are reluctant to invest in equipment which will increase labour productivity. Only a system of hiring workers at regular wages would make such investments attractive. The spectre of unionization, in turn, reduces the interest of firms in this option.

CONCLUSIONS

The cluster of firms described here appears to be a typical example of IDs in developing countries. While it matches some elements of the definition of IDs, it also differs in certain important respects. Principally, unlike the IDs in developed countries, the firms in Okhla show a general lack of innovative activity and rely on cheap labour for their competitive strength.

Garment exporters operating in the cluster have a number of advantages. Primarily, they do not have to set up in-house production facilities. Facilities for dyeing, fabrication and packaging are all available within a few kilometres. There is also an abundant supply of cheap but skilled labour in the area. The cluster, with its well-developed linkages, provides considerable economies to all the firms operating in it.

Our evidence supports the view that, at least in developing countries, IDs are not characterized by a high degree of technological activity. In fact, we find that there are in-built conditions in these clusters which, while providing them with much of their competitive strength, prevent the adoption and diffusion of advanced technologies. However, we must emphasize that most studies of IDs in developing countries, including this one, concentrate on craft-based low-tech industries. Further research on developing countries should be directed at studying the small-firm clusters in relatively technology-intensive areas. (Some of the examples of these are textile machinery and pump industries in Coimbatore and machine-tool industry in Ludhiana.) When such industries have been studied, the role of IDs in the adoption and diffusion of technology in developing countries may be better understood.

NOTES

1.   The author has greatly benefited from the following papers:

   (i)   Asheim, Bjorn, "Industrial districts, inter-firm cooperation and endogenous technological development: the experience of developed countries", reference paper for the UNCTAD/GATE symposium on the role of industrial districts in the application, adaptation and diffusion of technology, Geneva, 16 and 17 November 1992.

   (ii) Nadvi Khalid, "Industrial district experiences in developing countries", reference paper for the UNCTAD/GATE symposium on the role of industrial districts in the application, adaptation and diffusion of technology, Geneva, 16 and 17 November 1992.

   (iii) Van Dijk, M.P ., "The interrelations between industrial districts and technological capabilities development", reference paper for the UNCTAD/GATE symposium on the role of industrial districts in the application, adaptation and diffusion of technology, Geneva, 16 and 17 November 1992.

2.   The following firms were studied:

   (i)   Mohan Exports;
   (ii) Sanjana Garments;
   (iii) Arun Sales Corporation;
   (iv) Name withheld on the request of the owner (a fabricator).

Discussions were also held with the following: Mr. I.K. Puri, President, Okhla Industries Association; Mr. J.C. Maggon, Officer-in-Charge, Okhla Industries Association.

3. In an earlier study of adoption of technology by small firms in India, we found this tendency to be widespread in other sectors as well. See, Alam Ghayur, "Impact of non-economic factors on choice of technology and organization of production: a study of small industrial firms in India", prepared for ILO, December 1991.

INDUSTRIAL DISTRICTS IN DEVELOPING COUNTRIES

Liew Mun Leong *

INTRODUCTION

Thirty years ago, Singapore's economy depended almost entirely on commerce and entrepot trade. Today, it is a newly industrialized economy with strong capabilities in manufacturing and services, supported by good infrastructure. Singapore's strategic thrust for the 1990s is to become a developed country by the end of the decade. To achieve this, it will need to compete in the league of the developed countries: the super-league. Quality and innovation will be the twin engines for moving into and competing in that league. The Singapore Technology Corridor, the district where technology is developed and disseminated, will be pivotal in providing Singapore's industries with the competitive edge through higher quality and innovation. This paper presents the Singapore Technology Corridor and discusses its role in the adaptation, application and diffusion of technology.

A. Country overview

Before delving into the subject, it may be instructive to look briefly at Singapore and the state of its economy. The Republic of Singapore is an independent city State with a total population of over 2.7 million. Together with its 58 islets, the Republic's total land area is 633 square kilometres. Situated in South-East Asia, Singapore is part of the fast-growing Asia-Pacific region. At independence in 1965, Singapore's GDP was US$ 2 billion (at current market prices). This translated into a per capita GDP of US$ 979. The GDP in 1991

---

* Chief Executive, Singapore Institute of Standards and Industrial Research and Executive Director, National Science and Technology Board, Singapore.

was US$ 43 billion with per capita GDP at US$ 15,625, representing a 22-fold and 16-fold increase, respectively (figure 1).

The economy has also become more diversified, with manufacturing (27 per cent of GDP) and finance and business services (26 per cent of GDP) as the two mainstays (figure 2).

Figure 1

GDP and GDP per capita (1965 - 1991)

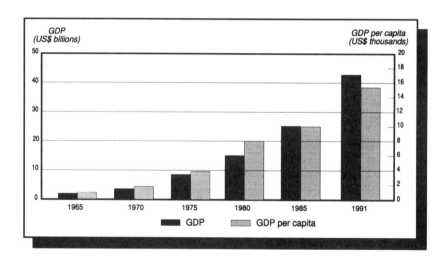

Figure 2

GDP by industry (1965 and 1991)

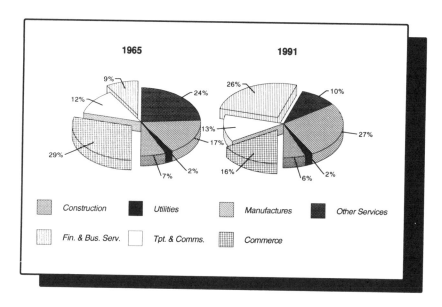

B. Overview of the Technology Corridor

Spanning some 15 kilometres, the Singapore Technology Corridor is modelled on other world-class technopoleis such as "Silicon Valley" in the United States, Sophia Antipolis in France and Multi-Function-Polis in Australia. The need to develop a Singapore technopolis was prompted by the observation that knowledge-based activities thrived best in a community that combined tertiary institutes, high-technology industries, R&D-oriented companies and research centres blended with a complete working, social and living habitat. Given the traditional concentration of research-oriented establishments on the south-western part of the island, a decision was made to develop this belt into a technopolis, so as better to exploit its potential. The Technology Corridor currently comprises a rich mix of research institutions, training establishments and manufacturing companies. The major ones are:

(a) National Promotion and Funding Agencies, namely the National Science and Technology Board (NSTB) and the National Computer Board (NCB);

(b) Tertiary institutions, such as the National University of Singapore (NUS), Nanyang Technological University (NTU), Ngee Ann Polytechnic and Singapore Polytechnic;

(c) Research institutes: All eight national research institutes are located here. They are: the Singapore Institute of Standards and Industrial Research (SISIR), Institute of Systems Science (ISS), Information Technology Institute (ITI), Institute of Molecular and Cell Biology (IMCB), Institute of Microelectronics (IME), Institute of Manufacturing Technology (IMT), GINTIC Institute of CIM and the Magnetics Technology Centre (MTC);

(d) Technical training institutes, such as the French Singapore Institute and the German Singapore Institute;

The Corridor also has two major infrastructure establishments where the manufacturing companies and their R&D facilities are situated: the Singapore Science Park and the Jurong Industrial Estate.

C. Roles of the various institutions

The Singapore Technology Corridor is a well-integrated community with the elements needed for the adaptation, development, application and diffusion of technology. Today, it houses the entire spectrum of institutions needed for research and development of new products. As an illustration, the product development cycle and the involvement of the institutions can be summarized in the figure below.

Figure 3

Institutions in the product development cycle

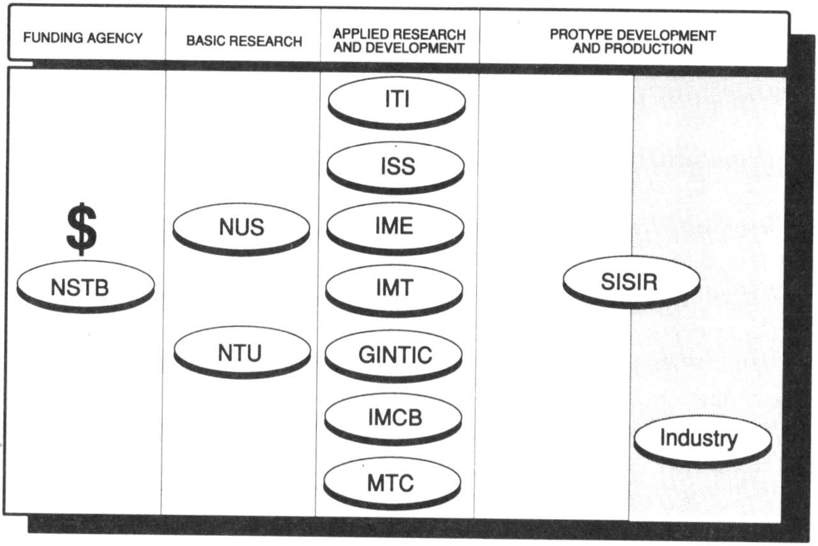

FUNDING AGENCY	BASIC RESEARCH	APPLIED RESEARCH AND DEVELOPMENT	PROTYPE DEVELOPMENT AND PRODUCTION
$ NSTB	NUS NTU	ITI ISS IME IMT GINTIC IMCB MTC	SISIR Industry

The contributions of each group of institutions within the Corridor can best be understood by examining their respective roles.

Universities

Universities provide the base of academic R&D resources. Specifically, NUS and NTU provide a steady source of highly-trained scientists and engineers for the research institutes and industry and conduct high-end basic research.

Polytechnic and technical training institutes

The polytechnic and technical institutes provide application-oriented training and ensure an adequate supply of trained technicians and technologists. In addition, these institutions also provide basic technical services to industry, such as testing and measurement services, and related consultancy; they assist in information transfer by maintaining up-to-date technical information on areas under their purview and offering access to it; they also provide some design and development capabilities.

National research institutes

The research institutes and centres are key players in providing the enabling resources of manpower, skills, technology, knowledge, products and processes for industry. Specifically, these institutions provide direct contract R&D services to industry along with a steady stream of research scientists and engineers (RSEs) with practical R&D experience who can be immediately deployed by industry. They are also a good source of information on new technologies and knowledge that may be tapped by industry; they develop new products and technologies which can be disseminated to industries and spin off new companies for new products which become commercially viable, either through their own staff's efforts or in collaboration with industry.

The research programme of the existing institutes covers a broad spectrum. A brief insight into the mission and research focus of each of these institutes is given in annex B.

National Funding Agency

NSTB was set up to promote research and development of technology at the national level. Its operations and contributions are discussed later.

D. Additional supporting infrastructure

In addition to these institutions, there are two key infrastructure establishments within the Corridor which are critical to Singapore's drive towards higher quality and innovation. They are the Singapore Science Park and the Jurong Industrial Estate.

Singapore Science Park

The Singapore Science Park provides the infrastructure for companies to perform R&D. Initiated in 1983, this 30-hectare site now has some 100 establishments, including technology centres of transnational corporations (TNCs) such as Rank Xerox, Du Pont, Fujitsu, Sony and Seagate, local start-up companies, supporting Government agencies such as SISIR, NSTB and NCB, and commercial supporting laboratories such as Det Norske Veritas. Prompted by the success of Phase I of the development of the Park, Phase II, the development of an additional 20 odd hectares, was initiated in 1992.

Jurong Industrial Estate

There are currently 2,300 transnational and local manufacturing companies in this estate with manufacturing activities ranging from chemical processing to electronics to shipbuilding. The companies include such transnational corporations as Shell, Sony, Far East Levingston and many local companies.

The presence of transnational companies' R&D facilities helps to generate secondary R&D activities among the local supporting industries and also to train a pool of local manpower in R&D work. The efforts of NSTB and the Economic Development Board further help to encourage the transnational companies to upgrade their manufacturing presence into one of research and development.

E. The National Science and Technology Board

Formed in January 1991, the Board's mission is "to develop Singapore into a centre of excellence in selected fields of Science and Technology so as to enhance our national competitiveness in the industrial and services sectors".

The NSTB is working towards establishing itself as the leading promoter and facilitator of R&D in Singapore. It intends to achieve this by:

(a) Strengthening the infrastructure required for technology development by:

   (i) Developing the Science Park as the focal point of the Technology Corridor;

   (ii) Creating an environment conducive to interaction between the R&D community of the manufacturing sector and the higher tertiary institutions. This has been facilitated by locating the Science Park next to the NUS and the National University Hospital;

   (iii) Encouraging a mix of R&D organizations, from tertiary institutions to TNCs and local manufacturing companies, to cultivate synergy between these organizations.

(b) Creating financial incentives to encourage local companies and TNCs to undertake R&D. Schemes offered by NSTB include:

   (i) *Research & Development Assistance Scheme (RDAS)*: This scheme is open to all R&D projects arising from industry, or those involving joint collaboration between industry, universities and research institutes/centres. Under this scheme, NSTB will fund up to 70 per cent of the total direct project costs;

   (ii) *The Product Development Assistance Scheme (PDAS)*: This scheme is specifically targeted to development of products. Under this scheme, NSTB will fund up to 50 per cent of the costs directly associated with product development;

(iii) Funding of research institutes and centres: NSTB funds all the national research institutes and centres. Moreover, NSTB also funds the setting up of local R&D centres by transnational companies. A recent case was the Apple-ISS R&D Centre. The funding of similar centres is under study;

(iv) *Manpower development schemes:* NSTB has set aside Singapore dollars 400 million to develop R&D manpower with the aim of raising the number of RSEs from 29 per 10,000 labour force in 1990 to 40 per 10,000 in 1995. Without an adequate pool of RSEs, the Corridor will not be able to develop into a vibrant technological industrial district.

F. Role of the Singapore Institute of Standards and Industrial Research

Having the infrastructure, manpower and funds is not sufficient to elevate the level of technology in industry. SISIR has been established to provide the necessary interface between the research institutions and industry. SISIR is a self-financed, not-for-profit, government R&D institute with the mission "to excel as the National Standards Authority and to lead Singapore industry towards greater international competitiveness through quality and industrial technology". Embodied in this mission are two main roles: (a) to serve as Singapore's national standards authority; and (b) to be the leading technology resource centre in Singapore, focusing on industrial R&D, and the commercial application of technology.

SISIR's role as the national standards authority

As the National Standards Authority, SISIR promotes the use of international standards and provides independent certification of a company's products, processes, services and quality management systems that meet international requirements. In this capacity, SISIR provides the following benefits:

(a) As custodian of the national standardization programme, SISIR is able to guide the strategic efforts of local enterprises as well as promote safety, quality and efficiency of products and processes in industry for local and international markets;

(b) Through participation in international standardization efforts, SISIR is able to monitor the latest international activities and trends. This information can then be disseminated to industries for their benefit;

(c) Metrological services at national level. This is critical since high-end metrological support is a key cornerstone for advanced manufacturing industries;

(d) Through certification and testing, companies are encouraged to upgrade their quality system. The SISIR ISO 9000 certification scheme is one example of a company's quality management system being regularly monitored to ensure that it is up to par and is so certified by an independent and recognized authority.

SISIR's role as a technology-resource centre

As a multi-disciplinary technology resource centre, SISIR undertakes applied research along with developing mechanisms to transfer technology to industry. As a one-stop technology-resource centre, it offers with a wide array of R&D expertise supplemented by extensive technical services. In addition to these competencies, SISIR has also established a Technology Transfer Division (TTD) to facilitate the transfer to, and adoption of, appropriate technologies by Singapore industry.

In carrying out its role, TTD provides specialist services such as expert sourcing programmes, patent search and filing assistance, technology market programmes, where buyers and sellers of technology are matched, "incubator programmes", where entrepreneurs are given financial and technical assistance to transform their innovative ideas into commercial reality, and "soft-start" R&D options to help companies minimize the costs of starting R&D. As the interface between industry and the research institutions, SISIR looks towards hastening the pace of technological development and upgrading in local industry.

G. Benefits of the Technology Corridor

Compared to the other technopoleis in the world, the Singapore Corridor is still relatively young. Yet, even at this early stage, there are already several clear benefits evident in nurturing the growth of this community:

(a) The Corridor is a one-stop district for R&D and related support services. It has a concentration of R&D, technical information agencies, testing and certification facilities, technical consultancy services, and manufacturing support services, all conveniently integrated within a dedicated geographical enclave;

(b) Because of physical proximity, the Corridor facilitates interaction and formal, as well as informal, exchange among researchers and scientists. They can thereby develop new ideas and/or obtain alternative views on projects being worked on;

(c) Since the Corridor includes other segments of the business community, such as industrialists, financiers and managers, closer interaction can be fostered between researchers/ scientists and those who may contribute creative ideas and/or have the ability to exploit the commercial potential of new products and technologies;

(d) Good communications facilities within the community and with other research communities worldwide can be more easily provided. As an example, because of the physical proximity of institutions, it has been easier to link them to the national R&D computer network, Technet, and plug them into the international network, Internet;

(e) A comfortable and pleasant living community equipped with the necessary recreational and family support facilities can be provided. Because of a more homogeneous community, it is easier to develop specific facilities in response to social needs and preferences.

H. The case of Eutech Cybernetics

Through NSTB's help, several projects within the Corridor have been commercialized. The case of Eutech Cybernetics is highlighted here to depict one manner in which resources within the Technology Corridor can be used to improve quality and innovation in industry.

Eutech Cybernetics was the brainchild of Dr. Hari Gunasingham. As a chemistry lecturer at NUS, Dr. Gunasingham's idea was to develop a chemical sensing system for monitoring glucose and neurotransmitters in human body fluids. In October 1985, he was awarded over $600,000 through the RDAS to develop the system. A team of 17 researchers was subsequently formed and a start-up unit under SISIR's "incubator programme" was established. SISIR's expertise in product design and system integration was solicited to assist in the development of the prototype.

At the end of the RDAS project, the group published 18 research and review papers and filed two United States patent applications. Five honours students were also exposed to the pioneering work done by the unit by doing their final-year research projects in the enzyme sensor field. In addition, a prototype was developed and subsequently tested in both animal and clinical trials. The analyser, having aroused much commercial interest on the part of both local and foreign companies, was subsequently commercialized in 1990. In the following year, using the technology and know-how acquired from the RDAS project, a commercially viable product, the Electrascan

EC-1, was introduced. Subsequent sales are expected to be in the region of US$ 60 million.

This case illustrates how an idea which originated in a basic research establishment was brought through institutions in the product-development process to arrive finally at the manufacture of a commercially viable product. Through that process, manpower was also trained and some improvement, albeit small, in prestige of the local R&D community has been achieved.

J. Lessons learned

Looking back at our case, the following paradigms appear in the Technology Corridor model:

(a) There should be a central national body (the NSTB in this case) that provides the incentives and physical infrastructure to encourage the collaboration between research institutions and industries, as well as coordinate the national technology programme;

(b) Transnational corporations should be encouraged to set up R&D facilities in the industrial district, as this will help spur other R&D activities by local companies. TNCs bring with them instant R&D expertise and ability to train locals in R&D;

(c) Centralizing the technical support facilities within a geographical locale provides operational conveniences and reduces the costs of undertaking R&D. Such centralization would also make technological resources easily accessible. These facilities would be particularly advantageous for TNCs in high-value-added industries where services such as metrology, calibration, testing and certification are regularly needed;

(d) Manpower development is critical to the success of an industrial district when it comes to development of technology. A national effort is needed to train R&D manpower to meet the anticipated demands;

(e) There has to be a mix of academic institutions, research institutes, technical training institutes, industrial R&D outfits, and the manufacturing industries for technology to be synergistically applied, embodied in the products, and marketed in global markets.

CONCLUSION

To become a developed country, it is imperative that Singapore have a strong R&D base to fuel its manufacturing and services sectors. The Singapore Technology Corridor is the principal vehicle through which this R&D capability will be developed. By providing the research and manufacturing community with a fully integrated work and social habitat, we hope to achieve the objective, that is, to promote a conducive environment to accelerate the adaptation, application and diffusion of technology and through that, drive Singapore to its national goal of being a developed country by the end of this decade.

ANNEX A

Locations of institutions and establishments

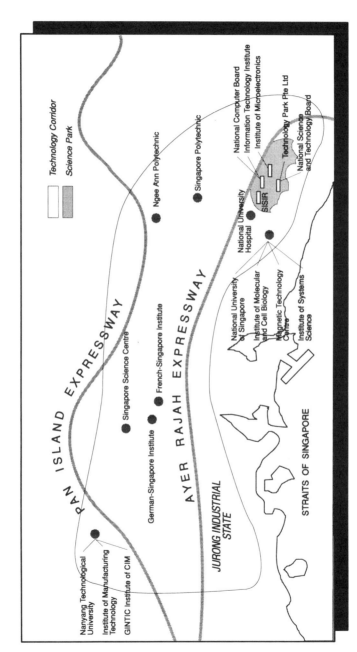

Annex B

Areas of research undertaken by institutes

<u>Institute of Systems Science (ISS)</u>

1. ISS was established in 1981 primarily as a teaching institute. Its R&D programme commenced in 1986 with the broad goal of advancing the state-of-the-art information technologies that will eventually replace existing ones.

2. ISS's research focuses on producing technical inventions and prototypes which will lead to the development of next-generation information systems. One specific aspect common to these systems will be their multimedia orientation and relation to "intelligent" systems, with an emphasis on connectionism and natural language processing.

<u>Information Technology Institute (ITI)</u>

3. Founded in 1986, as the applied R&D arm of the National Computer Board, ITI's mission is to create and deploy useful innovations using advanced information technology (IT) to benefit IT companies and user organizations.

4. Its research programmes are focused on advanced information management, multimedia, computer communications, artificial intelligence, high-performance computing applications, and software engineering.

<u>GINTIC Institute of CIM</u>

5. The Grumman International/Nanyang Technological University (GINTIC) Institute of Computer Integrated Manufacturing (CIM) was set up in 1985, with the assistance and expertise of Grumman International. Its mission is to

develop local expertise in CIM application and development by working with industry through cooperative R&D.

6. GINTIC's R&D activities are aimed at upgrading the country's manufacturing capabilities through the application of advanced information technology. The eight programmes being developed are: (a) flexible manufacturing systems; (b) simulation and modelling; (c) concurrent engineering; (d) computer-aided product design and process definition; (e) communication networking for manufacturing; (f) integrated knowledge-based systems; (g) computer-based manufacturing management, planning and control; and (h) strategic planning and standardization.

Institute of Microbiology (IMCB)

7. IMCB, predominantly a basic research institute, was established in 1987 to develop and foster a modern research culture for biological and biomedical sciences, and train scientists.

8. The institute's main areas of research can be divided into six major groups: (a) cell regulation; (b) molecular genetics/protein engineering; (c) plant molecular biology; (d) molecular neurobiology; (e) tumour immunology/virology; and (f) microsequencing and peptide synthesis service.

Institute of Microelectronics (IME)

9. IME was set up in April 1991 to serve as Singapore's central facility for enhancing its industrial capabilities in the area of microelectronics technology. Initially, the Institute will focus on four major areas which are of critical importance to its industrial collaborators in the microelectronics sector. They are: (a) silicon technology; (b) microelectronic component reliability and failure analysis; (c) very large-scale integrated

computer-aided design, circuit design and test; and (d) microelectronic systems and applications.

Institute of Manufacturing Technology (IMT)

10. IMT was set up in 1991 to establish and promote advanced manufacturing technologies that are of strategic significance to Singapore's economic growth. The Institute was expected to focus its research on five major areas: (a) net shape manufacturing; (b) surface technology and environment; (c) assembly and materials handling; (d) measurements and quality control; and (e) precision machining.

Magnetics Technology Centre (MTC)

11. Established in July 1992, MTC was set up to boost Singapore's lead in the magnetics industry. The Centre was expected to focus its research on design and control (actuator and motor), coding and data communication, magnetic film and media, and electromagnetic interference and compatibility.

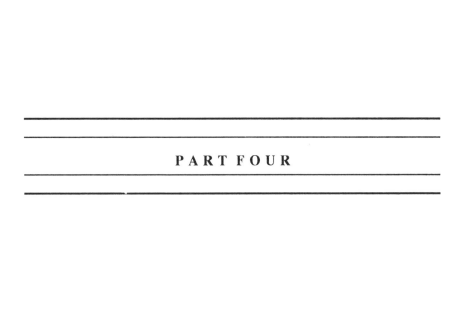

PART FOUR

IMPLICATIONS OF INDUSTRIAL DISTRICTS FOR UPGRADING SMALL FIRMS IN DEVELOPING COUNTRIES: A SYNTHESIS OF THE DISCUSSION

Brigitte Späth

INTRODUCTION [1]

The recent work on successful small-firm development in European industrial districts has captured the attention of a substantial body of researchers and policy-makers alike, and across a wide range of countries and organizations. As a consequence, the debate at the joint UNCTAD/GATE Symposium on the Role of Industrial Districts in the Application, Adaptation and Diffusion of Technology, was not only vivacious but also highly controversial, given the interest and background of the participants. The discussion synthesized below covered a wide range of subjects which will be subsumed under around five key rubrics:

(a) Is the European experience of successful small-firm development in so-called industrial districts of equal importance to countries at lower levels of industrialization and for all industrial subsectors?

(b) Can the organizational principles inherent in these industrial districts, or similar ones, be found in developing countries?

(c) In what way do the economic, social, political, institutional and cultural structures in these countries facilitate or, on the contrary, obstruct the types of industrial district strategies that have succeeded elsewhere?

(d) What are the resultant effects, (in terms of economic and social benefits derived for different groups, such as entrepreneurs, workers etc.)?

(e) What policy measures would enhance and sustain the development of successful industrial districts in these countries?

Underlying these questions is an overall concern for technology and, in particular, its role in the emergence and consolidation of such districts. What implications could be derived for technology policy?

I. FROM CONCEPTS AND DEFINITIONS: TOWARDS AN OPERATIONAL APPROACH

Various definitions and concepts presented to the Symposium met with controversy in the discussions. They are contained in this volume. A principal issue was whether industrial districts could serve as a model for developing countries, and if so, what adaptations would be necessary so as to make the concept operational in these countries.

A. Industrial districts as a concept of advanced market economies

Definitions and concepts of industrial districts have essentially been derived by abstracting from a stylized description of particular cases in industrialized countries. However before entering into details of the discussion, it is worth recalling briefly the origin and context in which the notion of industrial district evolved as well as its principal features. Although the significance of industrial districts for local industrialization had already been recognized by the turn-of-the-century economist Alfred Marshall,[2] new impetus undoubtedly came from Italy. This occurred when it became obvious that, contrary to mainstream economic theory, small firms did not wither away gradually, but in some regions, such as in the north-central and north-eastern parts of Italy, now called the "Third Italy", they appeared to be rather efficient, flexible and dynamic.[3] A decisive contribution has been made by Becattini (1990), who applied Marshall's concept of industrial district to these territorially defined productive systems in the "Third Italy". At the same time, he contended that the unit of analysis was no longer a single firm but a cluster of interconnected firms located in a small area.[4]

Thereby, the crucial characteristic of an industrial district becomes its organization which, although it may vary at the margins, typically contains a number of key principles, namely:

(a) **specialization** of the district in a principal industry, in the sense of containing most of the upstream and downstream processes and services going towards the manufacture of a family of products;

(b) inter-firm **division of labour** in different phases or activities of the production process;

(c) inter-firm **cooperation** among the specialized and segmented population of firms;

(d) the existence of **entrepreneurial dynamism** and the availability of a **skilled labour force**, where entrepreneurs and workers alike are versed in the various functions and processes associated with the manufacturing and marketing of the main product of the district;

(e) social, cultural and territorial **embeddedness** of the economic activities, which enhances a shared value system, trust and cooperative attitudes;

(f) **institutional thickness**, based upon the existence of (i) strong production and information networks among firms; ii) interest groups, such as employers' organizations and trade unions; (iii) self-help groups and sectoral associations; (iv) the back-up by regional and local authorities and (v) specialized support and real service institutions.

It is important to recognize that these are not individual or independent features but are interrelated, a fact which is sometimes overlooked. Industrial districts are not merely an industrial network of firms but an economic, social and cultural phenomenon, which is best portrayed by the notion of "embeddedness of economic relations into a deeper social fabric" (Asheim) or the "thickening of industrial and social inter-dependencies" (Bellandi; Becattini 1990).[5] It is exactly this specific combination of economic, social and institutional arrangements which provides the conditions for a number of subsequent developments: (a) external economies, (Asheim); (b) economies of scale and scope, and efficiency, both individually and at the level of the district (Sengenberger/Pyke 1992); (c) agglomeration economies (Asheim); (d) innovative capabilities, synergies or decentralized industrial creativity (Bellandi) and (e) a potential for regional and local endogenous development. Also it is important to note that the economic success of the European industrial district has come not through advantageous access to low-cost factors of production - cheap labour, land or capital - but rather from a particularly effective social and economic organization based on small firms.

In addition, industrial districts soon became associated with the notion of flexible specialization, coined by Piore and Sabel (1984) in their study of the crisis of the Fordist mass production paradigm in advanced market economies.[6] The notion of flexible specialization, in turn, is identified with flexible production based on increasingly productive and widely applicable technology, a polyvalent labour force and the manufacture of differentiated goods to meet a rapidly changing demand in constantly shifting markets. The pursuit of flexible specialization can be either on a large- or small-scale level. The small-firm and craft-based variant of flexible specialization is an advanced form of industrial district, which is also termed Marshallian industrial district (Becattini 1990) or Mark II district (Brusco 1990).

In the ideal case, these districts seek their competitive edge not just on cost-cutting and price differentials, but on a range of dimensions, such as improving productivity, quality, design, flexibility and exploring new markets. In this context, industrial districts epitomize a new form of industrial organization, which calls into question the previous trends of industrialization geared to a more or less continuous centralization of the industrial structure and the steady enlargement of both enterprise and production units, and hence, forming part of an larger process of industrial restructuring, modifications in the organization of production and differentiation of markets.[7]

Recent research on industrial districts and flexible specialization has stimulated the industrialization debate by questioning how firms can be efficiently structured; how they relate to markets, suppliers and their direct competitors; the role played by the labour force and skills; how innovation takes place and how technologies are diffused; and how governments and institutions can most effectively implement industrial policies. Thus, the reserach has cast new light on a number of old issues, such as firm-size, inter-firm relations, industrial relations, the implication of technology supply, the choice of technique, and the appropriate form of financial markets and support, and capturing new ways of industrial and economic organization.

B. Limits to the advanced market-economies' model of industrial district

Industrial districts have so far mainly been studied and identified in developed market economies.[8] Scholars of the Italian industrial districts (Amin, Asheim and Bellandi) have stressed the theoretical rigour of the concept and point to the uniqueness of the Italian situation in that it provides a peculiar cultural embeddedness of industrial districts (in Emilia Romagna or Tuscany). The same holds true for Baden-Württemberg. The social underpinning of these "productive cultures" has often evolved over a long period of time; it is culturally rooted in traditions of family business, such as the *famille communautaire*, share-cropping or the *metayage system* in agriculture and in craftsmanship, or the medieval guilds and German *Handwerkskammern*. These socio-historical and cultural features have furthered the formation of a distinct entrepreneurial culture, craft pride, tacit knowledge and a consensual environment.

The existence of close-knit communities with common value systems facilitates the creation of trust and cooperative attitudes, on which various forms of collaboration and exchange of information are based, and which reduce potential sources of conflict (*cf.* Pyke 1992). The performance and dynamics of a district depend on close interrelationships between the different social, political and economic spheres. The functioning of one, say the economic, is shaped by the functioning and organization of the others. Nevertheless, acting according to principles of trust does not imply that people cease to act in their own self-interest; rather, it means a specific, broader understanding of self-interest which includes the welfare of others and one's own future welfare (*cf.* Sabel 1992). It is precisely this feature, so distant from prevailing conceptions of economic rationality, which leads to the assumption that the European industrial districts are unique historical artefacts which can be found but not made (*cf.* Zeitlin 1992, p.286f). The limits of the conceptual framework is underlined by this apparent dependence on a highly specific socio-historical context.

The first conclusion would therefore point towards the relative uniqueness of industrial districts and towards their unsuitability as a model for developing countries. However, according to the empirical evidence of advanced market economies presented in this volume (*cf.* Amin; Asheim; Bellandi; Kozul-Wright) the performance of industrial districts inside and outside Italy varies widely. Experiences range from (a) traditional or prototype industrial districts in Italy, Slovenia and Sweden, which have achieved certain externalities, but few economies of agglomeration and a low potential for technological capability-building; (b) industrial districts with some innovative capacity in Italy; (c) to advanced forms of industrial districts with a good to high potential for innovation as found in Italy, Norway and

Germany. This holds even more so for the case studies on developing countries, surveyed by Nadvi, and the other examples presented (e.g. Alam, Villarán) and discussed at the meeting.

Given this diversity of experience with industrial districts in advanced market economies, it was concluded that it would be wrong to over-generalize, and or stick too closely to "narrowly" or "thickly" defined concepts. Even for advanced market economies, the application of normative concepts such as the Marshallian industrial district or the Mark II district appears difficult in practice: "Despite its many valuable insights, the canonical model of the Marshallian industrial district now appears too rigid, too exclusive and too closely bound up with the experience of a particular time and place to accommodate convincingly the diversity displayed by contemporary districts..." (Zeitlin 1992, p.284).

In contrast to that, Van Dijk applied the notion of industrial district in rather elusive terms, which leads finally to the conclusion that the concept lacks all recognized and agreed definitional rigour. Accordingly, it was emphasized that a direct transfer or replication of such a model originating from advanced market economies would be neither feasible nor desirable for developing countries. Consequently, a need for an adaptation of the concept was explicitly expressed.[9]

C. Towards an adaptation

There is much confusion over the way the concept has been set forth and associated with dissimilar ideas. Therefore, it is worth summarizing, what an industrial district is not. First, an industrial district is not a company group, with or without a common shareholder, within the same manufacturing sector and operating in a limited geographical area. Secondly, it is neither just a business, science or technology park, nor an export zone. Thirdly, it must not be confused with the small-enterprise promotion concept of industrial estate, defined as a collection of disparate firms on a special site, and where sometimes material infrastructure is provided, such as factory space, electricity and water supply and other services.[10] Finally, it encompasses more than franchising, subcontracting or ancillary relations between firms.[11] Whereas some of these elements may pertain to industrial districts, an industrial district is much more than that. Rather, it is the *modus operandi* of a community of firms that brings about what is termed "collective efficiency".[12]

For further investigations, a common working understanding would be needed, one which would include a diversity in economic performance, internal organization and social complexion in developing countries. A decisive step in this direction has been taken by Nadvi, who abandons the rigidity of the Marshallian industrial district concept by emphasizing a view of the industrial district as a specific example of the more generic process of clustering. In doing so, it is possible to derive an operational approach, which is much looser and more easily adaptable to widely differing circumstances and different types of small-enterprise clusters in developing countries.

The point to be made is that the unit of analysis should no longer be the individual firm, but rather the sectorally-specific clusters of firms, which are a necessary, if not a sufficient condition for collective efficiency and technological capability-building. The analysis should focus on essential characteristics, such as (a) the nature of the relationships between firms, (b) the nature of embeddedness and (c) the nature of institutions. At the same time, attention should be given to processes and dynamics: how collective efficiency and innovative capacities are or are not achieved. Since the formation and vitality of industrial districts are furthered by non-firm related catalytic externalities, it seems to be crucial to embark on an interdisciplinary analysis, and to take into consideration the totality of economic, technological, political, social and cultural aspects in which these clusters operate. A more holistic approach such as this would help to see beyond the narrow (micro-) economic concepts and progress towards an understanding of the political economy and social organization of enterprises.

An obvious need for more research on this matter was expressed. The concept of clustering has to be developed through both theoretical and empirical work. While it is improbable that an ideal type of industrial district will be found in developing countries, a normative concept is nonetheless important for indicating what kind of development is anticipated. A blend between a normative and positive approach would contribute to a more structured and operational concept of clustering which could later facilitate the formulation of adequate policies.

II. SMALL FIRMS AND COLLECTIVE EFFICIENCY
IN DEVELOPING COUNTRIES

A. Implications of industrial districts at different levels of industrialization

A principal issue discussed at the meeting was whether the experience of small firms' industrial districts is of equal importance to countries at different levels of industrialization. Already for industrialized countries Amin (p.1) argues that "...the dynamics of growth in craft-based industrial districts are quite different from those in other examples of local agglomeration such as high-tech complexes...". This suggests that implications derived from the industrial district concept will also differ for developing countries, since economic conditions, the degree of industrialization, technological capabilities, the labour market, and the markets vary widely from region to region, from country to country and within one country, as well as from industry to industry.

The group of newly industrializing countries (NICs) in East and South-East Asia and Latin America, as well as some export-oriented zones, are affected in a different way by the crisis of the Fordist mass production paradigm - as suggested by Piore and Sabel (1984) - than the group of least developed countries, e.g. in Africa. The integration of the first group into the world market is essentially based on the Fordist pattern of accumulation, production, and consumption with a distinct international division of labour. These countries are increasingly under pressure from two sides:[13] On the one hand, they are in danger of losing the competitive edge they derived from low labour costs to the second generation of newly industrializing countries, e.g. Indonesia, Malaysia, Thailand. On the other hand, their international competitive position is jeopardized by advanced market economies, emanating from the constant introduction of more efficient production technologies and management concepts of best-practice producers. Consequently, if the NICs do not want to lose ground, they will have to develop new competitive advantages which will essentially be knowledge- and technology-based. Whereas these countries have already achieved a level of industrialization, in terms of industrial structure, institutional infrastructure, technological and management abilities, which gives them ample scope to pursue a strategy of flexible specialization, new competitiveness (Van Dijk) or some other form of radical innovation (Asheim), they are also forced to do so.[14] This may also hold for export-oriented industries and zones in other developing countries, unless their competitive edge is entirely built on cheap-wage labour.

However, the group of lower-income developing countries seems currently to be mainly preoccupied by regaining economic growth and curbing their high rates of unemployment, a fact strongly emphasized by Villarán. Already, the oil shocks of the 1970s have left enduring scars on most developing economies. Followed by crises encountered in the 1980s, some of these countries have experienced dramatic declines in economic growth, employment and social conditions, coupled with the adoption of austerity measures. Economies which were already struggling to overcome internal problems have been caught between escalating debt payments and decreasing export revenues. Against this background, it is increasingly recognized that future economic progress will depend mostly on the expansion and revitalization of the private sector, and the mobilization of local resources. From a policy point of view, a collective ability to innovate and adapt to disruptive circumstances of crisis and a growth strategy primarily rooted in local and endogenous capabilities such as small-firms clusters will be crucial.[15] Furthermore, for these countries it appears also less relevant to produce for a diversified, high-income and export market, than to cater for basic needs in the internal market constituted by a broad group of middle- and-low income consumers. Competitive pressure to innovate will therefore mainly come from large enterprises and from imports. Hence, achieving collective efficiency in mostly craft-based or small-firm clusters, ensuring economic growth, employment creation and incremental innovation, such as a gradual improvement of quality and processes, and increasing technological capability as such, will be of immediate relevance to this country group.

Given the divergent conditions in these two country groups, the implications derived from experience with industrial districts in each group of countries will differ in terms of number and quality of external interventions and type of technological change. However, the fundamental organizational principles of industrial districts, such as sectorally specified clustering, inter-firm division of labour, a peculiar blend of cooperation and competition, and territorial embeddedness of the material production relations set in a deeper social fabric, will be of equal importance to both groups. In relation to the latter characteristic, it is this inter-penetration of economic exchange relations and social relations which provides the conditions for the creation of an "industrial atmosphere" (Amin, Asheim, Becattini 1990) or "decentralized industrial creativity" (Bellandi) as a major driving force for innovation.

B. Why small firms?

Among the more general issues raised by some of the participants in the meeting was why there should be a focus on small enterprises rather than on large enterprises. This question reflects a widespread attitude and a long-lasting controversy about the role of small versus large firms in economic development. Questions raised therefore included: are small enterprises or clusters actually more viable than medium- and large-size enterprises, in terms of productivity, innovative capacity, employment generation and social relations of production? What differences exist (e.g. types of technology in use, capital/labour ratio, productivity, employment of capacity) between large and small firms and clusters? Can small firms or clusters thereof ever compete successfully in the long term on both national and international markets against the huge resources of large integrated firms? What about the latters' advantages in terms of economy of scale, research and development, financial resources and advertising and marketing capabilities? Although this is not the place to prove the viability of small firms, it is nevertheless worth scrutinizing some principal considerations.

Since quite some time, small enterprises have been regarded as a historical vestige: they were expected to wither away in the course of economic modernization.[16] For a long time, many developing countries have been pursuing a strategy of accelerated industrialization, devoting substantial resources to the promotion of large enterprises as cornerstones for economic progress and growth. Through credit policies, investment incentives, trade regulations, licensing, etc., macroeconomic and technology policy has essentially, if somewhat inadvertently, discriminated against small firms. In spite of such an unfavourable environment, small enterprises have not only persisted, but in some cases they have proved to be remarkably efficient, resilient and dynamic. In many developing countries various crises have helped small firms to come (back) into business, compensating for the decline in both output and employment of large enterprises and the public sector.[17]

However, the development of small firms is not just an outcome of pressure and constraints but also of opportunities and initiatives. In most developing market economies, small firms predominate in the industrial tissue, both in terms of numbers of enterprises and employment generated. Against this background and in the course of structural adjustment, an increasing surge of interest in small-firm development may be observed. This is part of a larger concern over deregulation, privatization and related efforts to remove artificial restrictions on individual enterprises and initiatives. Consequently, expectations have been raised. Small-firm growth is expected to lead towards easing the pending need for adjustment, to stimulate economic regeneration and to resolve pressing employment problems.

Despite the rhetoric and an ever-increasing amount of scholarly literature, the underlying issue of the viability of small firms remains unclear.[18] Some of the expectations raised in extolling the merits of small firms may prove unfounded, such as the claims made for large firms in earlier years, since a real understanding of the differences between small and large firms and their innate economic superiority is incomplete. Although the number and the employment share of small firms have shown a remarkable increase, the experience is mixed in qualitative terms. The small-firm sector is extremely heterogenous. While in some regions, countries and industries, small enterprises appear to have achieved remarkable growth and competitiveness, for others the situation looks far more bleak. In the latter cases, the small-firm sector has been stagnating, and trailing the large-firm sector by a wide margin not only in terms of economic capacity, but also with regard to social standards, such as wage level, working conditions, human-resource development, etc. The coexistence of success and failure of small firms calls into question the view that it is enterprise size as such that plays a crucial role in determining economic efficiency and vitality. If efficiency and dynamism were inherent to small-scale activities, all small firms should do well. Little *et al.* (1987), in their comparative analysis of small manufacturing enterprises in India and other developing countries, have found that firm size is insignificant as an economic variable: small producers are neither more nor less efficient than medium or large enterprises in the same industry.[19] Hence, empirical research so far does not allow for a generalization about the growth potential of the small-firm sector.[20]

Moreover, the overall performance of small firms does not yet appear to have come up to expectations, and the success of policy initiatives designed to deliberately encourage small-enterprise development has been decidedly limited.[21] Thus, it is doubtful whether the economic vitality of a sector of independent small firms hinges primarily on technical inputs, capital infusion, and subsidized services. The principal weakness of the individual small firm does not seem to be a matter of size nor of technical and productive inefficiency *per se*, but rather its lack of capacity for self-determination.[22] This may be particularly pronounced in an environment aligned to large-scale enterprises which, owing to their greater financial and organizational strength, impose an overall pattern of accumulation and competition. Since the 1980s, the emphasis on small-firm promotion has gradually moved away from social issues towards greater economic emphasis in the sense of recognizing the strength of small enterprises not only in terms of generating employment and income, but also as an essential ingredient of a consolidated and diversified industrial structure.

As small firms constitute an important part of the economic and social reality of most developing market economies, it was finally acknowledged that an evaluation of a concept which seems to be promising for upgrading small-firm sectors would be vital.

C. Sectorally specified clusters

In many developing countries, sectoral agglomerations of firms exist. Consequently, considerable discussion focused on the following questions: What is the origin of clustering of small firms? Is it the result of purposeful action on the part of small entrepreneurs, or is it the fortunate outcome of unrelated historical circumstances and even chance? To what extent can external interventions, such as the creation of learning institutions, technology development centres or large firms induce clustering? What is the size composition of such clusters? Have firms in clusters graduated from small, to medium or large? Why do clusters disappear?

As Marshall had suggested: "Many various causes have led to the localization of industries, but the chief have been physical: such as the character of the climate and the soil, or the existence of mines and quarries in the neighbourhood, or within easy access by land or water" (1928, p.151). Most available research on small-firm clusters in developing countries indicates that clustering has mainly occurred unplanned and spontaneously.[23] This holds particularly in the artisan sector (textiles and garments, leather and footwear manufacturing, carpentry and furniture, and metal products) where sectoral clustering has been encouraged by the availability of raw materials, and local expertise in crafts or artisanal goods and services along with a custom of self-employment and entrepreneurship. As most of these activities have traditional links with the agricultural economy, either in agricultural produce or in providing inputs for the agricultural sector, it would be valuable to inquire into such growth linkages between agriculture and off-farm activities.[24]

Even crises can stimulate the formation of sectoral agglomerations, when technical staff of retrenching large enterprises make a virtue out of necessity - in the absence of alternative forms of employment - by starting up their own businesses and by seizing market opportunities. This may occur because of shortages of foreign currency for importing. This was the case in Kumasi, Ghana, where the economic crisis experienced in the early 1980s gave rise to the formation of a metal-working cluster. Formally trained workers withdrew into self-employment; a large share of machine tools found their way into the small-enterprise sector; owing to the absence of imports, there was an increasing need for repair shops and components (Dawson 1992, p.35).

Some sorts of intervention have resulted in the consolidation of existing sectoral agglomerations. For example, in Trujillo, Peru, where clustering was encouraged by the availability of leather, this effort has been consolidated by a vocational training course in footwear production held in the regional prison, and by the establishment of subcontracting links with two large shoe manufacturers from Lima (Villarán 1993 p.182f). In the rattan industry of Tegalwangi, Indonesia, clustering was also encouraged by an abundant supply of raw material, such as rattan and other cane and the existence of traditional skills; however, it benefited later from sectoral interventions by the Government aimed at international competitiveness of the Indonesian rattan industry (Smyth 1992 p.51). Moreover, the examples presented for Singapore (*cf.* Liew) and for India (*cf.* Alam) point to the importance of public interventions in terms of zoning, provision of real services and infrastructure.

In more advanced sectors and technology-based activities, the role of purposeful public intervention in the formation of clusters, particularly the establishment of vocational training centres and engineering schools, along with technology research and transfer institutions, seems more obvious. The city of Santa Rita do Sapucaí, in the State of Minas Gerais, Brazil, is one such example, where first a technical college for electronics and later a National Institute for Telecommunications was created. This stimulus resulted in the creation of a cluster specializing in electronics and telecommunications.[25]

In technology-based and new high-technology industries clustering of firms of various sizes has also deliberately, sometimes unintentionally, been encouraged in the realm of large enterprises, production conglomerates and specific production zones. While in some countries and industries the establishment of clusters has already been promoted by an active policy of development of supplier, feeder and ancillary industries,[26] the recent impetus has been due to technical and organizational changes in large enterprises. Large enterprises engaged in the manufacturing of new commodities are increasingly out-sourcing, or farming out, parts of the production process, as they need many parts and components and often highly-specific products and services.[27] As a result, new firms come into being, sometimes as direct spin-offs from the main enterprise, e.g. created by technicians in order to realize a product idea, while other firms have been attracted by the technological and physical infrastructure and the market opportunities (*cf.* Cho 1992; Marcovitch 1993 p.152f). Once clustering has taken place, it attracts complementary industries and services.

At the meeting, it was felt that very little was known as yet about the origins of clusters; doubts were raised as to whether clusters could be promoted or not. It was suggested that the development of clusters would be better promoted by building on existing specializations, skills and resources rather than by seeking to transplant wholly new productive activities. Clustering in itself may yield external economies, such as reduced transaction costs. The particular vitality of a cluster was considered to result from the interaction between the firms within it, independent of their size.[28] Accordingly, the questions raised at the beginning of this section deserve some further study. Nevertheless, the chief interest should be in the nature of the interaction between firms and the related dynamics and processes concerning economic growth and the enhancement of technological capabilities.

III. TECHNOLOGICAL CHANGE AND INNOVATIVE CAPACITIES

The focus of the symposium was on the lessons to be drawn from experience with industrial districts in advanced market economies for application, adaptation and diffusion of technology in small-firm clusters in developing countries, an issue which will be addressed below. Four papers presented at the symposium and included in this volume explicitly dealt with the issue of technology: Bellandi, on innovation "from below" or decentralized industrial creativity in the tradition of the Italian industrial districts; Asheim, on the potential for endogenous technological capability-building and innovation in industrial districts in advanced market economies; Villarán with a critical appraisal of a practitioner in a crisis-stricken country; and Liew with a specific example of institutionalized support for technology development in Singapore.

It should be underscored that sectorally specified clusters will not, on their own, solve the overall problems of technology and technological capabilities in developing countries, since these are linked to structural problems and broader policies in the area of education, vocational training and technology. They are also linked to market distortions and the existence of labour surplus conditions. Technology was broadly defined as encompassing everything pertaining to the transformation of inputs into outputs (Fransman 1984, p.9). This definition includes three aspects which are worth making explicit: (a) technology includes the social organization of the production and labour process; (b) knowledge embodied in hardware and software, in people and institutionalized practices and procedures plays a central role in transforming inputs into outputs; (c) the way in which inputs are transformed into outputs, particularly by enterprises, is intimately influenced by external events, of which competition is the main vehicle.

Concerning technological change, "minor" or "incremental" innovation as the result of the continuously ongoing process of transforming inputs into outputs is distinct from "radical" innovation, a discontinuous event.[29] Technological capabilities involve the following kinds of activities: (a) the search for available alternative technologies and the selection of the most appropriate technology; (b) the mastering of technology; (c) the adaptation of technology in order to suit specific production conditions; (d) the further development of the technology as the result of minor innovation; (e) the institutionalized search for more important innovations with the development of R&D facilities; (f) the conducting of basic research (*cf.* Fransman 1984, p.10). The latter is expected to go beyond the scope of individual districts because it is often complex and costly and therefore usually linked to specific public or private research institutes and universities (Asheim). Both the concept of technological change and the linear hierarchization of technological capabilities were challenged by some participants.

A. Division of labour and inter-firm cooperation

Clustering of small firms would offer few benefits if they consisted merely of enterprises producing more or less the same commodity. The existence of strong networks of producers engaged in inter-firm cooperation and, through specialization and subcontracting, dividing among themselves the labour required for the manufacture of a particular good, is a distinct characteristic of clusters endeavoring collective efficiency. Such an increasing division of labour - among the firms of the cluster - represents a explicit change in the social organization of production and therefore constitues technological change, whether or not it necessarily embraces a change in the physical means of production. Among the issues discussed were: Are existing agglomerations of small firms merely a multiplication of producers making similar products or has specialization and inter-firm division of labour occurred? Does it also include a network of suppliers (of raw materials, equipment, spare parts and repair services) and of purchasers (of intermediate or final products)? How does such cooperation and division of labour emerge, particularly in the context of a small-firm sector, which is generally perceived as highly atomistic and exhibiting strong competitive behaviour? What forms of inter-firm cooperation exist? What is the nature of the relationship between large and small firms? Do large firms contribute to the growth dynamics of small-firm clusters, e.g. through subcontracting arrangements? If so, do such arrangements yield mutual benefit? How could such linkages be promoted?

Whether there is scope for a division of labour depends largely on the nature of the product. For discrete products with a homogenous production process, entering into a vertical division of labour with other firms is deemed to be unlikely. Conversely, if the product is complementary, allowing division of the production process into various steps, prospects exist for inter-firm division of labour, particularly when specialization results in efficiency gains, both individually and at the level of the cluster.

Four forms of inter-firm cooperation may be distinguished, (a) vertical cooperation in a production chain; (b) diagonal cooperation between complementary specialists; (c) horizontal cooperation between producers of the same product; and (d) cooperation in a field of interest distinct to a larger group of the cluster or to the cluster as a whole. These forms of cooperation among firms of the cluster are essentially characterized by the absence of a single one acting as a centre for strategic decision-making.

Vertical cooperation and specialization in the various upstream and downstream activities required to manufacture the main product of the cluster can be economically rational, particularly if the individual firm does not lose economies of scale but rather gains from it. Greater economic effectiveness and technological competence can be achieved simply because individual small firms do not need to have a full-fledged production line, but rather to specialize. Thus, the firm can invest in special and/or even expensive equipment for producing inputs or services for a larger number of firms in the cluster. Sectoral agglomerations provide a critical mass of enterprises for which increased differentiation, specialization and cooperation may not only be feasible but may offer great advantages in the form of external economies.

Diagonal cooperation between manufacturers, who are not producing for exactly the same market and are therefore potentially not direct lateral competitors, can occur between specialists producing complementary products, sometimes very similar but not identical, e.g. a varied range of qualities or designs. Diagonal collaboration could range from the sharing of common facilities to an agreement to participate in the production of a complementary range of goods produced according to a common design specification to be marketed as a collection (Pyke 1992, p.4).

Horizontal cooperation of producers of the same product seems to be more arduous, since they may compete in the same market. However, in some cases there might still be perceived advantages in cooperation rather than competion, at least at certain times or in certain circumstances. For example, periodic collaboration, such as work-sharing arrangements, might be conceivable to fill an order that no one individual firm could handle. Alternatively, they could engage in periodic subcontracting for one another. Other potential areas of collaboration would include joint procurement of raw materials and inputs; joint marketing and advertising, and even the creation of a common brand name. Cooperation is not limited to production or marketing because, for a group of enterprises or the entire business community, there might be areas of common interest encouraging collective actions. Possible areas of common concern are the establishment of joint services and facilities, such as accounting, quality testing, storage facilities, joint design and R&D centres, etc. Particular problems could be approached through self-help groups. Problems mentioned at the symposium included power cuts as a result of power shortages in India. For securing constant energy supply, a collective response would be the joint acquisition and utilization of a diesel generator. Other common areas of concern could on be environmental issues, such as recycling, re-use and treatment of waste and effluence discharge. Finally, collective actions may also be required for negotiating with local and regional authorities, in respect of zoning, infrastructure provision, public transport, etc.

Nevertheless, particularly in developing countries, the role of larger enterprises and traders introducing a form of contractor-subcontractor relationship with the firms of a cluster seems to be pertinent. In the course of recent industrial restructuring, the establishment of such subcontracting relations has been governed by new production and organization concepts, which favour the externalization and specialization of the manufacturing process among technically different firms (*cf.* Cho 1992; Nadvi). The production objectives of both groups are common and intertwined; therefore they are more associative and collaborative. While in some cases such subcontracting relations may offer mutual benefits, in others - mostly in traditional sectors - they may yield asymmetric exchange relations, in which large firms buffer costs and risks to the detriment of the small subcontractors.[30] These subcontracting relations mainly concern hierarchical ties with a leading enterprise or entrepreneur - which may be large or not - controlling the complete production cycle and marketing all or part of it owing to superior access to resources and information (*cf.* Knorringa 1992: 7; Nadvi). In such cases, it appears unlikely that small firms could develop a substantial independent potential. Viable small-firm development may be inhibited unless the small firms organize horizontally, in some sort of business or sectoral associations, in order to strenghten their bargaining position, and hence improve their exchange and trading relations.

Inter-firm collaboration is furthered by non-firm related catalytic externalities, such as a shared value system, which enhances cooperative attitudes and trust among the different actors in a cluster. An important issue therefore is whether only a pre-existing cultural consensus accounts for the development of trust and interdependencies within the industrial and social community. The most obvious ties which facilitate cohesion are a common cultural background, such as caste, class, ethnicity, kinship or religion.[31] Yet recent research indicates that, under the right circumstances, any set of collective experiences can form the basis for a common culture, and hence for at least a minimum degree of trust (*cf.* Sabel 1992). A wider set of formative *milieux*, such as a common professional identity (engineering college), craft pride among artisans, or common origin (migration, work in the same large firm) and political affiliation, can also serve the purpose. Cooperation may occur spontaneously. It may also come about through some kind of external intervention, such as counselling by experts, technical or management training programmes.[32] It may start at a very low level, particularly in areas of mutual benefit, where external economies can be achieved. Thus, trust relations in industrial districts seem to be more a consequence than a precondition of practical cooperation among local actors, while social consensus may be less an antithesis of conflict than an outcome of its successful resolution.

It was therefore concluded that there were a number of rational economic and technical reasons for a functional division of labour and for inter-firm cooperation among the firms of a cluster. Firms would endeavour cooperation in areas where no individual competitive advantage could be achieved, but not in those areas where there was fervent competition. For further investigations into the immediate advantages of differentiation, both specialization and cooperation are of interest. Of equal importance is whether the firms and the various actors of a cluster benefit equally from increased economic efficiency; and whether this leads to an egalitarian type of development or rather to an exacerbation of economic differentiation. This should also cover the nature of the relationship between firms of various sizes and between contractors and subcontractors. Research into these "productive cultures" should pay attention to the social and cultural mechanisms and the dynamics, which may both facilitate and obstruct the creation of trust and cooperative attitudes. Therefore, distinct social categories, dominant social values, family structure and gender relations should be included. Another issue, albeit not explicitly raised at the meeting, may nevertheless be important. This relates to the internal organization of production; whether the internal division of labour is based on single- or multi-tasking; whether the management style is hierarchical, paternalistic or participative; the type of communication between technical and managerial staff is likewise important.

B. Endogenous technological capability-building

Endogenous technological capabilities depend essentially on knowledge, whereas, generally, knowledge is quite unevenly distributed at any point in time and the accumulation of knowledge is a highly specific process. Among the issues discussed were: What is the source of skills and knowledge in a cluster? Are sectorally specified clusters particularly prone to generate endogenous technological capabilities? Is there an entrepreneurial culture? What is the role of formal vocational training and of learning institutions? Is there transfer and diffusion of know-how from large firms to small firms?

The availability of a skilled and qualified labour force is regarded as a vital source for enhancing the technological capability of a cluster. In general terms, in many developing countries there appears to be a lack of established, generalized and socially acceptable systems of occupational profiles and vocational training (cf. Dombois 1993). Even in the modern sector, skills may often be acquired through on-the-job training. National vocational training programmes have almost exclusively been geared to the needs of modern industry and skilled workers are normally absorbed by large firms, which can provide more attractive employment and working conditions as compared to small firms. Consequently, small firms have usually benefited little from such training programmes.[33] Only in some of the newly industrialized countries is there a high degree of labour skill and an organized labour market;[34] these are the principal attributes which will help these countries to meet the international competitive challenge with a strategy based on innovation. Thus, it is not surprising that, in small firms, particularly in less developed countries, informal acquisition of skill and training usually predominates.

The origin of basic skills and knowledge in a sectoral agglomeration depends largely on the main industry present. In artisan sectors - textiles, woodworking, leather manufacturing, metalworking - skills are usually acquired by informal or on-the-job training and apprenticeship. Skills are usually handed down from generation to generation. Whereas in more modern, technology-based industries, such as electronics and machine tools, formal education and training received from vocational schools, engineering and professional colleges, and even university education is of relevance. However, these skills are only the starting point, since sectoral agglomerations, embracing various or almost all steps related to the manufacturing of a particular product, are particularly disposed to generate tacit knowledge, which goes beyond codified scientific, engineering or vocational knowledge (*cf.* Asheim, Bellandi). Technical routine, learning-by-doing, learning-by-using and the daily interaction among the workers of the same firm and between firms, as well as the circulation of the labour force among the different firms of the cluster, contributes to an accumulation of practical knowledge. If the working climate is favourable, minor innovations can be introduced at the shop-floor level, such as improving the layout of the workshop, the processes, quality and design, cutting back waste production, saving of raw materials and energy, etc. Furthermore, the existence of tacit knowledge strengthens capabilities for the mastering of new technology and for the adaptation of technology to specific production conditions within the firm or cluster.

Moreover, competent entrepreneurship, embracing both technological capabilities and business acumen, is an important ingredient for the growth potential of these clusters. The importance of a tradition of self-employment and entrepreneurship has been stressed above; this applies particularly to the existence of an entrepreneurial culture which encourages productive investment, rather than discourages it. Competent entrepreneurship may result from persons setting up their own business, after gaining experience working in one of the enterprises of the agglomeration. Over the years, workers will not only accumulate knowledge about their own particular trade, but familiarize themselves also with the network of firms, and the spectrum of managerial tasks and functions, the more such tasks are delegated to them by their employer. Furthermore, workers could be encouraged and sometimes supported by other enterprises of the cluster to set up their own firm and realize a business idea that will supplement the activities of the cluster. In addition to such a backing of business start-ups by the community of firms, it is also important that, in case of failure, entrepreneurs and the labour force can be reintegrated back into the local business community through offers of employment in an enterprise. Generally, the creation of new firms, and hence the growth of clusters, is facilitated by the existence of a favourable regulatory environment, which not only eases formal entry into business but also any exit.

A further source for endogenous technological capability-building is the face-to-face relationship between, on the one hand, complementary manufacturers, buyers and users throughout the vertical production process, and producers and sellers, on the other hand. In the ideal case, clusters also include the producers of machinery and equipment, firms engaged in one of the successive vertical stages of production, final assembly, product designers, marketing firms, export specialists, etc. Given the division of labour within a cluster, interaction between the various groups can induce strong complementary effects leading towards upgraded technology at the various levels of the production process. This is reinforced by the development of strong information networks among the firms and various actors in the business community.

Concerning endogenous technological capability-building, it was concluded that a high potential existed for sustained learning and creative effects of specialized practical knowledge in sectoral agglomerations. Furthermore, there was an evident ability to reproduce this knowledge - an essential factor for inducing technological change. Thus, industrial districts offer the possibility of breaking away from the highly specific process of accumulation of knowledge prevailing elsewhere. Similarly, the geographic concentration of enterprises permits the development of various channels for the dissemination of information. Individual expertise and capability can be perceived as part of a collective resource pool. Further research should therefore cover: How does the distinct learning process take place within a cluster? What are the channels for disseminating information and knowledge? Are there direct links between capital goods producers and users, as well as between producers and consumers? What effect does this have on technological capabilities? Moreover, the relationship between labour conditions in clusters and innovation deserves some attention. For example, to what extent do personnel policies and labour conditions of small firms attract certain types of workers and how does this affect the technological capability of the cluster?

C. Cooperation plus competition equals innovation?

The relationship between clustering, specialization, cooperation and technological and innovative capabilities seems to be one of mutual reinforcement. However, a major stimulus for innovation that is external to the firm and the cluster is competition. In a sectoral agglomeration, competitive pressure comes either from other firms within the cluster or from firms outside the cluster and imports. Among the issues discussed were: Does inter-firm cooperation and competition go together? For what kind of market does the agglomeration of small firms produce? Is it for a differentiated, mass or a highly specified niche market? For final consumers or inputs for other enterprises? For domestic, local or export markets? For what income group? Which are the areas of competition (low-cost/low-price, design/quality, copy/innovation)? What sort of effect does it have? What causes innovation? How is information disseminated? In what way does the labour market (e.g. existence of labour surplus, segmentation of the labour market, deregulation, etc., affect the competitive strategy of the firms in a cluster?

Whereas there are a number of rational reasons for enterprises to enter into some form of inter-firm cooperation, nonetheless, collaboration does not deny conflict or competition among firms of a cluster. The fact that firms make similar products and compete for the same customers tends to inhibit cooperation and the exchange of information at first sight (Pyke 1992, 4). Clustering makes the market more transparent. Whereas product similarity is likely to induce horizontal competition, it will also spur innovation. Within a cluster, demonstration effects can be quite strong. They reinforce a process of copying or imitation.[35] This not only concerns the product itself (e.g. design) but also the transmission of know-how and the diffusion of technology. Because the firms are located in close geographic proximity, entrepreneurs can visually absorb new processes and see new machines in operation, for example. There is a lower risk in absorbing new technologies which have already been tested by other firms of a cluster; moreover, there is a competitive pressure to keep up with other enterprises. At the same time, collaboration in certain areas (e.g. vertical cooperation) may also aid competition in others (e.g. external to the cluster) and thus promote competitive efficiency in other contexts. Nevertheless, excessive competition may weaken an agglomeration, while a certain degree of inter-firm competition stimulates the innovative atmosphere of a cluster.

Furthermore, pervasive trust can introduce an essential dynamism into the economy because it removes the paralysing inertia that can occur when entrepreneurs are afraid to take action for fear that others might take advantage of any temporary weakness (*cf.* Sengenberger/Pyke 1992:19). It may even reduce considerably the risk, in the sense that a firm can engage in investment on the understanding that other enterprises will buy the products of this investment. In fact, vertical division of labour among members of a cluster will encourage the acquisition and application of specialized technology, and make it rewarding to an extent. Otherwise an individual small firm could hardly dare to venture. The beneficial influence of homogeneity clearly helps to bind members of a small-firm community around a common goal; it inhibits people from transgressing acceptable business practices and industrial relations and helps to overcome possible sources of conflict. It also enhances the ability of the actors of a sectoral agglomeration to perceive problems internal to the cluster, to intervene and to introduce solutions quickly.

Besides the demonstration effects within a cluster, the existence of trust and of collective institutions reinforces the dissemination of information among the various segments of a sectorally specified cluster (*cf.* Asheim, Bellandi). It allows people to exchange commercial information and ideas about new technologies, processes and products, knowing that partners will not abuse them. The collection and diffusion of information is crucial for the ability of the cluster to respond fast and flexibly to a rapidly changing market. The passing on of information available within a sectoral agglomeration can accelerate the dissemination of knowledge as well as reduce costs for it considerably. Nevertheless, this does not imply that enterprises will share unanimously all information. They may share information in areas where technology is uniform or similar, or along the vertical line of production, but will withhold strategic knowledge giving them a competitive advantage.

Even when competition is reduced within a cluster, incentives for innovation remain by virtue of the presence of external competition. Depending on the industry or branch, and the market segment in which the cluster specializes, competitive pressure comes either from other small firms, or from national medium- and large-scale producers or imports. Generally, small firms have been identified with niche and low-income markets, which are indifferent to large firms. As a result of recent changes in technology and demand structure, it has become feasible for individual small firms to advance in technology-based production, such as the production of specific machine tools, software and high-quality and differentiated consumer goods. However, compared to large enterprises, small firms have normally less resources to call upon and fewer possibilities for strategic behaviour, namely the ability to influence and shape their markets. In contrast, sectorally specified clusters appear to be better set to control their own destinies and to choose their competitive strategy.

Two principal approaches whereby enterprises, industries or clusters can try to meet the external competitive challenge may be distinguished: the "low road" and the "high road" to industrial growth (*cf.* Nadvi; Sengenberger and Pyke 1992:11ff.; *ibid.* 14f.). The first approach consists of seeking competitive advantages through cost-cutting or "passive pliability". This means that the firm or the cluster yields to outside pressure, such as an economic crisis or pressure from customers, by passing the flexibility requirements onto the workforce, reducing production volumes, cutting corners by using inferior inputs or resorting to informal types of business - sometimes with the aim of evading taxation and regulations. Particularly under the labour surplus conditions prevailing in most developing countries, a great opportunity presents itself to commence clustering with a competitive strategy based on low labour costs. Although such an option may be economically opportune in the short run,[36] it does create unfavourable prospects for medium- and long-term improvements, because it deprives the cluster of opportunities to innovate and enter new markets.

The second approach, the "high road" to constructive competition, is based on efficiency enhancement and innovation. This also involves versatility through exploring and exploiting market niches, and responding rapidly to demand changes. The cluster competes not just on price, but on a range of dimensions, such as increased productivity, quality improvements, design and fast response to changing markets. The pursuit of a strategy of active flexibility depends largely on the technological capabilities available in a cluster, that is, on the existence of a qualified labour force and competent entrepreneurship. This offers the prospect of considering labour not simply in terms of costs, but rather as resources. A more differentiated approach towards surplus labour is needed. The labour available may not be the type required in sectorally specified clusters. Especially in more advanced and high-quality craft sectors, labour skills required may often be in relatively short supply and imply extensive (on-the-job) training.

Doubts were raised during the symposium as to whether, in the circumstances, clusters of firms in developing countries would embark on the "high road" to meet competition. It was argued that the best solution might be a "hybrid" form, somewhere between a "low road" and "high road" growth path (*cf.* Nadvi). In some cases, a selective disadvantage in the more basic factor endowments could actively encourage a small-firm community to innovate; thus what would appear to be a disadvantage in a static model of competition would be an advantage in a dynamic one (*cf.* Porter, 1990, p.78). It must be recognized that a qualitative jump is required in moving from the former to the latter. The ability of, and constraints on, firms and clusters to make this jump may be important in determining long-term progress. As a result of the particular form of economic and social organization, it was concluded that, in clusters, there exists an enhanced capability for seeking available alternative technology and choosing the most appropriate one for mastering technology and adapting it to specific production conditions and furthering technological development. However, owing to the prevailing factor endowment, sectorally specified clusters are more susceptible to incremental innovation than to radical innovation, because the latter is more complex and costly and will have to be initiated from outside the cluster.

D. Institutions and technology development

The role of institutions in fostering technological upgrading of clusters in developing countries occupied a large part of the discussions, since the experience of advanced market economies (*cf.* Amin, Asheim, Bellandi) had accentuated the importance of institutions in promoting innovative cooperation and in ensuring or maintaining an optimal technological dynamism in industrial districts. The role of institutions in introducing more radical technological change and in strengthening a process of creative growth of clusters appeared to be crucial. The overall question therefore was, how institutions could strengthen the technological capability of clusters and introduce technological change. Research should focus on how the transfer of new technology and radical innovation takes place in clusters. How can already existing technology transfer, support and training institutions become more effective and more responsive to the actual and specific needs of communities of small firms?

Whereas informal cooperation may be sufficient in the formative period of a sectorally specified cluster, at a later stage enterprises may find it worthwhile to engage in activities which go beyond the functional division of labour among firms and to create more formal collaborative institutions in order to compensate for their fragmented industrial structure. A wide range of possibilities exists between informal and formal institutions; however, it is up to the people concerned to choose an adequate form of organization, depending on the purpose, and the political, social and cultural background.[37] Some possible areas of mutual interest which encourage collective action have already been mentioned above. They concern technological change and depend on the resources of a cluster, the establishment of production and information networks, common facilities, design and training centres. In that respect, small-enterprise associations and organizations can be important means of communicating with, and providing services to, a large number of small firms. For example, daily interaction among members of the labour force, professional groups and entrepreneurs engaged on an informal basis in the various production steps furthers the exchange of information within the cluster. In order to assure the constant flow of information, it may be vital to institute more formal information networks among the various actors. This could include members of sectoral associations, self-help groups, training institutions, technology-transfer and support institutions. Subsequent research should therefore look into the issues of (a) whether collective actions to pursue common interests (e.g. business or employer associations, self-help organizations) are of importance in existing clusters; (b) whether the type of leadership (paternalistic or participatory) and organization (formal or informal) influences these actions; and (c) how these types of institutions shape the innovative capacity of a cluster. While organization from below may be able to identify and compensate for many of the weak spots, constraints and bottlenecks, while seizing the opportunities within the cluster, small-firm clusters are usually ill-equipped to conduct formal basic research and development.

The institutionalized search for more important innovations normally takes place outside the material production sphere of an enterprise: in universities and technology research institutes.[38] Technology institutions could perform a crucial role in fostering radical innovation by developing local technology or adapting technology to local conditions. However, these institutions are usually detached from the potential users, and one important issue, therefore, is the diffusion to small-firm clusters of the results of formal research and development. The fact that sectorally specified clusters have a low potential for inducing more radical innovation on their own does not mean that they are not susceptible to innovation given their high capacity to generate endogenous technological capabilities. In most cases, however, the results of formal research and development efforts as well as basic research are not amenable to direct application in the specific context of small-firm clusters; usually they require translation by intermediaries.

Therefore, technology transfer and support institutions play a key role in diffusing technology. It was concluded that the development of sectorally specified clusters is better promoted by building on existing specializations, skills and resources rather than by seeking to transplant wholly new productive activities. Technological corridors, as suggested by the example of Singapore (*cf.* Liew), emphasizing the importance of effective State support and involving a high degree of sophistication, appear to be feasible only for newly industrialized countries. Many governments have already introduced specialized support institutions, often with the assistance of multilateral and bilateral aid agencies,[39] to help small firms to overcome their perceived weaknesses: (a) multi-purpose institutions have been created to cater for different services and training requirements; (b) industrial estates with a material infrastructure have been set up; (c) development and commercial banks have operated special credit schemes; and (d) technology institutions have been established for the development of appropriate technology, adaptation and diffusion of technology. However, an evaluation of this type of assistance has shown that most of these measures are isolated interventions with significant limitations, benefiting only a small number of usually better-off urban-centred enterprises.[40] Such institutions apply a rigid set of rules and regulations, and suffer from bureaucratic inertia and inability to innovate and take risks. In addition, there is rarely cooperation between the different support institutions - sometimes not even between branches or extensions of the same institution. The result is a fragmented approach which wastes human and financial resources and obstructs inter-institutional complementarity.

It seems therefore to be less a question of building up new institutions than of making existing ones more effective and adjusted to the specific requirements of sectorally specified clusters. From a policy point of view, this could be envisaged by linking institutions for greater complementarity. A narrow sectoral focus would enable these institutions to tailor their interventions to the needs of particular sectors and trades. By doing careful studies of a sector, possible points of intervention could be identified. Thereby, a well-grounded understanding could be gained of sector-production processes, sources of supply, product markets and industry structure; when working well, they might become an integral part of a specific sector.

The provision of various "real services" and the transfer of new technology was considered vital for fostering and sustaining an innovative strategy of sectoral agglomeration. Furthermore, instead of rendering free or heavily subsidized services, the introduction of market mechanisms could yield mutual benefits. On the one hand, most enterprises would presumably be willing to pay for a good quality service and appreciate it to an extent they might never do with "free" assistance; on the other hand, the institutions would be impelled to improve and to upgrade constantly their expertise.

Moreover, the role of training and learning institutions in strengthening the technical and managerial capability of clusters is vital, especially in view of the already observed importance of labour-force qualifications in reinforcing the technological and innovative potential of clusters. In a prospering cluster, the returns gained from a skilled labour force and the possible creation of an intra-cluster labour market may outweigh the individual small firm's inherent indifference to human resource development. Joint interest in qualifying and upgrading the skills of the labour force could be enhanced by the formation of a labour pool from which all the firms of the industrial network could recruit workers. Training programmes should therefore cater to the specific needs of sectorally specified clusters and relate to the observed practices of learning-by-doing and learning-by-using. By offering continuous training and upgrading of skills, they could sustain the technological capability of clusters.[41] Furthermore, training programmes should impart cooperative attitudes by including industrial networking, inter-firm division of labour and collaboration in their curricula. To make training schemes more suitable and cost-effective, it was suggested that enterprises, associations and, if feasible, also labour representatives should be involved in the planning and running of training programmes, and possibly also contribute financially.

IV. UPGRADING SECTORAL AGGLOMERATIONS OF FIRMS: SOME POLICY IMPLICATIONS AND PERSPECTIVES

The last set of policy issues addressed at the symposium was the role played by public policy in sustaining and diffusing dynamic sectorally specified clusters. It was agreed that clusters of firms were unlikely to produce the desired result unless there was a conducive environment.

Although the papers presented paid little attention to the macroeconomic conditions under which clusters had developed, whether successfully or not, the discussion emphasized that prospects for growth and innovative dynamism of sectorally specified clusters depended largely on factors external to the district, such as the country's overall economic performance, rapid changes in the pattern of international trade, or the emergence of dynamic forces that compel the cluster to meet competitive challenges through innovation. With the exception of the newly industrializing countries, where a booming economic situation and the existence of macroeconomic stimulus can be observed, it was suggested that the situation looked far bleaker for other countries. The crises encountered by most developing countries have negatively affected the development of all enterprises, whether small or large and whether located within clusters or outside. However, in spite of a relatively unfavourable setting, small-firm clusters have emerged in these countries and, although they may currently not grow and innovate, they do manage to survive. Accordingly, it was found that the persistence of small firms in clusters can already be an important objective in an economy under pressure. Unquestionably, reviving the economy and restoring industrial growth, are essential for enhancing greater diffusion and dynamism of this particular type of industrial organization.

Another important aspect is the policy environment in which small firms and clusters operate. If it is badly distorted, special incentives and direct assistance programmes are unlikely to be very effective; in fact, they may well make things worse.[42] In the course of structural adjustment adopted by many developing countries, some governments have also begun to examine the scope for amending, simplifying and streamlining regulations and administrative practices which currently present obstacles to private sector development. However, mere reliance on market forces may not be feasible, since the State has an important role to play not only in setting the basic framework in which economic activities take place, but also in supplying important goods and facilities, not provided by market mechanisms alone, such as infrastructure, e.g. roads, transportation, electricity, water, telecommunications; education and training; and health services. The question is not whether the State should involve itself in economic regulation, but rather how it can introduce creative and effective policies to support private sector development.

Policies, programmes, regulations and incentives are implemented by administrative authorities. Good governance is directly related to the administrative structure; the issues are what should be in the sphere of the central government and what should come under regional and local authorities and how administrative constraints and bureaucratic inertia can be eliminated.

Experience from industrial districts in advanced market economies strongly emphasizes the role of regional and local governments in strengthening the development potential of sectorally specified clusters (cf. Amin, Asheim, Van Dijk). Likewise, in developing countries regional and local authorities shape the immediate environment of small firms and are important on account of their regulatory function, such as enforcing municipal by-laws, health and environment regulations. Their development function related to zoning, provision of infrastructure and educational and training facilities is also important. However, in most places an administrative and institutional setting which is hardly supportive and frequently discriminatory often prevails.[43] Regional and local administrative units are often not sufficiently equipped with competent staff, resources and decision-making authority. In fact, initiatives by local authorities to promote private-sector development are often stifled by a centralized decision-making process and dependence on outside transfers of resources. There are also few incentives for local and regional officials to take initiatives and risks, since these administrative levels offer few career prospects in the civil service. As things stand, most regional and local authorities would not themselves profit much from local economic growth, since most taxes and other income generated in the area are channeled to the central administration. This suggests that regional endogenous development favouring the growth of sectoral agglomerations can only be stimulated by simultaneously fostering regional and local governments through administrative reforms, embracing new incentive structures and a corresponding autonomy to use the benefits independently and properly.

A final set of policy issues goes beyond a narrow understanding of institutions, in the sense of public or semi-public institutions and regulations, to the creation of a consensual environment which will enhance and sustain the establishment of new institutions, administrative reforms and recognized practices for conflict resolution. In many developing countries, a top-to-bottom approach still prevails in policy formulation and implementation. The actual target group is excluded from this process, which is often confined to a small group lacking transparency and accountability. With regard to small-enterprise development, small entrepreneurs have, as a rule, not been integrated into established interest groups, such as employer organizations, sectoral federations and associations, or Chambers of Commerce and Industry, and are thus excluded from any political bargaining process.[44] The same applies to workers in small firms, whom trade unions generally have neglected.[45] However, any policy needs the support of the potential beneficiary if it is to be effective and produce permanent results. This may have momentous implications in the near future, as, in recent years, a weakening of public institutions paralleled by a strengthening of political interaction has been observed. Many countries have progressed towards more pluralist, participative and democratic societies. It is expected and hoped that others will follow. It is increasingly recognized that this is the context in which economic strategies and policies must be formulated and applied (*cf.* ECLAC, 1990). As for the strengthening of sectorally specified clusters, it is imperative that the various actors organize themselves, in order to voice their interest, to improve their political standing, and to participate actively in the shaping of their policy environment. Furthermore, the capacity of business organizations, trade unions and other interest groups should be reinforced. At the same time, institutional mechanisms of conflict resolution and dialogue should be established between the various actors. The crucial task is to initiate an "industrial public sphere", making an organic link between a broad variety of actors, such as regional and local authorities, support institutions, business associations and trade unions.

At the same time, there is a quest for a new reassignment of tasks between public and private sector. Which tasks should be confined to public institutions and which would be better organized by the private sector was one of the questions raised. It would be too narrow an approach to concentrate only on the supply-side of authorities and support institutions. The question not only concerns how institutions and administrations become more efficient but also whether they could be strengthened by communities of small firms. Endogenous regional or local economic development is more effectively promoted by strong regional and municipal authorities; decentralized institutions are more likely to improve their institutional performance in an efficient working environment based on dialogue and consensus-building among the various interest groups. A flourishing and organized industrial network could in fact support political and administrative reforms by strengthening - politically and financially - regional and local authorities. Furthermore, through participation, they could exert the public control which is currently lacking, and thus make public authorities accountable to an extent that cannot be achieved by most administrative rules. In turn, sectorally specified clusters may be in a position to internalize the costs and benefits of collective services and regulatory mechanisms, and accordingly ease the budget and administrative load of public institutions.

To conclude, although there is still much controversy, the industrial district concept, once adapted to the specific circumstances prevailing in developing countries, appears to be immensely fruitful in focusing attention on a dynamic form of economic and social organization of mainly small firms. It demonstrates how small firms can redress obvious economic and technical disadvantages which they experience individually in relation to large enterprises by virtue of what has been called collective-efficiency. This fact is of particular relevance in view of the predominance of small enterprises in developing countries. Moreover, it seems to be a concept that embraces key areas of development policy concern, such as economic efficiency and growth, employment and income generation, human resource development, technological and organizational innovation, institutional change, and endogenous regional development.

However, our understanding of sectorally specified clusters needs to be developed further through both theoretical and empirical work adapted to the specific conditions of developing countries. First insights into the reality of small-firm clusters in developing countries indicate that the best path would probably be a "hybrid" form. Particularly under labour surplus conditions, the danger of non-evolutionary growth of clusters of small firms is real, but the conditions which determine their potential vary and must therefore be studied and specified. Yet, the issue is not whether the ideal type of industrial districts already exists in developing countries, but rather under what conditions clusters of small firms will have the potential for growth and innovation and what policies can sustain successful development. There is also scope for action-oriented research or research-oriented action. This would require the adoption of an experimental and flexible approach to assistance programmes, in which activities are accompanied by research, so that they can constantly be adapted.[46] Experience has shown that policies and supportive measures should be constantly adjusted. A great number of issues were raised at the symposium and a few questions were answered; most deserve further investigation. A decisive need for more case studies, if possible comparative and interdisciplinary, was expressed. They are needed for understanding more about the inherent dynamics and processes of sectoral agglomerations of firms and for coming up with appropriate policy recommendations.

REFERENCES

Alexim, J.C., 1993, "Training programmes for small firms: an overview", in Späth (ed).

Alam, G., 1992, "Industrial districts and technological change: a study of the garment industry in Delhi", paper presented at the joint UNCTAD/GATE Symposium on the Role of Industrial Districts in the Application, Adaptation and Diffusion of Technology, Geneva, 16 and 17 November.

Amin, A., 1992, "The potential for turning informal economies into Marshallian industrial districts", paper presented at the joint UNCTAD/GATE Symposium on the Role of Industrial Districts in the Application, Adaptation and Diffusion of Technology, Geneva, 16 and 17 November.

Anderson, D., 1982, "Small industry in developing countries: a discussion of issues", in *World Development*, vol.10, no.11, November.

Asheim, B., 1992, "Inter-firm linkages and endogenous technological capability-building", paper presented at the joint UNCTAD/GATE Symposium on the Role of Industrial Districts in the Application, Adaptation and Diffusion of Technology, Geneva, 16 and 17 November.

Assunção, P. *et al.*, 1993, *Internationale Organisationen, Entwicklungs-ver-waltungen und Kleingewerbeförderung in der Dritten Welt*, Baden-Baden, Nomos.

Becattini, G., 1990, "The Marshallian industrial district as a socio-economic notion", in Pyke *et al.* 1990, pp.10-19.

Bellandi, M., 1992, "Decentralized industrial creativity in dynamic industrial districts", paper presented at the joint UNCTAD/GATE Symposium on the Role of Industrial Districts in the Application, Adaptation and Diffusion of Technology, Geneva, 16 and 17 November.

Brusco, S., 1990, "The idea of the industrial district: its genesis", in Pyke *et al.*, 1990, pp.10-19.

Cawthorne, P., 1989, "The labour process under amoebic capitalism: a case study of the garment industry in a South Indian town", paper presented at the Workshop on Development and Change in the Labour Process in the Third World and Advanced Capitalist Countries, held at the Institute of Social Studies, The Hague, 14-15 April 1989.

Cho, M.-R., 1992, "Weaving flexibility: large-small firm relations, flexibility and regional clusters in South Korea", paper prepared for the EADI Workshop on New Approaches to Industrialization: Flexible Production and Innovation Networks in the South, held in Lund, Sweden, 26-27 June.

Dawson, J., 1992, "The relevance of the flexible specialization paradigm for small-scale industrial restructuring in Ghana", in: *IDS Bulletin,* vol.23, no. 3, pp.34-38.

De Soto, H., 1989, *The Other Path: The Invisible Revolution in the Third World*, New York, Harper & Row.

Economic Commission for Latin America and the Caribbean (ECLAC), 1990, *Changing Production Patterns with Social Equity: The Prime Task of Latin American and Caribbean Development in the 1990s*, Santiago, Chile, ECLAC, March.

Elsenhans, H. and H. Fuhr (eds.), 1991, *Administrations and Industrial Development: Case Studies of National and International Assistance*

329

Programmes for Small Enterprises in LDCs, New Delhi, National Book Organization.

Fransman, M., 1984, "Technological capability in the Third World: an overview and introduction to some of the issues raised in this book", in Fransman, M. and K. King (eds.).

Fransman, M. and K. King (eds.), *Technological Capabilities in the Third World*, London, Macmillan.

Fuhr, H., 1993, "Mobilizing local resources in Latin America: decentralisation, institutional reforms and small-scale enterprises", in Späth, B. (ed.).

Fuhr, H., 1987, "Economic restructuring in Latin America: towards the promotion of small-scale industry", in *IDS Bulletin*, vol.18, no.3, pp.49-53.

Fuhr, H. and B. Späth, 1989, "International organizations and small-scale industry promotion: genesis, implementation and evolution of a development policy concept", in *Labour and Society*, vol.14, no.3, July, pp.213-228.

Gabriel, A. *et al.*, 1992, "Technological modernization in small and medium industries in Korea, with special emphasis on the role of international enterprise cooperation", Berlin, *Research Report*, German Development Institute.

Gosses, A. *et al.* (eds.), 1989, "Small enterprises, new approaches", proceedings of the Workshop on Small Scale Enterprise Development in Search of New Dutch Approaches, The Hague, 6-7 March 1989, Ministry of Foreign Affairs.

Haan, H. 1989: *Urban Informal Sector Information: Needs and Methods*, J.-B. Célestin (ed.), Geneva, International Labour Office.

ILO, 1989, *World Labour Report* no.4,

ILO, 1991, *The Dilemma of the Informal Sector*, International Labour Conference, 78th session, Geneva, ILO.

Jeffrey, J. and A. Bhalla, 1991, *Microelectronics, Flexible Specialization and Small-Scale Industrialization in the Third World*, Geneva, ILO, WEP 2-22/WP220.

Jeffrey, J. and S. Watanabe, 1985, *Technology, Institutions and Government Policies*, London, Macmillan.

Kashyap, S.P., 1992, "Recent developments in the small-scale enterprise sector in India: economic and social aspects", Geneva, International Institute for Labour Studies, *Discussion Paper*, no. 48.

Knorringa, P., 1992, "Adaptive capabilities in the Agra footwear cluster", paper presented at the EADI Workshop on New Approaches to Industrialization: Flexible Production and Innovation Networks in the South, held in Lund, Sweden, 26-27 June.

Kozul-Wright, Z., 1992, "Organizing flexibility: a comparison of the Italian and Slovenian furniture industries", paper presented at the joint UNCTAD/GATE Symposium on the Role of Industrial Districts in the Application, Adaptation and Diffusion of Technology, Geneva, 16 and 17 November.

Kulessa, M. (ed.), 1990, *The Newly Industrializing Economies of Asia*, Heidelberg, Springer-Verlag.

Liew, M. L., 1992, "The Singapore experience", paper presented at the joint UNCTAD/GATE Symposium on the Role of Industrial Districts in the Application, Adaptation and Diffusion of Technology, Geneva, 16 and 17 November.

Little, I.M.D., Mazumdar, D. and J.M. Page, 1987, *Small Manufacturing Enterprises: A comparative Analysis of India and Other Economies*, New York, Oxford University Press (for the World Bank).

Maldonado, C., 1989, "The underdogs of the urban economy join forces", in *International Labour Review,* vol.128 (1), pp.65-84.

Maldonado, C.and S.V. Sethuraman (eds.), 1992, *Technological Capability in the Informal Sector: Metal manufacturing in Developing Countries,* Geneva, ILO.

Marcovitch, J., 1993, "Technological innovation and small firms in Brazil", in Späth, B. (ed.), pp.150-157.

Marshall, A. (1892), 1928, "Elements of economics of industry", *Principles of Economics* (first volume), London, Macmillan.

Mead, D. C., 1984, "Of contracts and subcontracts: small firms in vertically disintegrated production/distribution systems in LDCs", in *World Development,* vol.12, no.11/12.

Medeiros, A. J., 1990, *Les Nouvelles Technologies et la Formation des Pôles Technologiques Brésiliens,* Sao Paulo, Centre Universitaire de Documentation Scientifique et Technique - CENDOTEC, (mimeo).

Moser, C., 1984, "The informal sector reworked: viability and vulnerability in urban development", in *Regional Development Dialogue,* vol.5, no.2, Autumn.

Nadvi, K., 1992, "Industrial district experiences in developing countries", paper presented at the joint UNCTAD/GATE Symposium on the Role of Industrial Districts in the Application, Adaptation and Diffusion of Technology, Geneva, 16 and 17 November.

Piore, M. and C. Sabel, 1984, *The Second Industrial Divide: Possibilities for Prosperity,* New York, Basic Books.

Porter, M. E., 1990, "The competitive advantage of nations", in *Harvard Business Review,* March/April, pp.73-93.

Pyke, F., 1992, *Industrial Development through Small-Firm Cooperation*, Geneva, ILO.

Pyke, F., 1991(b), *Upgrading Industrial Sectors: Creating an Institutional Framework*, study prepared for INDUSTR/ILO, Geneva, (mimeo).

Pyke, F. and W. Sengenberger (eds.), 1992, *Small-Firm Industrial Districts and Local Economic Regeneration*, Geneva, International Institute for Labour Studies, ILO.

Pyke, F., Becattini, G. and W. Sengenberger (eds.), 1990, *Industrial Districts and Inter-Firm Co-operation in Italy*, Geneva, International Institute for Labour Studies, ILO.

Rasmussen, J., Schmitz, H. and M.P. Van Dijk, 1992, "Introduction: exploring a new approach to small-scale industry", in *IDS Bulletin*, vol.23, no.3, pp.2-6.

Sabel, C.F., 1992, "Studied trust: building new forms of co-operation in a volatile economy", in Pyke and Sengenberger (eds.), pp.215-250.

Sanders, T. G., 1985, "Brazil's microbusiness law", in *UFSI Reports*, no.26, pp.1-6.

Schmitz, H., 1992(a), "On the clustering of small firms", in *IDS Bulletin*, vol.23, no.3, pp.64-68.

Schmitz, H., 1992(b), "Industrial districts: model and reality in Baden-Württemberg", in Pyke, F. and Sengenberger, W.

Schmitz, H., 1990, "Small firms and flexible specialization in developing countries", in *Labour and Society*, vol.15, no.3. pp.257-281.

Sengenberger. W. and F. Pyke, 1992, "Industrial districts and local economic regeneration: research and policy issues", in Pyke and Sengenberger (eds.), pp.3-29.

Sengenberger, W., Loveman, G.W. and M.J. Piore (eds.), 1990, *The Re-emergence of Small Enterprises: Industrial Restructuring in Industrialized Countries*, Geneva, International Institute for Labour Studies, ILO.

Smyth, I., 1992, "Collective efficiency and selective benefits: the growth of the rattan industry of Tegalwangi (Indonesia)", in *IDS Bulletin*, vol.23., no.3., pp.51-55.

Späth, B. (ed.), 1993(a), *Small firms and development in Latin America*, Geneva, International Institute for Labour Studies, ILO.

Späth, B., 1993(b), "Small firms in Latin America: prospects for economic and socially viable development", in Späth, B. (ed.), pp.1-37.

Tendler, J., 1989, "Whatever happened to poverty alleviation?" in *World Development*, vol.17 (7), pp.1033-1044.

Tokman, V. E., 1991, "Informal sector in Latin America: from underground to legality", in Standing, G. and V.E. Tokman (eds.), *Labour Market Issues and Structural Adjustment*, Geneva, ILO.

Turnham, D. *et al.*, 1990, *The Informal Sector Revisited*, Paris, OECD.

UNIDO, 1978, *The effectiveness of industrial estates in developing countries*, Vienna, UNIDO.

UNIDO, 1985(a), *Mechanisms for Small-Scale Industry Development: Ancillarization - Development of Feeder Industries*, Vienna, UNIDO/IS.151.

UNIDO, 1985(b), *Small-Scale Electronics Industry as Subcontractors in Asia and the Pacific Regions*, Vienna, UNIDO/IS.549.

UNIDO, 1986, *Policies and Strategies for Small-Scale Industry Development in Asia and the Pacific*, Vienna, UNIDO/IS.617.

UNDP *et al.*, 1988, *Development of Rural Small Industrial Enterprises, Lessons from Experience*, a joint study by UNDP, Government of the Netherlands, ILO, UNIDO, Vienna.

Van Dijk, M.P., 1992, "Industrial districts and development of technological capabilities: concepts and origins", paper presented at the joint UNCTAD/GATE Symposium on the Role of Industrial Districts in the Application, Adaptation and Diffusion of Technology, Geneva, 16 and 17 November.

Villarán, F., 1993, "Small-scale industry efficiency groups in Peru", in Späth, B. (ed.), pp.158-195.

Villarán, F., 1992, "Technological innovation and industrial districts: some comments and evidence", paper presented at the joint UNCTAD/GATE Symposium on the Role of Industrial Districts in the Application, Adaptation and Diffusion of Technology, Geneva, 16 and 17 November.

World Bank, *World Development Report*, 1991, Washington D.C.

Zeitlin, J., 1992, "Industrial districts and local economic regeneration: overview and comments", in Pyke and Sengenberger (eds), pp.279-292.

NOTES

1.   I would like to thank Helen Argalias, Ines Smyth, Roger Teszler and Ulrich Weigel for providing valuable comments about the conference and this synthesis.

2.   In the Principles of Economics and Industry being the first volume of *Principles of Economics* (first edition, 1892; 1928), Marshall stressed the economies which can often be secured by the concentration of many small businesses of a similar character in particular localities, pp.151-155.

3.   *Cf.* for the genesis of the industrial district concept, *cf.* Brusco (1990).

4.   *Cf.* Brusco (1990), p.14;   for an English review of the industrial district phenomenon in Italy, *cf.* Pyke *et al.* (1990).

5.   A fact which is particularly stressed by the scholars of the Italian industrial districts (*cf.* Becattini (1990);   Brusco (1990);   Bellandi and also Asheim).

6.   However, there is no clear definition of flexible specialization, and the concept itself is subject to much controversy and forms part of a wider debate on Post-Fordist industrial organization, *cf.* a critique by Amin and Robbins (1990) and the replies by Sabel (1990), Piore (1990) and Storper (1990); also Schmitz (1989).

7.   For the results of six case studies on industrial restructuring in OECD countries, *cf.* Sengenberger *et al.* (1990).

8.   Pyke *et al.* (1990);   Pyke and Sengenberger (1992);   also the contributions by Amin, Asheim, Bellandi, Van Dijk, Kozul-Wright in this volume.

9. This would just add to the long list of existing attempts to transpose and impose mechanical blue-print models, such as industrial estates, incubators, technology and/or business parks, etc.

10. For industrial estates as a industrial development concept, *cf.* UNIDO (1978) and UNDP *et al.* (1988), pp. 65ff; the failure of this concept is mainly due to the fact that the projected inter-firm cooperation and synergies did not occur.

11. These "foster models" are increasingly regarded as key instruments for upgrading small enterprises, since it is assumed that large firms transfer various resources, such as technical know-how, equipment, capital, managerial skills, qualified workers, access to markets, etc. to small firms; e.g. UNIDO (1985a); UNIDO (1985b); UNIDO (1986).

12. Schmitz (1990) has coined the notion of "collective efficiency" to bring out that clustering facilitates efficiency and flexibility rarely attainable by individual small firms.

13. This has also been termed "sandwich situation", *cf.* Gabriel *et al.* (1992), in their study on technological modernization in small and medium industries in the Republic of Korea.

14. The flexible specialization strategy may be feasible on either the small- or large-firm level, depending on the type of industry and the industrial structure of the country. *Cf.* the contribution on Singapore by Liew in this volume, on the Republic of Korea (Cho, 1992) and Gabriel *et al.* (1992), also Jeffrey and Bhalla (1991).

15. Small firms in clusters have already proved to be resilient: in the case of Peru, which is experiencing profound economic crisis, small firms in clusters may not be able to innovate, but they survive, *cf.* Villarán; more generally, *cf.* Schmitz (1990, p.281) and Rasmussen *et al.* (1992, p.2).

16.   The strong arguments in favour of small-scale industry, such as labour-intensiveness, advantageous utilization of local production factors, reduced dependence on imports, and their role in providing a seed-bed for indigenous entrepreneurship development and technological learning had already been confirmed by the mid-1950s.

17.   Often they constitute the only source of new employment. For example, PREALC estimates for seven Latin American countries that employment increased only 3.3 per cent between 1980 and 1987 in large private firms, while it reached 55.4 per cent in small firms, and 56.1 per cent in the urban informal sector. This phenomenon was even more striking during the severe recession of 1980-1983, when employment declined by 6.9 per cent in large firms, while increasing by 30 per cent in small firms and 24.1 per cent in the urban informal sector (PREALC, cited in ILO [1989, p. 31]).

18.   It is difficult to get a comprehensive picture of the quantitative development of large firms versus small firms - and even more so regarding their qualitative development - over the years, since reliable data on fixed assets, sales, labour and capital productivity for comparing their performances are rarely available. Hence, nothing definite can be concluded about total factor productivity or technical efficiency of either large nor small firms, *cf*. Späth (1993b) p.5ff, Little *et al*. (1987).

19.   *Cf*. Little *et al*. (1987);   this is also supported by a comprehensive review of small firm development in OECD countries, *cf*. Sengenberger *et al*. (1990).

20.   Useful reviews about what is known on the subject have been compiled by Anderson (1982); Haan (1989); Moser (1984); Schmitz (1982); Turnham *et al*. (1990).

21.   For a recent analysis of the relative (in)effectiveness of promotion programmes for small-firm development, *cf*. UNDP *et al*. (1988); for a thematic evaluation of the promotion of rural small-scale industry, *cf*. Gosses *et al*. (1989) and Assunção *et al*. (1993).

22.   Maldonado (1989, p.66) describes the principal weakness of small firms in developing countries as being: "...their isolation or their lack of organization on any appreciable scale. Bogged down in legal and administrative difficulties, they are left to wallow while the large enterprises are given every assistance the public authorities can afford."

23.   Most of the research available in this field has been surveyed by Nadvi and is presented in this volume.

24.   This touches also the important issue of labour surplus and rural-urban migration;   in most developing countries, it is in the countryside where the most disadvantaged producer groups, a high rate of labour surplus, unemployment and underemployment, and the lowest wages are found. It is worth pointing to the Republic of South Korea and Taiwan Province of China, where the process of industrialization has been furthered by land reforms assuring a relatively egalitarian distribution of income and resulting in internal demand for locally produced goods;   at the same time, the rural labour force was not pushed to migrate. Economic attractiveness of the countryside may help to mitigate the problem of migration and rapid growth of the urban agglomerations and thus, in the long run, counter the problem of unlimited supply of cheap and unskilled labour.

25.   Marcovitch (1993) and Medeiros (1990) have analysed some of the so-called Brazilian *technopoleis* which are found in various industries and branches, such as chemicals and pharmaceuticals, precision mechanics, electronics, telecommunications, informatics, aircraft, and military equipment. There has been fruitful collaboration among universities, research institutions and sectorally specified clusters of firms of different sizes;   sometimes researchers in the institutions accomplish projects by opening a business or starting a joint venture with a firm;   *cf*. ECLAC (1990, p.72) Villarán (1989) on technological innovation in the metal-working sector in Peru.

26.   *Cf.*, for example, UNIDO (1985a) on the development of ancillary and feeder industries in India.

27.   *Cf.*, for example Cho (1992) for the Republic of Korea, also, Gabriel *et al.* (1992).

28.   Also considered was whether networking of geographically dispersed firms in the same branch would yield similar results, given the new transportation and telecommunications technology. Certainly such networking will produce certain externalities; however, the dynamic influence of what Asheim calls agglomeration economies will be lacking.

29.   *Cf.* Bellandi; for the latter, Asheim, who also refers to two other types of innovation: (1) "new technological systems", consisting of clusters of radical and incremental innovations which are technologically and economically interrelated; and (2) "change in techno-economic paradigm". Both are judged as going beyond the scope of a single small-firm cluster.

30.   Such a cost-reduction strategy is paradoxically often encouraged by special incentives in favour of small enterprises, which exempts firms of a distinct size from minimum wage ceilings, labour regulations, environmental obligations, etc. or at least guarantees some special treatment, *cf.* Mead (1984) for subcontracting in general; for India, Cawthorne (1989), Kashyap (1992) and Knorringa (1992); for Indonesia, Smyth (1992) and also Nadvi in this volume.

31.   However, these features can also obstruct further coopera-tion and the development of trust across the various segments of society and the cluster. Knorringa (1992) points to the role of caste in the various segments of production and marketing in the shoe-manufacturing cluster of Agra (India), which seems to inhibit tight collaboration.

32.   *Cf.*, for example, Murray (1992) on the introduction of flexible specialization in Cyprus.

33.   For a recent change in training policies towards small enterprises, *cf.* for Latin America in general, Alexim (1993) and for Brazil, in particular, Silveira (1993).

34.   This fact is often neglected when innovation is discussed; however, Cho (1992) and Gabriel *et al.* (1992) point to the influence of increased bargaining power of the labour force in the Republic of Korea, which among other factors has encouraged a shift of competitive strategy away from cheap-wage production to high-technology production.

35.   Also Porter (1990, 81ff.) has pointed to the healthy influence of competition and rivalry among firms, by fitting it into his "diamond of national advantages" schema which comprises (1) factor conditions, (2) demand conditions, (3) related and supporting industries and (4) firm strategy, structure and rivalry.

36.   For example, Villarán pointed to Peru, where clusters are weathering the most severe economic crisis, reducing labour costs and allowing self-exploitation and family labour. Since labour relations in small firms are usually characterized by paternalistic relations between employer and employees, there is a strong moral obligation to care for the welfare of the worker, particularly if the economic situation of the firm allows it. Tokman (1991) has observed that the growth of more successful small firms has also resulted in improved standards for their employees, including paid vacations and the payment of bonuses.

37.   A major problem seems to be that some organizations are diversifying and expanding into more complex activities too quickly, and thus nascent self-help groups easily become overburdened; *cf.* Tendler (1989) who has studied self-organization in the case of Indian women's cooperatives and the Grameen Bank in Bangladesh. There are also possibilities for encouraging the formation of associations from the outside: e.g. the ILO has had first-hand experience in organizing artisans in French-speaking parts of Africa, *cf.* Maldonado (1989).

38.   *Cf.* Asheim; for the relation between technology, institutions and government policy, see for example, James and Watanabe (1985).

39.   For the generation and implementation of assistance programmes by multilateral donor agencies, *cf.* Fuhr and Späth (1989).

40.   *Cf.* UNDP *et al.* (1988); Gosses *et al.* (1989); Assunção *et al.* (1993): case studies in Ecuador, Peru, Senegal and Zambia; and Fuhr (1987).

41.   It was suggested that the introduction of a "dual vocational training" system - as practised in Germany - combining training on the shopfloor with theoretical qualification in schools, would also be of relevance to developing countries, in general, and to sectorally specified clusters. However, according to some recent information made available to the author, the German donor agencies are thinking of abandoning the promulgation of the dual system, since an appraisal of about 20 years of development cooperation in this field suggests that this type of training system is too complex for most LDCs.

42.   For example, by promoting the wrong kinds of activities, creating cumbersome bureaucratic procedures and encouraging small firms to build their competitive advantage on cheap labour, etc., *cf.* Späth (1993b).

43.   For example, entrepreneurs are facing excessive bureaucratic requirements and red tape if they want to register a business activity. The process of formalization is not only time-consuming and costly, but also constitutes a barrier equivalent to a prohibition to operate legally. For the bureaucratic constraints in Latin America, *cf.* Fuhr (1993); Tokman (1991); Späth (1993b); for Peru, De Soto (1989).

44.   There are signs that employer organizations are changing their attitude towards small firms, *cf.* ILO (1991 p.51ff).

45.　Workers in small units are usually not organized or covered by collective agreements, since trade unions have traditionally concentrated on modern large- and medium-scale enterprises. "The existence of the informal sector is the very antithesis of everything that the trade union movement stands for.... Trade unions in the past, like governments and employers, generally ignored the problem, in the commonly-held belief that, as a vestige of the past and a manifestation of underdevelopment, it would eventually be absorbed by the modern sector, and that those who worked in it could therefore eventually be covered by the trade union movement", ILO (1991, p.47), also Späth (1993b).

46.　A starting point is the dissemination of existing information among international and national planners and policy-makers, which could be followed by integrating the distinct and essential organizational principles into training and support programmes for regional and local authorities, and support institutions.

ANNEX

List of participants

Mr. I. Ahmed
International Labour Office
Geneva

Mr. A. Akpa
Officer-in-Charge
UNIDO Office
Geneva

Mr. G. Alam
Director
Centre for Technology Studies
New Delhi

Mr. L. Alcorta
The United Nations University
INTECH
Maastricht

Mr. R. Andreasson
Permanent Representative
World Assembly of Small
and Medium Enterprises
Geneva

Mr. B.T. Asheim
University of Oslo

Mr. D.B. Audretsch
Market Processes and Corporate
Development
Berlin

Mr. M. Bagachwa
University of Dar es Salaam

Mr. P. Bauer
Counsellor (Economic Affairs)
Permanent Mission of Germany

Mr. A.S. Bhalla
International Labour Organization
Geneva

Mr. M. Bellandi
University of Florence

Mr. M. Bouchrara
Afkar and Ich'Har
Tunis

Mr. P. Brath
Focal Point for Technology for
Developing Countries

Taastrup (Denmark)

Mr. Myung Rae Cho
Dankook University
Seoul

Mr. M.P. Van Dijk
Erasmus University
Rotterdam

Mr. G. Garofoli
University of Pavia

Mr. H. Habenicht
International Labour Organization
Geneva

Mr. M. Holmström
University of East Anglia
Norwich (United Kingdom)

Mr. R. Lemp
Permanent Mission of Germany
Geneva

Ms. Z. Kozul-Wright
Science, Technology, Energy,
Environment and Natural Resources Division
United Nations, New York

Mr. Mun Leon Liew
Singapore Institute of Standards and
Industrial Research
Singapore

Mr. S. Ludwiczak
Economic Commission for Europe
Geneva

Mr. C. Maldonado
International Labour Office
Geneva

Mr. A. Manuelli
IRPET
Florence

Mr. K. van der Ree
International Labour Office
Geneva

Mr. H.-C. Rieger
University of Heidelberg

Mr. B. Roux-Fouillet
Economic Commission for Europe
Geneva

Mr. S.V. Sethuraman
International Labour Office
Geneva

Ms. I. Smyth
University of Oxford

Ms. B. Späth
University of Konstanz

Mr. E. Stackelberg
Economic Commission for Europe
Geneva

Mr. R. Teszler
University of Amsterdam

Mr. F. Villarán
Pequeña Empresa Tecnología y Sociedad
Lima

Mr. E. Visser
University of Amsterdam

CAP CANAILLE

Christophe Gavat

Cap Canaille

Fayard

Couverture : Le Petit Atelier
Photo : © Getty/Nathan Swartz

ISBN : 978-2-213-71764-7

© Librairie Arthème Fayard, 2020.
Dépôt légal : novembre 2020.

Le prix du Quai des Orfèvres a été décerné sur manuscrit anonyme par un jury présidé par Monsieur Christian SAINTE, Directeur de la Police judiciaire, au 36, rue du Bastion. Il est proclamé par M. le Préfet de Police.

Novembre 2020

PRIX DU QUAI DES ORFÈVRES

Le Prix du Quai des Orfèvres, fondé en 1946 par Jacques Catineau, est destiné à couronner chaque année le meilleur manuscrit d'un roman policier inédit, œuvre présentée par un écrivain de langue française.

- Le montant du prix est de 777 euros, remis à l'auteur le jour de la proclamation du résultat par M. le Préfet de police. Le manuscrit retenu est publié, dans l'année, par les Éditions Fayard, le contrat d'auteur garantissant un tirage minimal de 50 000 exemplaires.

- Le jury du Prix du Quai des Orfèvres, placé sous la présidence effective du Directeur de la Police judiciaire, est composé de personnalités remplissant des fonctions ou ayant eu une activité leur permettant de porter un jugement qualifié sur les œuvres soumises à leur appréciation.

- Toute personne désirant participer au Prix du Quai des Orfèvres peut en demander le règlement au :

Secrétariat général du Prix du Quai des Orfèvres
36, rue du Bastion
75017 Paris

Site : www.prixduquaidesorfèvres.fr

E-mail : prixduquaidesorfevres@gmail.com

La date de réception des manuscrits est fixée au plus tard au 15 mars de chaque année.

Aux policiers, flics, keufs, condés...
Loin des âmes tièdes,
Cœurs brisés, trop souvent,
Cœurs brûlants, toujours.

« La vie est beaucoup trop courte et précieuse pour accepter de la ralentir dans la file d'attente des problèmes subalternes. »

Jean-Paul Dubois,
*Tous les hommes n'habitent pas
le monde de la même façon.*

Prologue

Drôle d'endroit pour mourir.

La beauté des lieux l'avait saisi. Il ne pouvait s'empêcher de s'émerveiller. Malgré les quatre hommes qui l'entouraient, le flingue qui le menaçait et la peur qui lui trouait le bide.

La lune était de sortie pour éclairer les dernières heures de sa courte vie. Elle lui permettait de voir comme en plein jour les falaises qui le dominaient et la mer qui l'aspirait. Qui l'espérait. 390 mètres plus bas.

Magnifique endroit pour mourir.

La journée avait été plombée de soleil. Il avait délesté ses rayons dans la Méditerranée. Pas un alizé n'osait braver le seigneur mistral. Virulent depuis plusieurs jours, il s'était tu, abattu par la chaleur ambiante.

L'homme n'avait pas l'habitude d'être philosophe. Pourtant il déplora de ne jamais être venu admirer ce point de vue. Devant ce spectacle majestueux, où la lune, amoureuse et mortelle, lui désignait son point de chute dans la mer, il le regrettait. Comme toutes ces choses auxquelles il n'aurait plus l'occasion de goûter. L'ivresse d'un baiser, la sensualité d'un fruit et le reflet de la lune dans la Méditerranée depuis les falaises du cap Canaille.

Jusque-là sa vie avait été marquée par la mort. Il n'avait pas hésité, quand certains voulaient l'empêcher de prospérer, de procéder à leur élimination. Deux selon la police, dix fois plus selon ses comptes personnels. Quand on prétend devenir le plus grand parrain de Marseille de tous les temps, plus puissant que Spirito et Carbone, plus malin que Mémé Guérini, plus violent que Francis le Belge et plus féroce que Farid Berrahma, il faut faire preuve de cruauté comme aucun de ses illustres prédécesseurs n'a osé le faire.

Quand d'autres avaient voulu prendre son territoire en éliminant les siens, il avait répondu par une application inflexible de la loi du talion, agrémentée de sa touche personnelle. Une exécution littérale des principes divins : ils n'étaient que poussière et retourneraient poussière. Même si sa préférence était de souffler sur leurs cendres. Poussières consommées, poussières brûlées.

La beauté du site ne recelait aucune échappatoire, à part le grand saut dans le reflet de la lune. Il aurait dû écouter sa mère. Elle lui répétait qu'il ne suffisait pas d'avoir une belle intelligence, encore fallait-il en faire un bon usage. Il avait dû merder quelque part sur l'utilisation de ses neurones.

À cette hauteur, avec la mer comme tapis de réception, il était trop tard pour se rappeler le premier adage du voyou. Pour survivre, reste à ta place. La présence des quatre hommes armés devant lui en était la démonstration. Il s'était vu trop beau, trop vite. Sa vanité avait obstrué sa lucidité. Il ne serait jamais le plus grand parrain de Marseille. Comme tant d'autres avant lui, connus ou anonymes, suicidés ou assassinés, il finirait en bas du cap Canaille. Au nom si prédestiné.

La main de l'homme qui tenait le flingue actionna la culasse. Pour faire couleur locale, il les traita d'enculés et se dit qu'il ne terminerait même pas en cendres, mais dans la gueule des poissons. Il trouva encore le moyen d'insulter leurs mères, et toutes les mères en général, sauf la sienne. Pensa : tout ça pour ça. Dans ces conditions, il serait impossible de retrouver ses restes. Il cracha par terre. Sale endroit pour mourir.

1

Un mois plus tôt,
vendredi 6 avril 2018, 18 heures.

Henri Saint-Donat, Canadien par son nom, british par l'allure et flic par vocation, est en plein doute. Du haut de ses 53 ans, de ses trente ans de carrière et de ses douze marathons, il se demande s'il a eu raison de confier le volant à Basile Urteguy, Basque par ses origines, lieutenant par son grade et minot par son affectation à la Crim' de Marseille. Son subordonné n'a même pas l'âge de sa carrière, 29 ans, l'arrogance de la certitude et l'insolence de sa jeunesse.

La Ford Mondeo couleur bleu gendarme circule à vive allure. Malgré son poids et sa longueur, Urteguy la manie avec dextérité. Compte tenu de la circulation ce vendredi soir en sortant de Marseille, il fait même preuve de talent. Il se tourne vers le commandant divisionnaire fonctionnel Henri Saint-Donat. Malgré le gyrophare qu'il a lui-même positionné sur le toit et la sirène qu'il a enclenchée, en mettant

17

au défi le jeune lieutenant de les conduire aux abords des Pennes-Mirabeau en moins de douze minutes, le commandant semble sur le point de défaillir. Quand il ouvre la fenêtre, Urteguy pense qu'il s'apprête à vomir.

– T'inquiète, j'ai fait le stage conduite rapide.

Ça ne rassure pas Saint-Donat. Cette formation se passe au Mans, sur circuit fermé, avec des Renault Mégane préparées pour la grande vitesse. Pas avec des Mondeo de plus d'une tonne et demie, affichant 250 000 kilomètres au compteur. Urteguy ne relève pas. Son supérieur hiérarchique lui a confié une mission, il tient à la remplir dans le temps imparti. Comme d'habitude, l'A55 est bouchée, il remonte le boulevard des Dames, circule entre les voitures avenue de la République et rejoint l'A7 en un temps record.

– Fin du calvaire dans quatre minutes et trente-sept secondes.

Le côté impertinent du lieutenant ne déplaît pas à Henri Saint-Donat. Il retrouve en lui des traits de son caractère au même âge. À l'époque où les lieutenants de police étaient encore des inspecteurs, et qu'il venait d'être muté à la Crim' du « 36 » à Paris.

Si la police judiciaire de Paris n'avait pas quitté son célèbre quai, il aurait aimé terminer sa carrière là où il l'avait commencée, et rester jusqu'au bout un orfèvre de la Crim'. Mais le déménagement de septembre 2017 lui avait fait prendre une décision radicale. Quitter le centre de la capitale avec vue sur la Seine, pour la porte de Clichy avec vue sur le périph, était une cause de séparation obligatoire avec le « 36 », et ce fut le moment de lancer sa moto Honda Goldwing 1 800 sur les routes ensoleillées du « 13 ». Le gamin de Paname avait décidé de terminer sa carrière chez les minots de la cité phocéenne. Mais toujours à la PJ. Quand on s'appelle Saint-Donat, il y a des limites à l'infidélité. Il n'aurait jamais pris une telle décision sans l'accord de l'amour de sa vie, Isabelle, sa femme depuis toujours et pour toujours. En tout cas depuis qu'ils s'étaient croisés, lui âgé de 27 ans, inspecteur au holster tout neuf, et elle, de 23 ans, vendeuse dans un magasin de fringues.

Elle s'imaginait styliste branchée, elle était devenue directrice d'une boutique tendance. Il espérait terminer sa carrière inspecteur divisionnaire à la police judiciaire de la préfecture de Paris, il était depuis huit mois commandant divisionnaire fonctionnel à la direction interrégionale de la police judiciaire de Marseille. Évolution normale en trois décennies de carrière, des grades, des corps et des esprits.

Il avait quand même eu du mal à quitter le quai des Orfèvres. Il le fréquentait depuis le 1er septembre 1986, frais émoulu de ce qui ne s'appelait pas encore l'Ensop*, mais l'ESIPN**. Son classement de sortie lui avait permis de choisir ce lieu mythique. Rentré comme inspecteur stagiaire, à la fonction de ripeur, il avait vite fait ses gammes et ses preuves, et avait gravi échelons et grades dans le saint des saints de la police judiciaire parisienne.

Pendant toutes ses années de carrière, il en avait vu, du voyou. Du délinquant récidiviste fiché au grand banditisme à l'occasionnel qui tuait par passion, bêtise ou accident. Il les avait tous vus monter les cent quarante-huit marches de l'escalier central. Il s'était pris d'affection pour quelques-uns et en avait détesté beaucoup.

---

* Ensop : École nationale supérieure des officiers de police, sise à Cannes-Écluse, nom donné depuis une réforme de 1995 à l'École des officiers de police, après qu'elle s'était appelée l'ESIPN.

** ESIPN : École supérieure des inspecteurs de la police nationale.

Et tout dans ce magnifique bâtiment lui rappelait ses affaires, qu'aucun film, aucune série télévisée ne pourrait jamais montrer dans leurs paradoxes psychologiques ; leur complexité et leur richesse.

Nostalgique de Paris, il avait vite repris le dessus, quand la CAP* des officiers avait donné suite à sa demande de mutation à la DIPJ** des Bouches-du-Rhône. Le directeur de Marseille, le contrôleur général Francis Larrivée, l'avait immédiatement nommé chef de groupe à la brigade criminelle, au cœur de la police marseillaise, à l'Évêché, situé au pied du populaire quartier du Panier, en face de la cathédrale de la Major, avec vue sur la Méditerranée et à deux pas du Vieux-Port. Il y avait pire comme situation géographique, et pour Saint-Donat une vraie cause de réjouissantes découvertes.

Quitter un service de police mythique au cœur de l'île de la Cité, pour la DIPJ de Marseille nichée dans l'ancien palais épiscopal, inscrit sur la liste des monuments

---

* CAP : Commission administrative paritaire, instance de représentation et de dialogue de la fonction publique.
** DIPJ : Direction interrégionale de la police judiciaire.

historiques, n'était-ce pas comme une sorte de continuité dans la légende ?

D'autant que, en termes de criminalité, le commandant sait bien que les voyous marseillais n'ont rien à envier à leurs homologues de la capitale. En matière de techniques pour tuer son prochain, bien que provincial, le Marseillais ne manque jamais d'imagination et tient à prouver au Parisien que, dans ce domaine comme dans celui du foot, il est le meilleur. Et ne craint *dégun**.

---

* *Dégun* : expression marseillaise signifiant : « personne ».

2

La découverte de cadavre sur laquelle il se rend à grande vitesse avec son jeune adjoint Basile Urteguy n'échappe pas à la règle. Il lui reste donc environ quatre minutes avant d'être confronté à la violence des hommes. Malgré ce qui l'attend, il se rappelle qu'il a aussi choisi cette mutation dans les Bouches-du-Rhône pour voir au-delà des images imposées sur les ondes médiatiques et découvrir l'autre réalité de Marseille et de ses environs.

Depuis huit mois qu'il est arrivé, il n'a pas été déçu. Cette ville ne recèle pas que des cités violentes, elle possède aussi un patrimoine historique, culturel et écologique magnifique. Avec Isabelle, il a pris l'habitude de partir à sa découverte. Et puisque le temps le permet plus souvent qu'à Paris, ils le font à moto. Il fallait bien qu'il y ait quelque intérêt à quitter l'île de la Cité. Celui de faire ronronner plus souvent sa moto Honda Goldwing 1 800, marche arrière incorporée, sous le soleil de la côte, en était un capital.

C'est ce qu'il s'apprêtait à faire il y a encore quelques minutes. Une randonnée à moto de plusieurs jours avec sa femme, juste avant que l'actualité policière en décide autrement. Depuis le temps qu'il est flic, il le sait pourtant, qu'il ne faut jamais prévoir des congés à la fin d'une permanence.

Alors qu'il s'apprêtait à faire démarrer sa si chère bécane, un appel téléphonique a bloqué ses plans. Au départ, il a cru à une mauvaise blague de son jeune adjoint, mais la voix déconfite de Basile lui a fait vite comprendre que son groupe héritait de la « bouse » du vendredi soir.

Les gendarmes des Pennes-Mirabeau venaient de découvrir une voiture entièrement calcinée aux abords d'un chemin forestier. Ce qui, jusque-là, ne posait aucun problème aux militaires de la brigade territoriale, même si dans l'immédiat il leur était impossible d'identifier la marque et l'immatriculation de cette dernière.

Mais les pompiers, par habitude et conscience professionnelle, avaient ouvert le capot et découvert à l'intérieur un corps, entièrement calciné.

– Un barbecue ! s'était exclamé Urteguy.

Mode opératoire local de règlement de comptes entre voyous, consistant à abattre son adversaire et le brûler dans le coffre d'un véhicule. Ce qui d'un coup dépassait les saisines habituelles de la gendarmerie et relevait bien de la compétence de la police judiciaire de Marseille.

En arrivant sur la scène de crime, Henri Saint-Donat regarde sa montre. Basile Urteguy a presque tenu le chrono, dépassé de deux petites minutes, ce qui, compte tenu de la circulation du vendredi soir, relève quand même de l'exploit, même avec un gyrophare et une sirène. S'il s'agit, comme toutes les apparences le laissent supposer, d'un règlement de comptes, malheureusement classique entre voyous des cités nord, il ne devrait pas rester sur place trop longtemps et pourrait avant 20 heures quitter les lieux et reprendre son programme initial. Il n'aime pas faire attendre sa femme et sa Goldwing.

3

La profession de Robert Battisteli ne lui avait pas apporté que du bonheur, bien au contraire. Il n'avait jamais fait les bons choix des établissements dans lesquels il avait exercé. Mais en 2013, à 47 ans, quand il avait appris que l'Hôtel-Dieu, ancien hôpital de Marseille situé dans le quartier historique du Panier, se métamorphosait en hôtel de luxe géré par le groupe anglais Intercontinental, il n'avait pas hésité une seconde.

Depuis, il jubile dans un langage qui lui est propre : un subtil mélange d'expressions anglaises et provençales. Un prétexte de moquerie intarissable pour sa compagne, Kimberley, une Galloise à l'humour dévastateur.

Chaque jour, en enfilant son costume de responsable de la réception à l'Interconti-nental, Robert Battisteli remercie la Bonne Mère. Exceptionnelle qualité du site, de ses collègues de travail, de sa direction, *« and last but not the least »*, comme il se plaît à le dire, des *« customers »*. Clientèle de charme, chic et argentée, qui lésine parfois sur les pourboires, mais jamais sur les éloges. Aucune raison de s'inquiéter. Même quand la femme de chambre en charge du quatrième étage l'avise que la cliente de la suite 412 n'a pas défait son lit depuis plusieurs jours. Habitué à l'excentricité de ses richissimes « patients », Robert Battisteli ne s'affole pas. Surtout quand il s'agit d'une cliente comme Mireille de Gounod ayant payé d'avance et en espèces son séjour de plusieurs nuitées.

En pensant à la femme de 54 ans qui occupe la suite 412, il sourit. Mirelle de Gounod ne laisse pas indifférent. Et ce n'est pas dû à son nom aristocratique. Elle a ce truc en plus. Cette chose infime et délicate qui fait basculer une jolie femme dans la catégorie des charismatiques. Les années n'ont eu aucun impact sur elle et semblent même accentuer l'aura, fascinante et mystérieuse, qui l'entoure. Robert ne se souvient pas de l'avoir croisée avec un homme. Pourtant, il en est certain, avec son sourire et ses yeux clairs, son allure noble et sauvage, Mireille est une séductrice.

Quand il arrive à la réception, il se souvient de la dernière fois qu'il l'a croisée à l'hôtel. Casque intégral à la main, elle portait un pantalon et un blouson de cuir, qui ne cachaient rien de ses splendides courbes.

Elle venait de rentrer de balade, avait laissé sa moto au voiturier et pestait contre la piètre qualité des conducteurs marseillais, en voiture ou à deux-roues.

– Tous des dingues. Et le pire, vous savez quoi, Robert ? Ils roulent en short et en tongs !

Autant par conscience professionnelle que par peur de dire une connerie, lui-même n'étant pas adepte des tenues de motard adaptées, Robert s'était contenté de hocher la tête.

– Faire du deux-roues dans cette tenue, ce n'est même pas de l'inconscience, c'est du suicide.

Ce mot résonne dans la tête de Robert quand il arrive derrière l'immense comptoir de l'accueil. Il souffle quelques mots à la réceptionniste. Pendant qu'elle consulte son ordinateur, il se demande si Mireille de Gounod pourrait être une femme capable de se donner la mort. Avec la joie de vivre et l'énergie sensuelle qu'elle dégage, il ne l'imagine pas capable d'un tel acte. L'hôtesse le sort de sa réflexion, le dernier passage de Mireille de Gounod à la réception remonte à trois jours. Elle a déposé les clefs de sa chambre et ne les a pas récupérées.

Si, jusqu'alors, Robert Battisteli n'avait pas de raison de s'inquiéter, un trouble le saisit.

Trois jours sans nouvelles d'une cliente, ce n'est pas normal. Dans un établissement comme l'Intercontinental, toute la chaîne hiérarchique aurait dû être au courant. Lui, le premier. Pas certain que sa direction, même avec son humour « *so typical British* », accepte ce genre de désinvolture.

Le cœur battant, il se précipite au garage de l'hôtel. Des Porsche, des Mercedes, des BMW et même une Aston Martin occupent tous les emplacements du sous-sol. Il ne voit pas le véhicule de Mireille de Gounod. Ce qui le rassure. Il souffle. Cette chère cliente aura donc avancé son départ et n'en aura pas prévenu la réception. Il repense à la crise d'angoisse qu'il vient d'avoir et s'imagine déjà en train de raconter cette anecdote à Kimberley et la façon dont elle va se moquer de lui.

Il se retourne. Pâlit. Son rythme cardiaque augmente de nouveau. Ce n'est pas bon pour son cœur. Kimberley aura bien une raison de se foutre de lui. Dans la deuxième partie du hall se trouve le parking motos, séparé de celui des voitures. Dix grosses cylindrées, aux couleurs variées, plus impressionnantes les unes que les autres, sont exposées côte à côte. Au milieu, comme une évidence : la Honda Goldwing Aventure bleu pailleté de Mireille de Gounod règne en maîtresse absolue.

4

L'horreur est là, sous ses yeux. Malgré ses trente-deux ans passés à la brigade criminelle, il ne s'y fait pas. Même si chaque scène de crime est différente, sa réaction reste la même. Il se laisse systématiquement surprendre. Le dégoût d'abord.

De ce qu'il imagine avant même de voir le corps. Le plus dur est de juguler son esprit, capable de se représenter le cadavre avant même de le voir. Il doit toujours jeter le premier coup d'œil, pour limiter les effets pervers de son imagination et appréhender la victime dans toute sa matérialité.

De ce qu'il sent, ensuite. Cette pestilence, âcre, nauséabonde. Tous ces cadavres sur lesquels il a enquêté lui ont appris une chose : la mort a une odeur. Différente et pourtant similaire à chaque fois. Même quand l'incendie a tout ravagé et que le corps brûlé n'est plus qu'un affreux tison, scrofuleux, recroquevillé, sur lequel il est difficile de différencier la tête des jambes. La fumée emporte avec elle l'odeur du corps. Elle se dépose sur ceux qui s'approchent, s'accroche entre les mailles des pulls et le coton des chemises.

L'effroi le saisit alors. Quand il réalise la violence et la haine qu'il a fallu pour éliminer son prochain de la sorte. Dire qu'il aura attendu sa mutation à Marseille pour découvrir ce mode opératoire hallucinant. Coutume locale, presque une signature, revendiquée par les voyous marseillais. Il se tourne vers Urteguy.

– C'est ça, un barbecue ?

– Oui. Règlement de comptes entre dealers de cité.

– Des gros cons.

Urteguy n'est pas habitué à de tels propos définitifs et vulgaires de la part du commandant.

– Déjà, se tuer entre eux, c'est triste. Et stupide. Mais cramer le cadavre et empêcher de prélever des organes, c'est vraiment très con.

Devant la malle arrière de la voiture, il regarde ce qu'il reste du corps. Un morceau de charbon d'un mètre sur trente centimètres. Voilà ce que fut un être humain. C'est noir, dégueulasse et ça pue.

Cinq autres policiers du groupe, ainsi que le docteur Faussier, médecin légiste, les rejoignent. Ce n'est pas le premier « barbecue » sur lequel ils interviennent. Pourtant habitués à ce type de scènes et prompts à faire des vannes de qualité douteuse, ils restent muets.

Pendant que le légiste commence ses premiers actes, Saint-Donat désigne trois collègues pour effectuer une enquête de voisinage. Compte tenu de la rase campagne où se situe la scène de crime, il leur demande de ratisser le plus large possible. Les autres prennent en charge les investigations sur la voiture brûlée. Avec Urteguy, en lien avec Faussier, ils assurent les constatations sur le cadavre.

– Alors toubib, notre macchabée du jour : jeune ? Vieux ?

Le légiste, la tête dans la malle, un masque sur le visage, reprend un peu d'air.

– À ce stade, je suis incapable de me prononcer.

Il n'a qu'une bonne nouvelle, les prélèvements effectués sur le cadavre devraient leur permettre d'établir le profil génétique du mort et, s'il est inscrit au Fnaeg*, de l'identifier formellement.

– Les mecs des cités, ils sont tous tombés au moins une fois. On devrait vite savoir qui c'est.

_____

* Fnaeg : Fichier national automatisé des empreintes génétiques.

La suite de l'enquête s'annonce plus compliquée. Depuis qu'il est à Marseille, Saint-Donat a compris que les clans des cités cherchent à implanter, intensifier ou reprendre leur territoire de vente de stupéfiants dans une guerre aux enjeux financiers considérables, qui conduit à tous les extrêmes. Les amis d'hier deviennent les ennemis d'aujourd'hui. L'ambition des gros bras conduit à éliminer ceux qui les dirigent. Les numéros deux cherchent à devenir numéro un. Tous, devant l'attrait de cette manne financière, rêvent d'être calife à la place du calife. Et sont prêts à toutes les trahisons.

L'argent a l'odeur de la drogue, et la came n'a pas d'honneur.

5

Saint-Donat vient à peine d'enfiler gants et masque de protection qu'il est obligé de les retirer. Son téléphone sonne.

– Saint-Donat, c'est Martin. Je te dérange pas ?

Martin Laval, son ancien adjoint lorsqu'il était chef de groupe au « 36 ». Lui aussi a quitté la brigade criminelle parisienne au moment de son déménagement, pour accrocher son galon de commandant, qu'il est allé prendre à l'antenne de police judiciaire de Melun.

– Martin ? Tu donnes pas de nouvelles depuis des mois, et tu m'appelles sur mon premier barbecue.

Laval aurait bien tenté une blague vaseuse sur la qualité des merguez, mais comprend que son ancien chef n'est pas en train de déguster rosé et chipolatas. En vieux flic, même parisien, il connaît les us et coutumes des voyous marseillais.

– Je te la fais courte. À Melun, je suis chef du GRB.*

---

* GRB : groupe de répression du banditisme.

– T'as chopé le galon de commandant ?

– Il était temps. Mais on n'est pas là pour ça. On a besoin d'un coup de main sur un braquage de fourgon.

– Je suis à la Crim', Martin, pas à la BRB*.

– Henri, je connais personne à Marseille. Si je passe par la voie officielle, j'en ai pour des plombes.

Laval est un vrai « poulet » et aime aller vite quand il suit une piste. Saint-Donat connaît le sens de la synthèse de son ancien adjoint.

– On a été saisis d'un braquage de fourgon, lundi dernier, le 26 mars. Des pros. Peugeot 308 et Ford Mondeo volées, plaques police et gyrophares. Ils ont piqué un million d'euros.

– Pas mal.

– Sur le braquage, on n'a rien. Pas de vidéo, pas de téléphonie, pas d'ADN.

– Tu l'as dit : des pros.

– C'est la suite qui est savoureuse…

Les braqueurs, après la commission de leur méfait, avaient prévu un parking isolé où se débarrasser de leurs voitures pour en récupérer d'autres. Contre toute attente, à ce moment et à cet endroit, un malfaiteur

---

* BRB : brigade de répression du banditisme, se différencie du « groupe » par une taille plus importante.

a lâché une rafale de kalachnikov sur un véhicule qui passait et a flingué la conductrice, une dame de 72 ans. Morte sur le coup.

– Un témoin gênant ?

– Je ne pense pas. Elle ne pouvait rien savoir du braquage qui venait de se dérouler vingt kilomètres plus loin.

– Bizarre…

Pris dans sa discussion, Saint-Donat en oublierait presque Urteguy et les constatations en cours. Il n'est pas inquiet, il a déjà vu le lieutenant à l'œuvre. Le jeune flic assure.

– Sur le parking, on a récupéré des étuis. Du 7,62. Sur l'un d'eux, on a prélevé de l'ADN. Le Fnaeg nous l'a sorti en fin d'après-midi : Yassine Hosni.

– Je ne connais pas.

– Ça m'aurait étonné, ce n'est pas ta génération. Il a 22 ans, né en 1996, tu sais où ?

– Je donne ma langue à Laval.

– À Marseille, mon vieux. Et il habite Bât B2, n° 12, allée des Pêcheurs, à la Cayolle. C'est chantant, non ?

Depuis huit mois à Marseille, Saint-Donat s'est habitué aux noms des cités. Il a déjà entendu parler de la Cayolle, plus pour sa proximité avec la calanque de

Sormiou, la magnifique, que pour la présence de voyous emblématiques, capables de monter sur un braquage de fourgon.

– Tu veux qu'on tape une « vérif de dom'* » ?

– Mieux, une « perquise », avec interpellation de Yassine Hosni, s'il est là.

– C'est pas précipité ?

– On n'a rien d'autre, Henri. Comme on ne comprend pas comment l'ADN d'un jeune voyou marseillais peut se retrouver sur un braquage de fourgon commis dans la région parisienne, on se dit que choper le minot est un bon début.

Pas question de ne pas filer un coup de main à son ancien adjoint. Solidarité de flic et d'ami.

– Contacte de ma part la capitaine Clert, chef de groupe à la BRB. C'est la meilleure.

Il percute. Il avait oublié un détail. Majeur.

– Tu la connais d'ailleurs, Lucie Clert, la fille de Louis.

– Louis Clert ? L'ancien CID** qui nous a formés au « 36 » ?

---

* « Vérif de dom' » : raccourci policier pour « vérification de domicile ».

** CID : chef inspecteur divisionnaire, ancien grade dans le corps des inspecteurs de la police nationale, avant la réforme de 1995.

Des années que Saint-Donat n'avait plus entendu parler de ce grade : le CID, le chef inspecteur divisionnaire. La police a toujours eu le chic pour trouver des acronymes improbables. S'il a connu des « CID », c'est qu'il commence à se faire vieux dans la boîte et qu'il va devoir passer la main. Il regarde Basile Urteguy s'affairer autour de la voiture et du cadavre. En d'autres temps, il aurait donc été le CID du jeune lieutenant. Il n'aurait jamais cru qu'il aurait cette pensée banale d'homme de plus de 50 ans : le temps passe si vite.

– Martin, fais attention quand même avec Lucie.

– Pourquoi ?

Il n'a pas besoin de lui expliquer. Laval comprend de lui-même.

– Oh, putain, elle a le même caractère de merde que son père.

Saint-Donat n'a pas dit toute la vérité au commandant de Melun. Lucie Clert a une personnalité encore plus trempée que son père. Pas besoin de lui gâcher cette bonne surprise.

Drôle de job. Il a appris le boulot avec le CID Louis Clert et travaille aujourd'hui avec sa fille, la capitaine Lucie Clert. Il remet gants et masque protecteur et regarde Urteguy aider le médecin légiste à sortir du coffre le corps carbonisé, qui apparaît dans toute son horreur. Il n'arrive pas à distinguer les bras des jambes, la tête des pieds. Il a même du mal à imaginer qu'il ait pu s'agir d'un corps humain. Une odeur âcre monte dans sa bouche. Envie de vomir.

Urteguy semble à l'aise et paraît supporter cette horreur. Avec Faussier, ils allongent le cadavre sur une bâche. Le lieutenant sort un décamètre de son gilet tactique et mesure la dépouille. L'attitude du jeune flic confirme la pensée de Saint-Donat : la relève assure. Pas besoin de lui. Ce n'est finalement pas un hasard s'il a répondu à l'appel téléphonique de son ancien adjoint. Il se fait peut-être vieux pour la police.

La roue tourne, les années défilent, la violence se perpétue. La connerie humaine reste. Combien de temps va-t-il être encore capable de supporter tout ça ? En a-t-il besoin ? Est-ce nécessaire dans l'ordre du monde ? Il ne le changera pas. À l'âge d'Urteguy, il y a cru. Au sien, il n'est pas dupe. Les beaux discours des politiques, des philosophes ou des religieux n'y changeront rien. Au contraire même. Les semeurs de violence se drapent volontiers d'une honorabilité de costume. Et la criminalité est immarcescible.

Urteguy lui fait signe. Le médecin légiste a décelé dans ce tison horrible qui a été un corps humain un trou au niveau de la nuque. Avant d'être brûlée, la victime a été tuée d'une balle dans la tête.

Devant ce corps carbonisé, Saint-Donat se sent vieux, usé. Le trop-plein déborde. Avec l'âge, l'accumulation dégueule. Mais qu'est-ce qu'il fout là ?

Il n'a qu'une envie : se serrer contre sa femme.

6

Il pleut quand Basile Urteguy gare la Ford Mondeo dans la cour de l'Évêché. Saint-Donat grimace. Pour son premier barbecue, il est gâté. Cadavre et pluie ne font pas bon ménage. Quelle drôle d'idée d'avoir quitté Paris, si c'est pour avoir des rincées au mois d'avril à Marseille ! Basile essaye de lui faire croire que, sur les bords de la Méditerranée, ce type d'intempéries est exceptionnel et annonciateur de très beau temps. Optimisme de Marseillais. Urteguy l'espère, dans quelques jours l'OM reçoit Lille et il n'est pas question que le match se joue sous un temps de Ch'tis.

Henri se déride aux propos du jeune lieutenant. Foutu pour foutu, il appelle Isabelle pour lui annoncer qu'il rentrera plus tard que prévu. Mais il y tient : ils maintiennent leur balade à moto. Isabelle connaît trop bien son mari. Elle ne veut même pas savoir les raisons de son retard. Leur confiance est infinie. Elle l'attendra devant une bonne série policière où les flics, ces héros, sont toujours à l'heure.

Il raccroche, souffle, chasse le blues qui l'envahit. Heureusement qu'Isabelle est là. Sans elle, après tout ce qu'ils ont traversé, il y a longtemps qu'il aurait quitté la boîte et serait parti vivre sur une île. Seul. Ou aurait même arrêté de vivre. Il lui doit tant.

Devant son bureau, la capitaine Lucie Clert, 37 ans, aussi brune que jolie, aussi sensuelle qu'acide, aussi caractérielle que pénible, aussi têtue et professionnelle que son père, cheveux défaits et yeux en pétard, ne lui laisse pas le temps de se poser.

– C'est qui, ces baltringues, Henri ?

Quand il a décrit Lucie à Martin Laval, Saint-Donat ne s'est pas trompé. Charmante et délicieuse.

– Tu as fait la connaissance de Laval ? Mon adjoint au « 36 ». Un excellent flic.

– À Paris peut-être. Mais, ici, il est *dégun*. Pourquoi ils ne sont pas encore là, les collègues de Melun ?

– Comment ça ?

– Putain, Henri, ils ont un braquage de fourgon avec la mort d'un témoin sur les bras. Ils identifient un lascar grâce à son ADN, ils devraient déjà être en planque devant son « dom' ». Mais pas du tout, ils nous demandent de faire le boulot à leur place. C'est quoi, ce bordel ?

Henri prend son temps, range son flingue, son brassard, et pose ses notes de la scène de crime sur son bureau, propre et bien rangé. Quelques rares photos sont affichées au mur. L'une représente le quai des Orfèvres à Paris et porte les dédicaces de ses anciens collègues du « 36 », une autre, la Honda Goldwing Aventure 1 800 cm³, couleur noire. Derrière son bureau, deux affiches de cinéma, *Ascenseur pour l'échafaud* et *Les Tontons flingueurs*, complètent la décoration. Des films d'un autre temps, révélateurs de son état d'esprit. Du sombre au farceur. Mais avec élégance, toujours.

Lucie est déjà entrée auparavant dans le bureau du commandant, mais ne s'en était jamais aperçue : il n'a pas affiché de photos personnelles. Seules quelques notes de service et numéros utiles finissent d'assurer le décor. Bureau neutre, ni triste, ni gai. Bureau de flic.

La voix d'Urteguy se fait entendre, les collègues chargés des constatations sur le véhicule brûlé l'ont identifié. Il se précipite chez Saint-Donat et sent tout de suite la drôle d'ambiance régnant entre la capitaine de la BRB et le commandant de la Crim'.

Lucie Clert piaffe. Pourquoi les collègues de Melun ne sont pas encore là ? Pourquoi la BRB de Marseille devrait se taper leur boulot ? Elle pose ses mains sur la table de travail d'Henri et se penche vers lui. Elle fait bouger le sous-main du commandant, dévoilant plusieurs photos et documents. Henri devient livide et lui hurle de ne pas y toucher. Il remet en place les clichés sous le rectangle de cuir. Son regard a changé. Il est devenu noir. Depuis huit mois qu'Urteguy fréquente le commandant, c'est la première fois qu'il le voit dans cet état. Le commandant reprend sa respiration.

– T'as quel âge exactement, Lucie ?

– Je vois pas le rapport.

– Un peu de lenteur vaut mieux que trop de précipitation.

Lucie, au bord de l'énervement, hésite entre l'envoyer bouler et modérer ses propos. Est-ce la présence d'Urteguy ou la réaction que le commandant vient d'avoir ? Elle choisit la deuxième option.

– J'ai 37 ans, Henri. Et tu sais ce que disait Corneille dans *Le Cid* : « *Aux âmes bien nées, la valeur n'attend pas le nombre des années.* »

– Moi, c'était ton père, mon CID.

L'ambiance se détend, Basile Urteguy pense qu'il peut intervenir.

– 37 piges. Tu les fais pas, la Vioque, j't'assure.

– Toi, la Freluque, c'est pas le moment !

Vieille habitude en PJ, trouver un surnom aux collègues. Il n'a pas fallu longtemps à Lucie Clert pour trouver celui du jeune lieutenant. Visage poupon, aspect juvénile et vanne facile, il s'est imposé de lui-même : freluquet. D'habitude orale en déformation argotique, « freluquet » est devenu « la Freluque », parfois même « lieutenant la Freluque ».

Basile Urteguy ne s'en offusque pas. Il n'est jamais le dernier pour se moquer des autres, surtout quand ils sont plus âgés que lui. Lucie Clert est devenue sa cible préférée. « La Vieille » quand il est gentil, « la Blèche » quand il veut faire le malin, et « Lilith » quand il fait semblant d'avoir des lettres. La première fois qu'il l'a appelée ainsi, Lucie s'est étonnée.

– Lilith, pourquoi ?

De ses grands yeux noirs, reflétant l'immensité de son impertinence, Basile a répondu en passant sa main dans ses cheveux longs et hirsutes.

– Un peu de culture, très chère : Lilith, c'est la femme de Lucifer.

Du fait des consonances de ses prénom et nom, Lucie Clert est habituée à entendre toutes sortes de jeux de mots relatifs à Lucifer. Celui-là a l'élégance d'être plus subtil. Le culot du jeune homme l'a immédiatement séduite.

À 29 ans, la Freluque traîne déjà une réputation de bon poulet. Rentré comme gardien de la paix dans la police, après quatre années à arpenter le bitume parisien, il a passé en interne le concours d'officier, qu'il a brillamment réussi. L'ascenseur social au ministère de l'Intérieur existe et il en est la preuve vivante. Après ses deux années de formation à l'Ensop, il a opté pour un poste à la DIPJ de Marseille, où son humour et son amour de l'OM en ont fait un élément apprécié de tous.

Et au charme duquel la terrible Lucie Clert n'est pas insensible, ce qui l'agace au plus haut point.

7

La tenue d'intervention d'Urteguy n'arrange pas les affaires de Lucie. Il porte encore son gilet tactique floqué « police judiciaire » et des traces de suie sur le visage. Même de retour d'une scène de crime, Basile apporte une lumière joyeuse. Elle se secoue, manquerait plus qu'elle le trouve beau. Elle connaît pourtant le dicton : « *No zob in job* », mais ne peut s'empêcher d'avoir une bouffée de désir au fond des reins. Et merde, pense-t-elle. D'autant qu'il reste insensible à ses propos agressifs.

– Henri, les collègues ont identifié la bagnole du barbecue. En grattant, ils ont récupéré le numéro de série. Renault Scenic, volée à la Soude, le 4 avril. Mercredi dernier. Y'a deux jours, quoi.

– C'est quoi, la Soude ?

– Une autre cité du sud. Entre les Baumettes et la Cayolle.

– Jolis cadres de vie.

– Je leur ai demandé de vérifier la vidéo-surveillance. On pourra peut-être la voir se faire voler.

– OK. On fait le point demain matin, 9 heures. Réunion ici.

Le commandant regarde Lucie. Il s'est aperçu de son trouble, qui le surprend, l'amuse et le rassure. Même une femme comme elle peut se retrouver muette devant un homme.

– Lucie, les collègues de Melun ne te demandent pas de faire leur boulot. Ils veulent juste une assistance. Quand t'arrives de Paname pour bosser à Marseille, c'est le minimum.

Henri reçoit un grognement en guise de réponse.

– Ensuite, c'est leur procédure, ils la gèrent comme ils veulent. Ils t'ont dit ce qu'ils voulaient exactement ?

– Une tombée à la dernière adresse connue de Hosni à la Cayolle.

Henri hoche la tête. Lucie s'apprête à sortir. Elle se retourne et lui confie.

– J'ai quand même envoyé la BRI* assurer une « reco** » et j'ai fait les vérifs. Dans la famille Hosni, y'a trois frangins avec des palmarès longs comme le bras, Khaled, Yassine et Bilal, tombés dans la même

_____

* BRI : brigade de recherche et d'intervention, appelée communément « brigade anti-gang ».

** « Reco » : raccourci policier de « reconnaissance ».

affaire de stups. Khaled, l'aîné, est au ballon, en provisoire aux Baumettes. Les deux autres sont sous « CJ* ».

– Quand tu commences, tu fais pas semblant.

– Je viens pas de Paname, mais je connais mon job par cœur. À Marseille, on craint *dégun*.

– Allez l'OM ! À jamais les premiers !

Urteguy n'a pas pu s'empêcher de rappeler sa présence. Il fait un clin d'œil à Henri et raccompagne Lucie. Saint-Donat l'entend échanger quelques mots dans le couloir avec la capitaine. Le jeune lieutenant provoque l'hilarité de Lucie. Quand son rire se calme, Henri perçoit ce qu'elle lui dit.

– Désolé, j'ai du boulot, la Freluque. Mais on remet ça plus tard. Promis.

Il ne sait pas ce qu'Urteguy a proposé à Lucie, mais il a un début de réponse à ses interrogations de fin d'après-midi macabre. Il est encore poulet, car il aime cette ambiance. Celle, feutrée et nocturne, de l'Évêché, où les pas résonnent dans les couloirs vides, où seuls quelques lumières de bureau, des cris, des invectives, laissent deviner que des flics bossent encore.

---

* CJ : contrôle judiciaire.

Bossent toujours. Surtout, il sait qu'il aime ces policiers aux caractères trempés, qui ne manquent ni d'énergie, ni d'abnégation, ni d'humour pour exécuter tous les jours avec passion leur métier, au point d'y passer leurs nuits.

Il prend son portable, envoie un message à Isabelle. « *Je plie, mon amour. Quitte tes flics de série, je rentre.* » Il attrape son casque et ses gants de motard. Son téléphone sonne, un texto en retour de sa femme. « *T'es le plus beau des vrais policiers. J't'attends la télé éteinte.* » Il sourit, fait sauter ses clefs dans sa main et s'apprête à partir, quand il se ravise. Retourne derrière son bureau, soulève son dessous en cuir et attrape une des photos que Lucie avait dérangées dans sa colère. Il la fixe quelques instants, la regarde tendrement. Et l'embrasse. Une larme aux yeux.

8

Marseille,
samedi 7 avril 2018.

Urteguy habite à deux pas de l'Évêché, place de Lenche. Douceur et couleurs avec vue sur le Vieux-Port. Terrasses de restaurants, parasols par tout temps, mouettes et goélands. N'était la vue sur la Bonne Mère, rien ne pourrait laisser penser que ce lieu se trouve dans une mégapole de presque un million d'habitants. Un peu plus de 890 000 pour être exact, mais à Marseille on ne chipote pas pour si peu. La place de Lenche ressemble plus à celle d'un petit village de Provence. D'ailleurs, à part les touristes, chacun connaît tout le monde. On se salue, on se hèle, on se paye le café et le pastis, on se moque et on vit ensemble, dans une harmonie de bonne humeur et de soleil.

Même levé à 8 h 50, Urteguy n'est pas en retard à la réunion prévu dix minutes plus tard à l'Évêché. Quatre cent trente-deux mètres exactement séparent son canapé-lit de son bureau à la Crim'. Il lui arrive de terminer sa toilette sous les douches de l'Évêché.

Tous les membres du groupe sont présents. Le commandant fait le point sur le « barbecue » de la veille. Les éléments sont minces. Un cadavre carbonisé, méconnaissable, découvert dans une voiture avec une balle dans la tête. Véhicule brûlé aux abords des Pennes-Mirabeau. Les constatations permettent de déterminer qu'il s'agissait d'une Renault Scenic, dérobée dans la nuit précédant sa découverte.

Les enquêteurs ont procédé à l'audition de la propriétaire, Mlle Oliveira Linda, demeurant à la Soude. La pauvre a pleuré quatre fois. Une première en apprenant le vol de sa voiture, qu'elle avait garée la veille sur son parking. Une deuxième, car ce vol l'empêchait d'accompagner ses deux enfants en bas âge à l'école. Une troisième quand elle a appris dans quel état se trouvait sa Renault Scenic de 458 000 km au compteur, et n'a pas pu refouler ses larmes une quatrième fois quand elle a appris ce que les enquêteurs avaient découvert à l'intérieur.

Persuadée depuis le départ de son concubin et père de ses deux enfants que la colère de Dieu et de tous ses saints s'était abattue sur elle, et que cette malédiction divine ne faisait qu'empirer depuis. Plus catholique que pratiquante, elle s'était quand même signée quatre fois, autant que ses pleurs, pour éloigner ce mauvais œil.

– On la raye de la liste des suspects. Elle n'a pas fourgué elle-même sa voiture aux mecs qui ont tué notre victime ! lâche Saint-Donat avant de demander à ses enquêteurs de poursuivre leurs investigations sur les circonstances et le lieu du vol.

– Vous oubliez rien, les gars. Le CSU*, la téléphonie, l'enquête de voisinage. Si on peut trouver un témoin qui a vu quelque chose.

Un soupir de protestation souligne cette dernière proposition. Urteguy s'esclaffe.

– On peut toujours rêver. Dans ces cités, personne ne cause aux flics. Trop peur de se retrouver dans le même état que la caisse de Linda Oliveira. Mais avec la grâce de Dieu, on ne sait jamais…

Leur priorité reste d'identifier le brûlé. Urteguy a un pote au labo, il le relance pour savoir si le Fnaeg aurait lâché un nom à partir de l'ADN prélevé sur le cadavre.

Saint-Donat demande enfin de vérifier les disparitions inquiétantes d'individus.

---

* CSU : Centre de supervision urbaine.

L'enquête fera un grand pas dès l'identification du macchabée. Il sera possible de connaître ses ennemis et ses amis, son emploi du temps et ses comptes en banque. Vérifier si quelqu'un avait une bonne raison de lui en vouloir au point de le faire brûler dans une vieille caisse volée.

– On croise les doigts pour que le Fnaeg nous crache son blaze, sinon on va se taper toutes les disparations depuis plusieurs mois sur toute la région avant d'envisager celles de la France entière.

Saint-Donat salue les enquêteurs, leur demande de finir la rédaction des procès-verbaux en cours et de mettre la procédure à jour, histoire qu'elle soit nickel pour la réunion de lundi matin dans le bureau du directeur interrégional.

– Après, vous y allez, les gars. Prenez des forces ce week-end, enfin, ce qu'il en reste, la semaine qui arrive va être rude.

9

Les fins d'après-midi à Marseille sont douces, surtout le samedi. Allongé sur son canapé, Urteguy rêvasse. Fenêtre ouverte, il écoute les bruits qui émanent de la place de Lenche. Une façon d'oublier un instant les saloperies sur lesquelles il bosse. Pieds nus sur la table, chemise ouverte, une bière dans la main, il essaye de se passionner pour le match de foot entre Guingamp et Dijon, qu'il regarde à la télé, sans le son. Quand l'OM ne joue pas, il ne trouve aucun intérêt à ces oppositions sportives et préfère la poésie outrancière des tenanciers aux commentaires superfétatoires des journalistes.

Son téléphone sonne. Il décroche avec nonchalance sans regarder le nom de l'appelant. Quand son interlocuteur se présente, il pose sa bouteille de bière sur la table. Et quand il lui rend compte de ce qu'il vient d'apprendre, il se redresse sur le canapé. Albert Lefret, son pote technicien du labo, a une réponse du Fnaeg concernant l'ADN du cadavre de la veille. En entendant l'identité de la victime, Urteguy s'étonne.

– T'es sûr ?

Basile ferme la fenêtre et note l'état civil que lui communique son pote. Il le remercie, relit ses notes plusieurs fois, épelle le nom qu'il vient d'écrire en se demandant ce que cela signifie, reprend son portable et compose un numéro.

Henri Saint-Donat sort de l'hôpital de la Timone. Il vient d'y passer deux heures. Son visage est triste et fermé. Son casque sous le bras, il s'apprête à enfourcher sa moto pour rentrer à La Ciotat. La sonnerie de son téléphone l'arrête. Contrairement à son jeune subordonné, il regarde le nom de l'appelant avant de prendre l'appel.

– Je t'écoute, Basile.

– A priori, on n'est pas sur un réglo classique. L'ADN relevé sur notre cadavre n'est pas celui d'un jeune con des quartiers nord. C'est celui d'une gonzesse.

– Une femme ?

– Oui. Et pas une toute jeune en plus.

Basile se rend compte qu'il dérape.

– Enfin, par rapport à moi. Parce que sinon elle est presque aussi jeune que toi, commandant.

– Envoie, Basile, de qui s'agit-il ?

– Nathalie Fournier, née le 23 août 1964 à Rungis.

Henri Saint-Donat blêmit, lui demande de répéter. Le lieutenant se moque de son chef. « Fournier » n'est pas un patronyme compliqué. Ils sont habitués à pire dans la police. À moins que ce ne soit un début précoce de surdité, à son âge, il devrait se méfier.

– Fournier, comme ça se prononce : F.O.U.R.N.I.E.R., comme le commandant Vincent Fournier dans *PJ*. Une vieille série policière que regardaient mes parents à la télé. C'est ta génération, ça, non ?

Saint-Donat ne s'était pas trompé, il avait bien entendu. Ses jambes tremblent. Entre ce qu'il vient de vivre à l'hôpital et ce qu'il vient d'apprendre, il est abasourdi. Il s'appuie sur sa moto, tente de mettre de l'ordre dans son esprit. Urteguy ne se rend pas compte de l'état d'Henri, il continue de lui lire la fiche Fnaeg.

– Elle avait un surnom original, Nathalie Fournier.

Il n'entend pas Henri murmurer en même temps que lui :

– La Carlton.

Urteguy poursuit.

– Comme le palace cannois. Original, non ?

Les interrogations déboulent en trombe et dans le désordre dans la tête d'Henri Saint-Donat. Comment croire que le morceau de charbon qu'il a vu hier soir dans le coffre de la Scenic calcinée soit celui de la sublime Nathalie Fournier ? Il essaye de reprendre le dessus, se secoue, s'interroge. Depuis combien de temps n'avait-il pas vu la Carlton ? Comment a-t-elle pu se mettre dans un tel pétrin ? Qu'est-ce qu'elle foutait à Marseille ? Comment une femme de sa trempe a pu se faire tuer de la sorte ? Dans quel guet-apens est-elle tombée ? Quel est le salopard qui lui a fait ça ?

– J'ai vérifié au TAJ*. Dis donc, que du braquage, propre, bien ficelé, sans dérapage. Elle a de jolis antécédents, la Carlton !

S'il savait, pense Saint-Donat nostalgique. S'il savait. Le plus beau palmarès de tout Paname.

---

* TAJ : Traitement des antécédents judiciaires.

10

Paris, mars 1998.

La grosse cylindrée remonte la rue de Rivoli. La pluie, menaçante en début de matinée, a abandonné l'idée de tomber sur Paris. Même si elle avait décidé le contraire, elle n'aurait pas dérangé le conducteur et le passager, confortablement installés sur leur deux-roues. Élégants et protégés dans leur combinaison, ils affichent tenue et casque similaires. Rien ne les perturbe. Pas même la sortie des employés des magasins de luxe de ce quartier historique au moment de la pause méridienne.

À hauteur du jardin des Tuileries, avec une coordination parfaite, ils se penchent à droite et tournent dans la rue de Castiglione. Ils se faufilent dans la circulation qui grossit, naviguent avec aisance au milieu de la foule. La moto remonte jusqu'à la place Vendôme, décor magistral au centre duquel la colonne éponyme rappelle la splendeur des victoires napoléoniennes. Les motards n'ont pas un regard pour ce mémorial guerrier, ils empruntent la contre-allée et remontent la place par sa droite. À aucun moment le conducteur ne pose son pied au sol. Il maîtrise parfaitement les 1 500 cm^3 et presque 400 kilos de son deux-roues.

Il sait parfaitement où il va.

Devant la bijouterie Van Cleef et Arpels, en face du ministère de la Justice.

Tout va très vite. Devant le sas de la joaillerie de luxe, le conducteur s'arrête. Pose ses deux pieds au sol. La moto stabilisée, le passager se dresse sur son siège, en descend et enlève son casque. Une chevelure longue, brune, ondulée, apparaît. La jeune femme est splendide. Fine, élancée, racée. Ses yeux d'un vert profond reflètent son rang de femme bien née et sa détermination. Le doute ne peut pas l'habiter. La vie ne lui refuse rien.

Elle descend la fermeture Éclair de sa combinaison, laissant plus deviner qu'apercevoir sa jolie paire de seins, secoue ses cheveux pour qu'ils retrouvent leur volume et affiche son magnifique sourire. Elle envoie un baiser à son chauffeur, se retourne, vive et radieuse, et sonne au sas d'entrée de la bijouterie.

Devant tant d'assurance naturelle, la porte lui est immédiatement déverrouillée.

À l'intérieur de la joaillerie, elle ouvre l'échancrure de sa combinaison, y glisse sa main droite et en sort un pistolet Smith & Wesson semi-automatique, de calibre 22. Petite arme de douze centimètres et de cent soixante-dix grammes, loin d'une kalachnikov aux dimensions plus imposantes, mais aux effets tout aussi dissuasifs.

Rosalie Duchemin, employée légèrement enrobée de 20 ans, perd son sourire obligé. Les idées les plus farfelues lui traversent l'esprit. Elle n'ose croire qu'une femme si belle est en train de la braquer. Elle cherche une caméra cachée, en vogue avec l'émission « Surprise sur prise » qui cartonne à la télé. Elle espère voir arriver Catherine Deneuve ou Isabelle Adjani, son lieu de travail s'y prête, même si, question de génération, elle préférerait voir surgir Vanessa Paradis. Mais, à part une grosse moto à l'extérieur, elle ne voit personne tenir une caméra, encore moins de célébrité franchir la porte de la bijouterie. Seule une belle inconnue la menaçant avec un pistolet qui n'a pas l'air de vouloir la filmer.

Elle regrette d'avoir refusé la proposition de son patron, Edmond Peeters, d'aller déjeuner avant lui. Elle a préféré faire bonne impression, en lui laissant la priorité.

C'est vrai aussi qu'elle doit surveiller sa ligne, si elle veut être sûre de rentrer dans les normes de l'entreprise qui l'emploie. Elle se met à pleurer. À quoi bon tout ce cirque relatif à son hygiène alimentaire et à sa silhouette, si c'est pour se retrouver entre midi et 14 heures menacée par une femme armée ?

11

La braqueuse n'hésite pas à menacer Rosalie Duchemin en lui glissant son flingue sous le nez. Elle lui tend un sac en toile.

– Deux minutes pour le remplir.

Le ton et l'arme employés ne laissent pas le choix à la vendeuse. Elle tremble de tous ses membres, tente d'ouvrir tiroirs et présentoirs. La braqueuse jette un coup d'œil à l'extérieur, où l'attend son complice sur la moto. Elle vérifie les caméras de surveillance fixées entre murs et plafond, se protège de leur champ. S'énerve, tape violemment sur les présentoirs.

Elle ne voit pas arriver Edmond Peeters. Il a mangé plus rapidement que prévu. À 55 ans, lui aussi doit pouvoir rentrer dans son costume de directeur de la bijouterie. Dans ce type d'établissement, l'élégance fine est de mise. Et depuis six mois qu'il est en poste, il a grossi. Bonne bouffe et responsabilités ne font pas bon ménage. Sans parler de sa peur des braquages. Dans sa dernière affectation, il en a connu trois, alors la direction de Van Cleef et Arpels l'a nommé responsable de la boutique place Vendôme, censée être plus protégée contre ce genre d'agressions. Une forme de remerciements de la direction, en compensation du préjudice subi. Mais il a encore en mémoire le fusil à crosse et canon sciés que le précédent braqueur avait posé sur sa tête et il s'est promis de ne plus jamais connaître ça.

Depuis plus d'un an, il a acheté un fusil à pompe Mossberg 500 calibre 12 et s'est inscrit dans un club de tir. Ce n'est pas interdit. Ce qui l'est en revanche, c'est de l'avoir caché dans la réserve de la bijouterie. Si elle l'avait su, la direction Van Cleef et Arpels ne l'aurait pas toléré. Pas question de transformer sa bijouterie à la réputation si parfaite en saloon de cow-boys.

Edmond n'a pas évacué ses peurs passées. Quand il voit sur la vidéosurveillance sa jeune vendeuse trembler comme une feuille devant un pistolet, sans hésitation, il récupère son arme, se précipite dans la boutique et, sans se demander si sa puissance de feu est proportionnelle à celle du braqueur, il lui tire dans le dos, sans sommation. La jeune femme s'écroule et tourne un regard incrédule vers la porte, tentant désespérément de voir son complice sur la moto. Pour lui sourire. Une dernière fois.

La détonation surprend Rosalie, qui se met à hurler. À l'extérieur, les pigeons s'envolent et le casque du pilote se retourne. Derrière sa vitre de protection, d'autres yeux remplis du même doute essayent de voir à travers le sas de la bijouterie. Le pilote abaisse la béquille de la moto pour en descendre.

12

À l'autre bout de la place, l'inspecteur de police Henri Saint-Donat se retourne. Un bouquet de fleurs à la main, pendant la pause déjeuner il vient voir son amoureuse, Isabelle, vendeuse chez Dior. L'envol des pigeons et le silence qui suit lui provoquent un sentiment bizarre. Il se passe quelque chose d'étrange devant Van Cleef et Arpels. Un motard descend d'une grosse cylindrée, casque vissé sur la tête, et se dirige vers le sas de la bijouterie.

Henri s'approche. Il pose sa main sous sa veste et se rassure en sentant la poignée de son Manurhin 357 magnum. De l'autre, tout en tenant serré contre lui son bouquet de fleurs, il s'assure que son brassard fluo « police » est toujours glissé dans la poche de son pantalon.

Devant lui les événements s'accélèrent. Devant le sas de la joaillerie, le motard recule en hurlant. Le son de sa voix n'est pas audible, mais Henri croit entendre : « Vous l'avez tuée… » La porte de la bijouterie s'ouvre. Un homme en sort, la cinquantaine bedonnante, en costume, chemise hors du pantalon et cravate défaite, l'air fou. Un fusil à pompe à bout de bras, il oblige le pilote à lever les mains.

Henri reste discret, mais accélère le pas. Il longe les murs, enfile son brassard et sort son arme, essayant de ne perdre aucune miette de la scène qui se déroule. Il croise des badauds, les force à se mettre à l'abri et leur demande d'appeler le 17. Ils l'interrogent, lui demandent si c'est pour le tournage d'un film. Tout ceci est si excitant.

L'homme porteur du fusil à pompe crie au motard de se coucher par terre, bras écartés devant lui. Sous la colère, son accent belge est encore plus prononcé. Henri ne comprend toujours pas ce qui se passe. Un homme à la prononciation bizarre sort armé d'une bijouterie et menace un pilote casqué. Où est le voyou ?

Le motard pose un genou à terre, puis le deuxième. Quand le bijoutier le met en joue et enclenche la pompe de son fusil, il n'hésite pas. Sa main cache un petit pistolet Smith et Wesson de calibre 22 similaire à celui de sa complice. Tout en roulant sur le côté, il tire sur l'homme qui s'apprêtait à l'abattre. Touché au ventre, Edmond Peeters tombe au sol, mais trouve la force d'appuyer sur sa queue de détente. La balle frôle le bras droit du motard.

Henri ne se pose plus de questions, il intervient, son 357 magnum à la main, son bouquet de fleurs dans l'autre, et hurle la première chose qui lui passe par l'esprit :

– Cessez le feu !

Conscient que ces souvenirs de service militaire ne seront pas suffisants, il ajoute :

– Police ! Jetez vos armes !

Le canon de son revolver fleuri menace tour à tour le motard et l'homme costumé au sol. Chacun de son côté se tord de douleur. Du pied, il écarte leurs armes. Les sirènes des voitures de secours annoncent leur arrivée imminente.

Des personnes accourent, portent de l'aide à l'homme costumé. Ils ont reconnu le nouveau directeur de la succursale Van Cleef et Arpels. Henri se penche sur le motard, il souffre du bras. Il lui retire son casque.

Son visage apparaît. Entre 25 et 30 ans, cheveux mi-longs, bruns, légèrement ondulés, yeux clairs, presque limpides, visage où se reflète autant de caractère que de beauté. Le motard est une femme. Elle essaye de sourire au flic qui vient d'intervenir, des fleurs à la main. Mais le cœur n'y est plus. Elle essaye de voir ce qui se passe à l'intérieur de la bijouterie.

– Il l'a tuée, hein ? Il a tué Elaia, ce gros con ?

Henri a peur de comprendre. Un équipage police secours vient d'arriver. Il lui confie la jeune femme et se rend à l'intérieur de la bijouterie, où l'attend une scène de désolation. Dans du verre brisé, entourée de bijoux et de montres, une jeune femme brune, très belle, en combinaison de motard, gît dans une mare de sang, le regard figé dans un sourire tourné vers la porte d'entrée. De l'autre côté des présentoirs, Henri entend des reniflements. Rosalie Duchemin en pleurs est incapable de bouger. Il l'aide à se relever au moment où entrent les pompiers.

Il n'y a plus rien à faire pour la braqueuse étendue au sol. Henri les laisse s'occuper de l'employée. Il ressort et cherche la motarde. Assise sur un muret, elle se fait soigner. Elle n'a pas besoin de lui poser de nouveau la question. Son regard suffit. La jeune femme comprend et ne fait rien pour empêcher ses larmes de couler.

Henri s'assoit à côté d'elle, ses fleurs posées sur les genoux. Et lui prend la main. La pilote est surprise, il est quand même policier et elle vient de participer à un braquage. Flic, voyou, Henri ne voit qu'une femme qui souffre, de la pire des douleurs.

Celle d'avoir perdu une âme chère. Il lui tend un mouchoir.

– C'était qui ?

Son regard embué ne lui enlève pas son air effronté.

– Elaia, la femme de ma vie. D'habitude c'est moi qui braque. Mais là, elle a tenu à le faire elle-même. Je suis enceinte.

Henri ne tique pas devant cette succession d'informations. Il accentue sa pression sur sa main. Il ne sait pas quoi dire, juste l'assurer d'une présence rassurante. Elle laisse sa tête tomber sur son épaule. Ses larmes coulent à flots, sans retenue. Elle pleure son amour, pleure la vie sans elle et cet enfant qu'elle ne verra pas grandir. Henri la laisse épancher sa peine, avant, tout en douceur, de lui demander son nom.

– Nathalie Fournier, monsieur le flic. Et toi ?

– Inspecteur Saint-Donat, du « 36 ». À la Crim'. J'étais là par hasard.

– Le hasard fait bien les choses.

– Pas toujours.

La foule se masse devant la bijouterie. Des hommes en uniforme tendent une rubalise, délimitent une zone protégée. Des policiers en civil arrivent, le commissaire de la BRB prend en main la direction des opérations. Henri lui explique ce qu'il a vu.

Tout en étudiant la scène de crime et ses protagonistes, le supérieur hoche la tête et lui demande de rester disponible pour l'enquête. Au moment où les flics se dirigent vers Nathalie, il les prévient :

– Doucement, les gars. Elle est enceinte.

Il l'aide à se lever et, sans tenir compte des regards circonspects de ses collègues, il la serre contre lui.

– N'oublie pas. Vous le vouliez toutes les deux.

La jeune femme se laisse appréhender par les policiers de la BRB, les yeux remplis de larmes et de doutes. En s'éloignant, elle ne parle pas, mais articule « merci » pour qu'il comprenne.

De l'autre côté de la zone de protection, il aperçoit Isabelle, étonnée de le trouver là. Malgré la lourdeur de son pas, il se hâte de la rejoindre. Il la serre si fort qu'elle comprend tous les messages. Pour l'instant surtout, ne lui poser aucune question. Rien d'autre que sa présence. Elle le connaît déjà trop pour savoir que plus tard, quand la pression sera redescendue, il ne lui cachera rien de ce qu'il vient de vivre.

Quand il s'écarte d'elle, il prend conscience qu'il a toujours son bouquet de fleurs à la main. Abîmé, mais pas fané. Avec un sourire lointain, il le lui offre.

13

Montereau-Fault-Yonne,
lundi 9 avril 2018, 5 h 45.

Le commandant Laval remonte son col. Les matins sont humides sur les bords de l'Yonne, encore plus les lendemains de week-end où il est de permanence. Celle-ci se termine le lundi matin à 8 heures, mais on l'a réveillé à 5 heures pour l'aviser de la découverte d'un noyé dans une écluse entre Montereau et Pont-sur-Yonne, dans les temps de son tour de perm'.

Quand il arrive sur place, il consulte sa montre : 5 h 45. Il pense au lieutenant Pierre Forest et au brigadier Joseph Labord, qu'il a désignés pour se rendre à Marseille. Ils ont dû se lever à 3 heures pour arriver en fin de matinée dans la cité phocéenne. En se levant à 5 heures, il est veinard. Il a grappillé deux heures de sommeil sur eux.

Le commandant n'est pas mécontent de lui. À son âge, même réveillé si tôt, il est encore réactif. Mettre quarante-cinq minutes pour avaler un café, s'habiller et arriver sur les lieux, il s'est bien démerdé. Lors de son réveil téléphonique, il a vite compris pourquoi les policiers de Montereau ne traitaient pas eux-mêmes cette affaire de noyé. Ils ont avisé le service départemental de nuit que le macchabée avait été retrouvé enroulé dans une bâche, entouré avec de la corde et du scotch. Après avis au procureur de la République, le commandant en charge du SDN* a alerté l'état-major de la DRPJ de Versailles. Le collègue lui a fait savoir que, dans ces conditions de découverte, le suicide comme l'accident paraissaient peu probables, à moins d'avoir un grand sens de l'imagination ou l'envie de se débarrasser d'un dossier encombrant.

Après vingt ans à la Crim' et malgré son âge qui avance, Laval ne passerait pas à côté d'un « bel homicide », surtout s'il paraît mystérieux et l'oblige à se lever dès potron-minet. Quel que soit le temps. Et ce matin, il fait vraiment froid. De la buée sort de sa bouche. De la vapeur monte de l'eau de l'Yonne. De la fumée sort de l'échappement de la péniche.

---

* SDN : service départemental de nuit, assurant avec plusieurs officiers la couverture judiciaire de tous les événements se déroulant la nuit sur le département.

C'est un marinier qui a découvert le corps. Alors qu'il venait de franchir avec sa péniche la première porte de l'écluse et que l'eau commençait à monter, il a remarqué en amont une bâche en plastique noire. Il a eu peur qu'elle soit aspirée par les turbines, il a hurlé de stopper les machineries.

En la dégageant, il s'est aperçu qu'elle entourait quelque chose. Dans l'Yonne, le batelier a déjà trouvé de tout et du n'importe quoi. Des voitures, des scooters, des bouteilles et même un casque sèche-cheveux de coiffeur. Pas un jouet pour petites filles rêvant de devenir coiffeuses, un outil de professionnel. S'il lui est arrivé de remonter des corps, noyés par suicide ou chute accidentelle, c'était la première fois qu'il remontait un macchabée ligoté dans une bâche, ficelé façon rôti.

Moins confronté à la violence que les flics, il se fait pourtant la même réflexion qu'eux. L'être humain est capable du pire pour se débarrasser de son prochain. Ça ne l'a pas rassuré sur la nature humaine et l'a conforté dans son choix de vivre en solitaire sur sa péniche.

Avec l'éclusier, ils ont remonté la bâche sur la rive. Ils ont coupé la corde gorgée d'eau, découpé le scotch et le plastique. L'odeur pestilentielle les a obligés à reprendre leur respiration avant de se pencher et de découvrir le corps d'un homme, complètement nu. L'eau n'avait pas terminé son œuvre de putréfaction. Le cadavre avait commencé à gonfler, mais les traits du visage étaient encore nets. L'homme était âgé de 25 ans environ, de corpulence normale, sans réel signe distinctif, à part deux traces sur le torse.

Pas besoin d'être médecin légiste pour comprendre qu'il s'agissait d'impacts de balles. Ils ont composé le 17. La roue judiciaire s'est mise en marche, pour finalement saisir le commandant Laval de permanence à la PJ. Le meurtre est évident. Le professionnalisme des auteurs aussi.

Martin écoute les explications du batelier. Regarde avec attention le cadavre de l'homme. Son visage ressemble à celui de tous ces jeunes qu'il a arrêtés au cours de sa carrière, entre 18 et 25 ans, mince, des tatouages disséminés sur le corps.

Il hoche la tête. Cela lui plaît. Pas de fringue sur le cadavre, une bâche noire comme il en existe des centaines, des cordes gorgées d'eau. Voilà une enquête qui s'annonce sans élément.

La difficulté l'excite. La curiosité est son moteur. Il veut comprendre et mettre un nom sur son noyé du matin.

14

Après le silence du week-end, l'Évêché se remplit de bruits. Contraste saisissant entre le calme du dimanche et la foire du lundi matin, où chacun retrouve ses collègues et ses manies du quotidien. Effervescence des débuts de semaine, les portes s'ouvrent, les baisers claquent. Façon banale de se dire bonjour à Marseille. Les blagues fusent sur la façon dont les uns ont passé le week-end, les vannes des autres en retour ne se font pas attendre, le tout au son chantant de cet accent du Sud, capable d'enjoliver le plus vulgaire des propos.

La cour trop petite a déjà atteint son seuil maximal de voitures, quelques rares deux-roues arrivent encore à s'y glisser. Depuis son affectation à Marseille, la Goldwing 1 800 cm^3 d'Henri Saint-Donat est repérée. Il n'a plus besoin de s'arrêter à la barrière, même lorsque le parking est complet. Tous savent que cette limousine à deux roues est celle d'un haut gradé de la PJ. Et Saint-Donat, malgré la taille de sa bécane, trouve toujours un endroit où la stationner.

Descendu de moto, il regarde sa montre. Malgré ses efforts, il n'arrive jamais à être à l'heure. Plus que tout le matin, il aime rester glissé au fond de son lit lové contre Isabelle et attendre le moment où elle se lève, pour prendre le petit-déjeuner avec elle. Le directeur ne manquera pas de le moquer pour ses retards répétés. Mais les quelques instants supplémentaires collés à l'amour de sa vie valent bien le risque d'une pique directoriale.

Il se précipite et accède au premier étage, siège de la PJ. La porte s'ouvre sur le large couloir et sur la présence de ses collègues, commissaires, commandants et capitaines, qui ne sont pas encore entrés dans le bureau du directeur. Lucie Clert le voit arriver essoufflé.

– Y avait match hier soir. Il ne nous a pas encore fait rentrer.

Henri comprend. À 59 ans, le directeur interrégional de la police judiciaire, Francis Larrivée, n'est pas un inconnu dans la police. De Lille à Lyon, sans oublier Toulouse, Montpellier ou Bordeaux, depuis trente-cinq ans qu'il est entré dans la police au grade de commissaire, avant d'atteindre celui de contrôleur général, il a traîné son flingue et son flair légendaire dans les brigades prestigieuses de nombreux services de police judiciaire de France.

Sa grande taille et sa moustache mousquetaire parachèvent sa réputation. Francis Larrivée est respecté et réputé pour ses deux passions.

La police d'abord, dont il a une connaissance encyclopédique et pour laquelle il ne compte jamais ses heures. Les policiers qu'il dirige savent qu'il arrive tous les matins à une heure où eux envisagent à peine de se lever. Et commence sa journée par la lecture de toutes les notes, tous les messages, toutes les synthèses, rédigés au cours de la nuit écoulée, relatifs aux événements qui ont eu lieu sur sa zone de compétence, s'étendant de Menton à Perpignan. Et il les retient tous. Relevant l'affaire qui intrigue, le détail qui choque et la faute d'orthographe qui chagrine.

Le sport ensuite, dont il a une gourmandise insatiable, même si sa pratique reste modeste et se limite à la marche à pied du week-end sur les plages du Prado, mais qu'il compense par une lecture assidue des magazines sportifs. Il lui est impensable de commencer une journée sans avoir lu *L'Équipe*, publicités et mentions légales incluses. Surtout les lendemains de match de football où l'OM a joué et gagné.

Et le match de la veille s'est bien passé, puisque le duel des olympiques a tourné court. Son équipe de foot de prédilection, Marseille, a gagné contre son équipe de désolation, Lyon, et avec la manière : les Phocéens en ont collé quatre aux Gones. Il s'autorise donc douze minutes de retard, et reste très souriant quand il convie les cadres de sa direction à entrer dans son bureau.

La grand-messe peut enfin commencer selon un ordre bien établi. Les directeurs des services extérieurs, Montpellier et Nice, égrènent les affaires dont leurs services sont saisis. Litanie des pires turpitudes commises au cours de la semaine écoulée sur les bords de la Méditerranée. Un braquage de banque à Menton, l'homicide d'une héritière à Nice, un cumulard de mandats électifs dans un village à côté de Montpellier, sans oublier l'antenne de police judiciaire de Perpignan, qui vient de mener à bien le démantèlement d'un important trafic de cocaïne entre Empuriabrava (lieu de villégiature espagnol, célèbre pour ses canaux, ses bars à putes et ses voyous) et l'agglomération grenobloise.

Vient ensuite le tour des services internes à Marseille. Le commissaire de la BRB laisse Lucie Clert présenter le dossier parisien. Sa synthèse est sans fioritures, directe.

– Un braquage de fourgon le 26 mars, cinq individus gantés, encagoulés et enfouraillés comme des porte-avions, lance-roquettes et kalachnikovs. C'est propre, bien fait, du travail de pro. Pas de coup de feu, pas de victime, tout à l'intimidation et ça marche. Ils se cassent avec un million d'euros en petites coupures à bord de fausses bagnoles de flics. Vingt-cinq kilomètres plus loin, petit parking discret, ils ont deux voitures relais, ils posent les premières, changent de caisses, et là, le grain de sable : une 307 Peugeot conduite par une dame âgée passe, d'après les témoins elle ralentit devant le parking et se fait « rafaler » par un des braqueurs. Panique chez les voyous. Ils s'engueulent entre eux. L'un d'eux hurle. Les autres chargent comme ils peuvent le tireur dans une bagnole et ils s'arrachent.

Le directeur, pourtant habitué au langage fleuri de Lucie et aux tribulations étonnantes des voyous, est suspendu à ses lèvres.

– Les collègues de l'antenne PJ de Melun de la DRPJ de Versailles sont saisis de toute cette merde. Sur les « constates* », ils découvrent plusieurs étuis de 7,62 qu'ils font analyser. Jackpot, y'a un ADN qui

* Constates : raccourci policier, signifiant « constatations ».

cause : Yassine Hosni, 22 piges, un minot de la Cayolle. J'ai eu les Parigots, ils débaroulent dans la matinée. La BRI est en planque devant le domicile familial. Pour l'instant ça bouge pas.

Le directeur, dubitatif, pense tout haut.

– Qu'est-ce qu'un môme de 22 ans fait sur un braquage de cette envergure à Paris ? Il n'y a pas beaucoup d'équipes de voyous en France capables de réussir un tel coup.

– Ce qui est étonnant aussi, monsieur le directeur, c'est le flingage qui suit. Ça fait amateur.

Francis Larrivée hoche la tête. Cet amateurisme a provoqué la mort d'une femme. Il a du mal à le supporter. Il demande à Lucie de le tenir au courant de l'arrivée des Parisiens. Il veut les rencontrer avant l'interpellation de Yassine Hosni. Bien comprendre tous les tenants et aboutissants de cette affaire. Il se tourne enfin vers Saint-Donat.

– Alors, la victime du barbecue a été identifiée, Henri ?

– Tout à fait.

– Nathalie Fournier, c'est ça ?

– La Carlton, oui monsieur.

Lucie, étonnée, se tourne vers Saint-Donat.

– Tu connais la victime ?

– Une vieille histoire.

– La « Carlton », pourquoi ?

Le directeur se charge de la réponse.

– Faut revoir vos classiques, capitaine. Votre père l'a forcément connue, la Carlton.

– On se dit pas tout non plus, avec mon père.

– La « Carlton » parce qu'elle passait sa vie dans les palaces. Avec une prédilection pour celui de Cannes. Aussi belle que dangereuse. Sachant jouer du flingue et de son physique. Un peu comme son illustre prédécesseur : la Dalton. La reine des braqueuses, autre chose que votre minot de la Cayolle, croyez-moi.

Francis Larrivée se redresse sur son fauteuil. Comme Saint-Donat, il se pose la question. Comment la Carlton a pu finir, façon rôtissoire, dans le coffre d'une bagnole, cramée comme un vulgaire petit trafiquant de stups des cités de Marseille ? Si, comme Nathalie Fournier, ces jeunes voyous ont choisi d'être hors-la-loi, à part ça tout les oppose : la génération, les méthodes, la culture. Et l'élégance.

Henri hoche la tête, sourire nostalgique. Malgré ses antécédents chargés, elle ne manquait jamais de classe, la Carlton.

15

Paris, quai des Orfèvres,
juillet 1998.

L'inspecteur Henri Saint-Donat descend les marches du « 36 » en prenant son temps. Il aime humer l'ambiance qui règne ici. Il pense à tous ces flics qui ont gravi cet escalier en rage ou en liesse, en fonction de l'avancée de l'affaire qu'ils traitaient. Il revoit aussi les malfaiteurs l'ayant monté l'air inquiet ou furieux de se retrouver entre ces murs, aussi mythiques que mystérieux, d'où il leur était impossible de s'échapper. Et où tant de rumeurs couraient.

Treize ans déjà, depuis sa sortie de l'École des inspecteurs de la police nationale, qu'il est en poste à la brigade criminelle du 36, quai des Orfèvres et il ne s'en lasse pas. L'accueil vient de le contacter pour lui indiquer qu'une personne l'attendait à l'entrée. Henri n'a pas de rendez-vous prévu, ses dossiers sont à jour, il est étonné de cette visite.

Quand il sort, il la reconnaît tout de suite. Ses cheveux ont poussé, son visage semble fatigué, mais la détermination dans ses yeux splendides est la même. Nathalie Fournier. La braqueuse à moto de la place Vendôme. Il hésite, mais Nathalie aussi l'a vu. Ils se regardent, se sourient, se rapprochent. Nathalie ouvre ses bras, laissant apparaître son ventre rond.

Henri l'enserre tendrement. Des collègues de la Crim' sortent et le reconnaissent. Le voyant enlacer une femme enceinte qui n'est pas la sienne, les quolibets et moqueries fusent. Saint-Donat n'en a cure.

– Tu l'as gardé ?

– J'ai déjà perdu la mère, je n'allais pas perdre notre bébé, l'enfant de l'amour.

Les questions se bousculent dans la tête d'Henri. Il ne sait pas par quoi commencer. Nathalie le sort de cette difficulté et l'invite à déjeuner. Sans attendre sa réponse, elle hèle un taxi et l'encourage à monter. Difficile de refuser. Henri la suit en souriant. Nathalie lance au chauffeur :

– Hôtel Crillon, les Ambassadeurs, place de la Concorde.

– Sortir du « 36 » pour aller dans un palace. Vous avez quelque chose à fêter, vous !

Nathalie va droit au but.

– La vie.

Le commandant regarde le flot de voitures et de piétons qui grouillent. Le taxi ralentit et s'immobilise dans un embouteillage. Henri lance un regard interrogateur à Nathalie et fait semblant de tenir un guidon, mimant l'accélération de la main droite sur la poignée. Nathalie lui répond sur le même mode, elle désigne son ventre qui grossit et fait semblant de bercer un enfant dans ses bras. Henri lui fait comprendre que c'est plus prudent ainsi. Leur chanson de gestes continue jusque devant le Crillon, où un concierge en tenue vient leur ouvrir la porte. Les deux se regardent et lèvent le pouce en même temps et éclatent de rire.

Le déjeuner est à la hauteur du lieu de prestige où ils se trouvent. Ils se régalent avec des plats aux noms aussi évocateurs que charmants. Prudents sur leur consommation d'alcool, ils s'autorisent à goûter un grand cru de gevrey-chambertin, « Mes Cinq Terroirs ». L'ambiance est douce, feutrée, presque sucrée. Elle appelle aux confidences.

Nathalie raconte ses quelques mois de détention. Après sa garde à vue pour le vol à main armée commis avec Elaia Da Silva, le juge d'instruction saisi du dossier l'a placée en détention provisoire à la maison d'arrêt de Versailles, connue pour avoir un quartier réservé aux femmes. Au bout de cinq mois, ses avocats ont obtenu une libération avec un placement sous contrôle judiciaire strict. Deux aspects ont plaidé pour elle. L'enfant qu'elle porte et la réaction disproportionnée du bijoutier belge au moment du braquage, assez éloignée pénalement de la qualification légale de la légitime défense. Pour autant, elle reste mise en examen pour vol à main armée et devra répondre de ses actes devant une cour d'assises.

Elle lui raconte surtout comment, quand elle a rencontré pour la première fois Elaia Da Silva Goncalves, cette Méditerranéenne magnifique, elle n'a plus jamais douté de sa sexualité et a su qu'elle était la femme de sa vie, aimant autant le vent, le soleil, la moto et le luxe qu'elle. Leur amour a été aussi violent que leurs envies. Elles devaient vivre vite, à fond, ensemble.

– On n'a besoin de rien d'autre dans la vie pour être heureux.

– D'un enfant, peut-être ?

Le visage de Nathalie se fait grave. Elle pose ses mains sur son ventre et le caresse avec tendresse. Le sourire lui revient, en même temps que le bébé se manifeste,

créant de drôles de bosses sur le ventre de
sa mère.

– Fille ou garçon ?

Nathalie ne sait pas et s'en fout. Quand
on est une femme comme elle, on vit dans
l'instant. Cet enfant est source de joie.
Qu'importe son sexe, ses origines, son père
biologique, elle veut juste profiter du bonheur de sa présence. Henri est totalement
d'accord avec cette femme que pourtant
tout oppose à lui.

– T'as pensé à des prénoms ?

– Elaia, pour une fille, c'est évident. Pour
un garçon ? J'en sais rien.

– T'as quand même cinquante pour cent
de chances...

Henri la trouve belle, très belle même.
Elle dégage quelque chose de spécial, un
magnétisme, une présence différente. Une
force profonde émane d'elle. Un mélange
subtil d'effronterie et d'élégance. Il prend
conscience qu'il ne la connaît pas. Il l'a
croisée dans des circonstances particulières et la rencontre aujourd'hui pour la
seconde fois. Pourtant leur connivence,
leur complicité coulent de source. Une
évidence. Comme s'ils se fréquentaient
depuis des années. Il regarde son verre de
gevrey-chambertin. Il devrait arrêter. Le

bourgogne a des effets inattendus sur ses pensées.

– Et toi, tu ne m'as pas dit. T'es papa ?

Le visage d'Henri s'illumine. Il hoche la tête.

– Fille ou garçon ?

– Un petit garçon de 3 ans.

– Son prénom ?

Nouveau immense sourire d'Henri.

– Octave.

– C'est original comme prénom, Octave. Mais beau. Tu l'élèves tout seul ?

Henri est surpris par la question.

– Les flics, généralement, vous avez des vies compliquées... assez dissolues même. Et quand on est beau garçon comme toi, les tentations sont nombreuses.

– Mauvaise pioche. Je suis un peu vieux jeu, tu sais, tendance romantique. Il n'y a rien de plus beau que de vieillir avec la même femme.

Nathalie se lève en se tenant le ventre et l'embrasse.

– Fais attention à lui. Et à la mère. Et ne change rien. Le romantisme te va très bien.

Il est déjà tard quand Henri reprend le chemin du « 36 ». Ils ne peuvent plus s'entendre quand il se retourne une dernière fois. Il porte deux doigts devant ses yeux, qu'il tend ensuite vers Nathalie, comme une façon de lui faire comprendre qu'il aura toujours une attention particulière sur elle. Nathalie communique sur le même mode, elle désigne son ventre rond et porte son index devant sa bouche, son pouce devant son oreille, façon téléphone. Elle ne le laissera pas sans nouvelles.

16

Marseille,
lundi 9 avril 2018, 10 heures.

– Saint-Donat ? Vous rêvez ou quoi ?

La voix de baryton de Francis Larrivée réveille Henri. Les rayons du soleil caressent son visage. Il est à peine 10 heures, mais il règne déjà une forte chaleur dans le bureau du directeur. Henri s'est abandonné à ses souvenirs. Une sombre histoire d'escroqueries sur fond de taxe fiscale a eu raison de sa concentration et provoqué sa somnolence. Il était au Crillon en train de déguster un turbot rôti en face de celle qui n'était pas encore la « Carlton ». Mais qui commen-çait à écrire son histoire, parce qu'elle avait choisi la voie de la voyoucratie ; pas pour être femme de voyou, mais pour être à leur tête ; totalement libre, et assumer avec insolence tous ses choix, de femme, de mère, de sexualité et de société.

Contrairement à sa promesse, elle ne l'avait pas contacté pour lui annoncer la naissance de sa fille ou de son fils. Il avait suivi ses exploits, relatés dans les journaux ou par ses camarades de la BRB, courant derrière celle qu'ils avaient enfin surnommée la « Carlton » pour sa capacité à commettre des braquages d'envergure avec des malfaiteurs de premier plan. La légende, son directeur vient de le rappeler, raconte qu'elle fêtait chacun de ses méfaits dans des palaces, celui de Cannes ayant sa préférence.

Les flics ont souvent cette forme d'admiration irrationnelle pour ces voyous capables de les faire courir, sans jamais ou rarement se faire arrêter, et n'hésitent pas à les affubler de surnoms plus ou moins flatteurs. La Carlton faisait partie de cette catégorie et était à elle seule un oxymore policier : une grande dame du banditisme.

– Et si les deux affaires avaient un lien ?

Henri a lâché la question comme ça, sans savoir pourquoi. Il a coupé la parole au chef de la financière, dont les propos se perdent dans sa barbe, et qui en a marre que ses affaires de taxes ne rapportent pas autant d'attention que celles d'homicides ou de braquages.

– La taxe fiscale et votre affaire de barbecue, Henri ? Vous plaisantez ?

– Je pensais plus à l'affaire du braquage meurtrier à Melun et à l'homicide de la Carlton.

Un brouhaha se fait entendre. Les participants à la réunion manifestent leur mécontentement. Quel lien faire entre l'ADN d'un voyou marseillais relevé sur un braquage parisien et le meurtre façon « barbecue » de Nathalie Fournier ? Certains persiflent, la douleur d'avoir perdu une ancienne connaissance fait dire n'importe quoi à Saint-Donat. D'autres grognent, les vieilles amours de l'ancien du « 36 » les fatiguent. Lucie se tourne vers Henri, ses yeux en disent long sur ce qu'elle pense. Saint-Donat est devenu dingue. Ils ont suffisamment à faire sur leurs dossiers pour ne pas faire de supputations sur les affaires des autres.

Le DIPJ se tait quelques instants, caresse sa moustache mousquetaire, signe d'une réflexion intense. Il abandonne les poils de sa bacchante, lève sa main pour faire taire les fâcheux.

– Henri a raison. Vieux principe policier, ne négliger aucune piste. Même si celle-ci peut paraître absurde. On a déjà vu des choses plus étonnantes dans la police.

Personne n'ose le couper. Chacun sent et sait au fond de lui que le directeur a raison. Ne serait-ce que parce qu'il est le directeur.

– Lucie, Henri. Vous échangez tous les éléments que vous avez sur vos dossiers respectifs.

Il les regarde tous les deux. Prend son temps avant de bien articuler :

– Et c'est un ordre. N'est-ce pas, Lucie ?

17

Le major René Malmaison, du service de quart de la division centre de la sécurité publique de Marseille, est bien emmerdé. Il aurait préféré ne pas être de permanence et ne jamais recevoir cet appel de Robert Battisteli, concierge en chef de l'Intercontinental lui signalant la disparition d'une cliente au patronyme qui fleure bon l'aristocratie et les emmerdes : Mireille de Gounod. Il est bien trop ancien dans la boîte pour savoir que ces derniers volent en escadrille. Cette réflexion n'est pas de lui, mais Malmaison aime citer les autres, une façon comme une autre de montrer qu'il a des lettres et est capable de retenir les déclarations des hommes politiques, même quand ils se prennent pour des humoristes.

Malmaison est tout à la fois de permanence et le chef du service de quart. Il ne pouvait pas faire autrement que de se rendre à l'Intercontinental pour y effectuer les premiers actes d'enquête. Prise de contact avec Robert Battisteli, qui a perdu toute trace d'accent ; visite domiciliaire de la suite 412 vide de tout occupant, mais où subsistent quelques vêtements épars ainsi que des produits de beauté dans la salle de bains, et constatations sur la moto Honda Goldwing avec relevé de son numéro d'immatriculation.

En vérifiant au SIV* à l'aide de son téléphone portable NEO**, Malmaison a confirmation de ce qu'il craignait : les emmerdes arrivent aussi vite que la vérole sur le bas clergé. Autre expression qui tend à prouver ses lettres. Même s'il est bien incapable de dire qui en est l'auteur. D'autant que le moment n'incite pas à ce genre de déclaration. Le concierge n'a pas une tête à prendre les enfants du bon Dieu pour des canards sauvages et n'a rien à faire des citations plus ou moins littéraires du chef de permanence du service de quart de la division centre de Marseille.

S'il peut être inquiet de la réaction de son public, lorsqu'il prononce des citations, Malmaison n'en est pas moins un policier aguerri et, une fois qu'il est saisi

---

* SIV : service d'immatriculation des véhicules, fichier recensant les véhicules immatriculés.

** NEO : nouvel équipement opérationnel, téléphone portable attribué à chaque policier sur lequel se trouvent les fichiers « police ».

d'un dossier, il ne laisse pas grand-chose au hasard. Surtout quand la disparition inquiétante qu'il traite concerne une femme dont il pressent qu'elle va intéresser au plus haut point ses collègues de la police judiciaire. Ils appartiennent quand même tous à la Grande Maison, et entre flics la solidarité est de mise et relève du minimum syndical. Même s'il ne porte pas les syndicats policiers dans son cœur, depuis qu'ils ne lui ont pas obtenu le grade de major RULP* à la dernière CAP. Ce qui lui aurait quand même permis de gagner entre 75 et 100 euros mensuels de plus.

Mais c'est une autre histoire, se dit-il, alors qu'il compose un numéro de téléphone qu'il aurait voulu ne plus jamais avoir à faire. Une raison supplémentaire d'être bien emmerdé.

---

* RULP : grade d'un major, signifiant « responsable d'une unité locale de police ».

18

À la sortie de la réunion du directeur, les cadres de la PJ s'éparpillent dans le couloir. Lucie se précipite sur Henri. En colère, comme toujours. Si l'humour est un art de vivre, ce n'est pas le sien.

– C'est quoi ces conneries, Henri ? Un lien entre nos deux affaires ? Tu plaisantes ? Ou alors t'as pas tout dit ? Les Parigots t'ont confié des trucs ?

La réponse de Saint-Donat la décontenance.

– L'intuition, Lucie. Comme m'a appris ton père.

– Lâchez-moi avec mon père. Il est à la retraite depuis quinze piges.

– Quand il était mon chef de groupe, il disait toujours qu'un bon flic suit son instinct jusqu'au bout.

Ce discours fatigue Lucie, elle n'y croit plus. Elle l'a trop entendu quand elle était môme, quand son père, Louis Clert, célèbre pour ses exploits en tant que chef inspecteur divisionnaire et ses gueulantes, tonitruait que, dans une enquête, avant de fermer des portes, il fallait vérifier ce qu'elles cachaient derrière. Moqueuse, elle l'imite quand il hurlait à qui voulait bien l'entendre :

– Le bon poulet vérifie tout ce qui se trouve derrière la lourde. Pas question de rester comme un con devant. Le con stagne, le flic avance. La lumière vient parfois de là où on ne l'attend pas.

– Tu vois, toi aussi t'as retenu la leçon.

– Il m'a tellement cassé les pieds avec, Henri. Mais c'est un discours de vieux.

Lancée dans sa diatribe, Lucie ne se rend même pas compte que sa sentence pourrait vexer Saint-Donat, de presque vingt ans son aîné.

– Henri, on est en 2018. On a l'ADN, la téléphonie. La PTS* a fait des progrès énormes en vingt ans. Ça marchait peut-être avant, son truc, mais c'est dépassé maintenant. Alors fous-moi la paix avec tes intuitions. La police bosse sur du matériel aujourd'hui, pas sur des états d'âme. Soit t'as des éléments pour établir un lien entre nos deux affaires et on échange. Soit t'as rien et tu fermes ta gueule.

Henri pourrait se vexer, rappeler à Lucie qu'il est à la fois son aîné et son supérieur hiérarchique, mais il préfère rester ludique.

---

* PTS : police technique et scientifique.

– Tu sais quoi, Lucie ? Y'a que les imbéciles qui ne changent pas d'avis. Je te parie une boule à zéro que ces deux affaires ont un lien. Celui qui perd se rase la tête.

Lucie se demande si c'est du lard ou du cochon, mais ne peut plus reculer. D'autres collègues ont entendu leur altercation. Elle tape dans la main qu'Henri lui tend. Persuadée qu'elle ne souffrira pas demain d'alopécie et qu'elle préservera sa belle chevelure brune.

Quand la sonnerie de son portable résonne, elle s'écarte du groupe et, téléphone collé à l'oreille, tente de répondre sans manifester trop de surprise à son interlocuteur.

19

– Le célèbre major René Malmaison de la « div' centre » lui-même ? J'y crois pas.

La voix de Lucie Clert réveille des souvenirs mal cicatrisés chez Malmaison.

– La douce et charmante Lucie Clert de la Crim' qui décroche, j'y crois pas non plus.

Un silence nécessaire pour que chacun d'eux remette en place ses pensées actuelles, repousse les anciennes et se concentre.

– Ça y est, t'as chopé le galon de l'exceptionnel* ?

– Depuis deux ans.

– Deux ans qu'on ne s'est pas vus, alors ?

– Deux ans, quatre mois et douze jours pour être exact.

Le côté précis de Malmaison l'a toujours autant éblouie qu'exaspérée. Lucie n'oublie pas ce qu'elle lui doit, mais aussi tout ce qui l'a poussée à le quitter. Ce n'est pas simplement leur douze ans de différence. Le côté pointilleux, tendance mesquin, de son ancien amant est une de ces raisons.

---

* Major de police à l'échelon exceptionnel (MEEX).

– J'attends le RULP, maintenant.

– Le quoi ?

– Le galon de major qui suit l'exceptionnel, c'est le RULP.

– Les acronymes policiers, j'en peux plus.
RULP, tu me rappelles ?

– Responsable d'une unité locale de
police. Je prendrai au moins entre 75 et
100 euros de plus. Tu te rends compte ?

– Ah...

En parlant argent, le couple retombe
tout de suite dans ses travers. Après leurs
folles étreintes, où leurs corps ne pouvaient
se détacher, ils avaient rapidement décidé
de s'installer ensemble. Deux ans de vie
commune et de quotidien, dans sa banale
habitude, sa vile condition matérielle et
le partage des frais, avaient eu raison de
leur passion charnelle. Malmaison était
aussi calculateur dans sa vie personnelle
qu'il était pointilleux dans sa vie professionnelle. Lucie avait vite compris qu'elle
ne pourrait pas passer le reste de sa vie
avec un type préférant acheter une demi-
baguette à une entière, au prétexte qu'elle
ne terminait jamais le pain et qu'il n'y avait
pas de petites économies.

Malmaison se l'était promis : ne plus
jamais parler d'argent avec Lucie. Il rede-
vient professionnel.

– Je t'appelle pour la disparition d'une cliente à l'Intercontinental qui pourrait intéresser la PJ.

– C'est pas trop de notre compétence, une disparition inquiétante.

– Mireille de Gounod, ça te dit ?

– Rien.

Lucie est curieuse et connaît le major. Elle sait qu'il aime ménager ses effets. Elle attend qu'il veuille bien continuer. Il ne s'est pas donné tout ce mal juste pour lui apprendre la disparition inquiétante d'une cliente richissime de l'Intercontinental. Mais sa patience a des limites. Malmaison ne l'a pas oublié.

– Mireille de Gounod : une aristocrate qui paye en espèces sa chambre à « l'Interco » et qui roule en Goldwing. Ça t'aurait pas étonnée ?

– Certainement.

– J'ai vérifié que la bécane n'était pas volée et que Mireille de Gounod en était bien la propriétaire.

– Et alors ?

– Je t'explique avec précision. Ce qui se conçoit bien s'énonce clairement...

– ... et les mots pour le dire viennent aisément. Moi aussi j'ai mes lettres.

– Après identification, la Goldwing est immatriculée au nom d'Octave de Gounod, né le 2 septembre 1998 à Annecy. 20 ans dans six mois. Un gamin, quoi.

– Certainement celui de ta disparue. Et pour l'instant, j'en ai rien à battre de sa bécane et de son môme.

Si Lucie Clert connaît bien le major (pas encore RULP) Malmaison et ses travers, l'inverse est vrai. Le policier de la division centre sait exactement comment attirer l'attention de la capitaine.

– J'ai appelé l'état civil de la mairie d'Annecy.

– Bon boulot de flic, félicitations !

– Octave de Gounod est bien né le 2 septembre 1998 et est bien déclaré comme étant le fils de Mireille de Gounod, mais… de père inconnu.

Lucie s'énerve. À sa façon.

– Et alors, bordel de Dieu, qu'est-ce que j'en ai à foutre qu'il n'ait pas de père, le minot ?

– À Annecy, ils ont noté la vraie identité de la mère : Nathalie Fournier. Mireille de Gounod, c'est un alias.

Lucie est encore sur le point d'envoyer balader son ex-amant, quand elle se reprend.

– Comment tu as dit ? Nathalie Fournier, c'est ça ? T'as vérifié sa date de naissance ?

Malmaison confirme, Nathalie Fournier, née le 23 août 1964 à Rungis.

– Merde, la Carlton !

René, pas peu fier de lui, précise :

– Quand j'ai lu le télégramme de diffusion de la PJ concernant la découverte du corps de Nathalie Fournier aux Pennes-Mirabeau, je me suis dit que ça pouvait peut-être vous intéresser de savoir qu'elle avait pris la chambre 412 à l'Intercontinental et que sa moto était toujours stationnée au parking du palace.

René savoure le moment. Pour une fois qu'il peut clouer le bec à son ancienne concubine, il ne s'en prive pas.

– Tu comprends pourquoi je m'en serais voulu de ne pas vous prévenir. Ç'aurait été un crime de lèse-policier. « Crime de lèse-policier », elle est de moi, cette expression.

Lucie est bien obligée de remercier le major et de lui souhaiter son galon de RULP au prochain avancement. Elle raccroche, songeuse, reconnaît que parfois les informations arrivent d'une façon étonnante dans une affaire judiciaire.

Elle se tourne vers Henri, en discussion avec le directeur dans le couloir de l'état-major. Elle s'étonne de cette tristesse nostalgique qui entoure le commandant malgré sa légèreté apparente. Même quand il parle, il semble ailleurs. Comme si peu de choses pouvaient avoir de prise sur lui. Elle repense à sa discussion avec Malmaison, de quoi faire avancer l'enquête dirigée par Saint-Donat sur la mort de la Carlton, Nathalie Fournier, alias Mireille de Gounod, qui roule sur une Goldwing, immatriculée au nom de son fils Octave.

Ce prénom résonne en elle. Elle l'a déjà entendu. Le fils d'Henri ? C'est étonnant que Nathalie Fournier et Henri Saint-Donat aient ces points communs, les motos et le prénom de leurs fils.

20

Le lieutenant Pierre Forest et le brigadier-chef Joseph Labord de l'antenne PJ de Melun sont surpris des couleurs de Marseille, du soleil méditerranéen et de l'accueil de Lucie. Quand ils apparaissent aux alentours de onze heures au fond du couloir de la BRB, souriants malgré leurs huit heures de route, elle regarde sa montre, outrée.

– Bien des Parigots, premiers au foot mais derniers en ponctualité.

Étonnés par cette entrée en matière ni amicale ni protocolaire, ils ne pensent pas à lui faire remarquer les 800 kilomètres qu'ils viennent d'avaler, ni l'heure matinale à laquelle ils se sont levés. Ils n'ont même pas le réflexe de lui retorquer qu'ils n'aiment pas le foot.

– Sympa, la collègue.

– Laval nous avait prévenus. Caractère de merde, mais bon flic, paraît-il.

– Il paraît, je demande à voir.

Lucie ne les laisse pas bougonner. Le directeur exige de les voir. L'accueil du DIPJ est plus chaleureux que celui de Lucie.

Ce n'est pas difficile. Les deux policiers lui relatent de nouveau le braquage de fourgon suivi de l'homicide sur lequel ils enquêtent et qui les conduisent aujourd'hui à l'Évêché. Larrivée, attentif au moindre détail, s'étonne de ce mélange paradoxal de maîtrise et de légèreté des voyous. Pour l'instant, Yassine Hosni est leur seule piste sérieuse. Il est urgent de l'interpeller.

– Y'a plus qu'à...

Le directeur conclut la réunion et, avec un sourire dont ils ne déterminent pas s'il est sincère ou ironique, leur précise qu'ils ont de la chance de pouvoir travailler pendant leur séjour avec la meilleure cheffe de groupe de Marseille : la lumineuse capitaine Clert.

Lucie n'a que faire des sous-entendus du directeur. Elle n'est pas flic pour plaire, elle veut juste arrêter des voyous.

Elle passe l'après-midi avec les flics parisiens à préparer l'opération du lendemain. Forest et Labord pensaient pouvoir, en force et en nombre, aller le jour même à la Cayolle. Lucie les tempère. Pas question d'intervenir en pleine journée, patience et prudence sont mères de sûreté. Dès six heures le lendemain, ils pourront planquer en toute sécurité sans prendre le risque de se faire « détroncher* » et de créer une émeute urbaine.

Son dispositif préparé, Lucie les accompagne à leur hôtel, sans se départir de sa moue irritée. Leur service de gestion leur a réservé des chambres au Tonic Hotel, à la situation rêvée. À l'angle du Vieux-Port et du quai des Belges, en face de la fameuse « Ombrière » conçue par Norman Foster, immense plafond miroir de 48 mètres sur 22, permettant de se protéger du soleil et de se mirer à l'envers. Les policiers parisiens observent cet ouvrage surprenant et pour la première fois entendent Lucie faire un trait d'humour, même s'ils ne sont pas certains qu'elle le fait exprès.

– Les Marseillais, pour se mettre à l'ombre, ils savent y faire.

Pour passer la soirée, elle leur conseille quelques restaurants, place d'Estienne-d'Orves ou place aux Huiles, tout en les mettant en garde de ne pas tomber dans la mauresque et dans le Vieux-Port. Ils ont « interpel' » demain matin. Et dans un sourire mi-figue, mi-raisin, leur demande d'être ponctuels. Histoire de les

---

* Détroncher : expression argotique policière, signifiant se faire remarquer.

changer des habitudes parisiennes. Leur confirmant ainsi son sens particulier de l'humour.

21

Marseille,
mardi 10 avril 2018.

L'ancien Hôtel-Dieu n'est qu'à quelques pas de l'Évêché, Henri s'y rend à pied avec Basile. Le commandant s'en veut de ne pas y avoir pensé. La Carlton ne pouvait pas être descendue ailleurs qu'à l'Interconti-nental. Élégance et panache. Bien dans son style. L'alias sous lequel elle est descendue dans cet établissement, Mireille de Gounod, ne l'étonne pas, même s'il l'intrigue.

– C'était peut-être une fan de musique classique, ta Carlton.

Les propos de Basile surprennent Henri.

– Je te rassure tout de suite, Gounod n'est pas mon compositeur préféré. Je pré-fère Chopin ou Mendelssohn.

Le look du jeune policier laissait plu-tôt penser qu'il était fan de Muse ou de Maroon Five.

– Je n'ai aucun mérite, la musique, je suis tombé dedans quand j'étais minot. Maman est pianiste et mon père chef d'orchestre.

Lourd héritage, je me suis tapé la totale :
solfège, cours de musique, rythmique et
tous les classiques.

Basile tape amicalement sur l'épaule
de son aîné.

– J'suis quand même premier prix de
piano au conservatoire Maurice-Ravel de
Bayonne.

Henri, empêtré dans ses certitudes, prend
conscience qu'il connaît peu son coéquipier.
Son job lui a pourtant appris à ne jamais
se fier aux apparences. Il a arrêté trop de
voyous pour savoir que l'expression « l'habit
ne fait pas le moine » n'est pas le fruit du
hasard. Derrière le grade ou l'uniforme se
cachent des femmes et des hommes avec
leur sensibilité et leur histoire. Derrière les
flics, des artistes sommeillent.

Après avoir traversé la place de Lenche,
ils empruntent la rue de la Caisserie. Leur
marche les pousse à la confidence.

– Le vrai hasard, c'est que je sois devenu
flic. La tronche de mes parents quand
je leur ai annoncé que j'avais réussi le
concours. J'étais programmé pour finir
soliste dans un orchestre philharmonique,
pas pour porter un flingue et des galons.

Henri comprend mieux les raisons du
capharnaüm dans le bureau du jeune

lieutenant, où guitares, accordéons et pianos électriques assurent la décoration.

– Maintenant je m'éclate en jouant avec « Papa Juliette 13 », le groupe de la PJ des Bouches-du-Rhône. Je suis à la guitare et au clavier. Toi, c'est la bécane. Moi, c'est la « zique ».

À l'évocation de sa passion pour la moto, Henri sourit. Il a d'autres secrets aussi, mais le moment n'est pas encore venu de s'épancher. Ils passent devant une boutique dédiée à Marcel Pagnol. Cela faisait un moment que Saint-Donat cherchait des affiches de films réalisés par l'auteur ayant bercé sa jeunesse. *Marius*, *César*, *Fanny*, *Angèle*, ils sont tous là, à deux pas de l'Évêché.

À l'angle de la place Daviel, ils empruntent la montée du Saint-Esprit menant à l'hôtel Intercontinental. Joli nom de rue pour accéder au palace, jamais loin du septième ciel. Emphase et humour des Marseillais si chers à Pagnol.

Les policiers se sont tus, ils connaissent cette bâtisse, mais chaque fois restent soufflés par sa majesté. En silence, tous deux se demandent si ce bâtiment a vraiment été le théâtre de la disparition de la Carlton. Comment Mireille de Gounod a pu passer de cette vie de luxe à un morceau de charbon au fond d'une voiture brûlée ?

22

Comme souvent à Marseille, le ciel se confond avec la mer. Le soleil invite au farniente. Une radio crépite dans l'habitacle de la voiture banalisée où Lucie Clert est installée depuis six heures, les deux flics parisiens avec elle. À la radio, de sa charmante voix, la capitaine rappelle pour la énième fois à tout le dispositif de surveillance les consignes élémentaires.

– On arrête de regarder le cul des gonzesses, les gars. Pas question de rater notre lascar.

Les flics de la BRB redressent leurs sièges et leurs lunettes de soleil. Ils regardent la cité de la Cayolle et se demandent comment leur capitaine peut deviner à chaque fois ce qu'ils sont en train de faire. Des grosses poubelles et des objets ménagers s'entassent aux angles des rues. C'est la journée des encombrants, les occupants entassent leurs vieux meubles, frigidaires ou machines à laver. Un va-et-vient s'est instauré entre les immeubles et les points de dépose.

– Ceux-là au moins, on les prendra pas sur la gueule.

La moquerie de Labord est sans effet sur Lucie, concentrée sur les habitants qui déposent leurs vieilleries ou récupèrent ce que leurs voisins ont déposé. Elle tapote nerveusement son volant. Forest tente à son tour d'entamer la conversation. La Cayolle, cité du sud de Marseille, l'étonne. Il s'attendait à une sorte de bastion imprenable, encadré par d'immenses tours de quinze étages, comme il en a connu au début de sa carrière, quand il exerçait en Seine-Saint-Denis, où le jeu préféré des habitants lors des descentes de police était de jeter toutes sortes d'objets ménagers sur les flics.

La Cayolle ne ressemble en rien aux cités parisiennes, où le béton fait la loi sur plusieurs hectares jusqu'à cent mètres de hauteur et où les espaces verts se résument aux pots de fleurs installés sur leurs balcons par les locataires, à côté de leurs paraboles.

Les Parisiens n'ont pas le monopole de la difficulté de vivre en cité, pense Lucie. La hauteur des barres n'est pas le seul critère de mauvaise qualité. L'habitat indigne a encore fait la une de l'actualité à Marseille. Un immeuble s'est effondré rue d'Aubagne, en plein centre-ville. La Cayolle est un agglomérat d'immeubles de trois ou quatre étages, où un dédale de ruelles permet d'accéder d'une résidence à une autre, en passant par des espaces verts, qui font la joie de ses résidents, mais compliquent l'accès des services de secours.

Rien ne laisse présager de la violence qui peut y éclater. Le chemin de Sormiou qui la longe permet d'accéder, quatre kilomètres plus loin, à la calanque éponyme, sans que la moindre habitation bétonnée vienne entacher le paysage. Un coin de paradis qui se jette dans le bleu infini de la Méditerranée, que des touristes viennent admirer l'été, s'ils réussissent à franchir la barrière du rond-point de Vaucanson, où parfois des hordes de jeunes de la cité les dévalisent, en commettant de véritables attaques de diligence. Ce qui fait dire aux flics lettrés, parodiant Albert Londres, que la Cayolle peut vite devenir l'enfer avant le paradis.

L'explication de Lucie n'allège pas l'ambiance. Loin de là. Mais elle fait comprendre aux Parisiens pourquoi ils attendent à l'extérieur de la cité, afin de s'assurer de la présence de Yassine Hosni pour l'interpeller, plutôt que d'aller directement au contact chez lui. Mis en place à six heures, ils quadrillent le quartier de véhicules banalisés. Lucie s'est positionnée allée des Pêcheurs, à quelques mètres à peine du Bât B2, n° 12, dernier domicile connu de la famille Hosni.

23

Robert Battisteli, le concierge de l'hôtel Intercontinental, est tendu. Il sent qu'il a fait une connerie. Les policiers en face de lui sont énervés. Quand il leur a annoncé que la suite 412 avait été nettoyée, leurs visages se sont transformés. C'est à peine s'ils n'ont pas crié. Il tente bien de leur expliquer que l'urgence commerciale commandait de rendre disponible cette suite, payée par ailleurs et dont la durée de séjour était dépassée. Ces arguments mercantiles ne touchent pas les policiers de la Crim'.

Basile lui explique qu'ils ont retrouvé le corps de madame de Gounod carbonisé dans une voiture calcinée. Mireille de Gounod, de son vrai nom Nathalie Fournier, n'était pas une femme du monde, mais plutôt du milieu, avec des antécédents judiciaires aussi lourds que les prix pratiqués à l'Intercontinental. Il aurait été souhaitable pour l'enquête de pouvoir accéder à sa chambre dans l'état où elle l'avait laissée pour y effectuer des recherches scientifiques.

La métaphore tarifaire d'Urteguy laisse de marbre Battisteli, perdu dans ses pensées. Il imagine déjà la réaction de Kimberley, elle ne le croira jamais. Lui, le p'tit concierge marseillo-britannique, mêlé à une affaire de meurtre, comme dans les films de série B qu'elle regarde à longueur de temps. On ne peut se fier à personne. Mireille de Gounod, une femme si classe. Il aurait bien tenté une expression du style « la robe ne fait pas le curé », mais face à ces deux flics en civil, aux tenues aussi différentes que disparates, il préfère « l'uniforme ne fait pas le policier ». Leurs regards noirs sont sans appel, ce n'était pas la bonne option.

Dans son bureau, il leur désigne un sac en toile dont la décoration et les initiales « LV » croisées dessus ne laissent aucun doute quant à la marque. C'est tout ce qui restait dans la chambre de madame de Gounod.

– Pardon, de madame Fournier.

Henri empêche Basile d'ouvrir le sac. Ils le feront plus tard, au bureau, avec les précautions d'usage. Battisteli les regarde, content de lui, il aura au moins réussi à préserver ça, et peut être que grâce à lui l'enquête va faire un grand pas. Saint-Donat lui demande :

– C'est tout ?

Le concierge va répondre « yes », puis se reprend. Il récupère en haut de son armoire un objet qu'il lui tend.

– Il y avait ce casque aussi, et sa moto, toujours stationnée au parking.

Battisteli, dans un geste mécanique, monte et descend la visière. Il regarde les policiers, sans comprendre leur œil mauvais.

– Vous voulez bien arrêter ça ?

– Quoi ?

Urteguy mime le geste d'ouvrir et de fermer la visière.

– Sans vos traces, ce sera mieux.

Paniqué, Battisteli lâche le casque, récupéré de justesse par Saint-Donat. Celui-ci regarde le concierge et lui demande de les conduire jusqu'à la moto en l'invitant à ne pas la toucher. Juste la leur indiquer de loin. Ils se chargeront du reste.

Après réflexion, Battisteli n'est pas sûr de raconter cette anecdote à Kimberley.

24

À 10 heures, la circulation se fait plus dense. Quelques jeunes roulent leur ennui et leurs joints au bas des immeubles. Les flics se tendent. Des habitants continuent à poser des encombrants sur les tas existants. Ça agace Lucie. Une Porsche Cayenne et un Touareg passent dans la rue. Ça n'étonne pas les flics. Dans ce quartier populaire, certains peuvent s'offrir ce type de véhicules. Ici, le trafic de stups est roi et permet aux petits dealers locaux d'engranger des sommes conséquentes.

Une grosse cylindrée s'arrête devant la résidence, le motard enlève son casque, récupère son portable et passe un appel. Les flics s'inquiètent. Qu'est-ce qu'il fout là ? Une jeune femme, seins apparents sous son sweat-shirt coloré, nombril exhibé, pantalon serré, sort de l'immeuble, embrasse goulûment le biker et monte derrière lui sans prendre la peine d'enfiler une protection pour sa tête. Tradition locale oblige. Les jeunes « shiteux » accompagnent leur départ de rires gras et de gestes obscènes.

Les policiers se lassent. Le camion-benne des encombrants arrive. Se stationne devant le numéro B2 de l'allée des Pêcheurs. Lucie ne voit plus l'entrée.

– Fait chier, celui-là. Il dégage ?

L'employé vide les poubelles, charge les encombrants dans la benne de son camion, qui repart.

– Pas trop tôt.

Dans la voiture, le brigadier Labord se redresse. Un individu sort du hall du n° 12 et s'approche des poubelles vides.

– C'est pas notre gus, ça ?

Forest a un doute. Avec Lucie, il jette un œil sur la photo anthropométrique de Yassine Hosni, avant de regarder de nouveau l'individu qui arrive à l'angle de la rue.

– Il lui ressemble. Tenez-vous prêts.

L'homme, en tenue légère, scrute à droite et à gauche, récupère une poubelle et retourne à l'immeuble.

– Qu'est-ce qu'il fout, ce con ?

Les flics, aux aguets, hésitent. La ressemblance avec la photo de Yassine Hosni n'est pas flagrante. En arrivant devant la porte du rez-de-chaussée, l'individu pose sa poubelle, glisse une clef dans la serrure, reprend la poubelle avec difficulté et entre dans le hall. Lucie regarde Forest. Ils se comprennent.

– La poubelle est chargée, on fonce !

La capitaine hurle le « top interpellation » à la radio. Quinze flics en civil, brassard police apparent, sortent de toutes parts et convergent en courant vers le Bât B2. Des guetteurs, chargés de surveiller le point de deal, gueulent :

– Ara, ara*…

Comme une volée de moineaux, les jeunes s'éparpillent, jettent leurs joints, se débarrassent de leurs sachets de résine de cannabis. L'homme à la poubelle accélère. L'ascenseur en panne l'oblige à prendre l'escalier. Il se retourne. Lucie pénètre dans le hall, les deux policiers parisiens derrière elle. Pas de doute, les flics sont là pour lui. Il monte les marches quatre à quatre, passe en soufflant le premier étage. Lucie se rapproche à grandes enjambées, elle gagne du terrain à chaque marche. Ses collègues ont du mal à la suivre. Au deuxième étage, elle est à deux mètres du fuyard, totalement essoufflé. Un dernier effort et elle pourrait le plaquer. Labord et Forest sont à la traîne. Mais l'individu ne cède rien. Il arrive au troisième étage. Lucie se jette en avant et lance son bras pour le faire tomber en

---

* « Ara » : cri poussé par les guetteurs des points de deal pour prévenir les dealers de l'arrivée des policiers.

glissant sa main sous sa chaussure. Façon cuillère, comme au rugby.

L'homme trébuche, mais ne tombe pas. Il donne des grands coups de pied derrière lui. Ses semelles heurtent le visage de Lucie. Dans un dernier coup de reins, il se projette en avant pour se dégager, pousse la porte de son appartement et se rue à l'intérieur, avant de la claquer devant le nez de la capitaine. Lucie, folle de rage, tambourine dessus.

– Ouvre, bordel, ouvre.

Les policiers parisiens arrivent, en même temps que les verrous s'enclenchent. Ils reprennent leur respiration. Forest remarque l'étiquette supportant le nom « HOSNI » sur la sonnette de la porte. Il lève son pouce à l'intention de ses collègues, ils ne se sont pas trompés d'individu. D'être passée si près met Lucie hors d'elle, elle balance des grands coups de pied dans la porte.

– Tu vas ouvrir, putain. Je te jure que tu vas l'ouvrir, ta putain de lourde, Hosni !

Puis elle réalise qu'ils sont au dernier étage : l'homme n'a pas d'échappatoire. Lucie place ces coéquipiers en sécurisation au pied de l'immeuble. Plus personne n'entre ni ne sort sans son autorisation. Le fuyard ne peut pas leur échapper. La faim, la soif, la peur ou l'envie le pousseront bien à sortir. La patience est la première vertu du policier.

25

La Honda Goldwing Aventure bleu pailleté 1 500 cm^3 de Mireille de Gounod règne au milieu du garage de l'Intercontinental. C'est la dernière version de sa moto de prédilection. Henri apprécie le goût sûr de la Carlton pour les bécanes de qualité et n'a qu'une envie, la chevaucher. Sans se faire d'illusions, il fait appel aux services de l'identité judiciaire, espérant que, contrairement à la suite 412, personne ne l'ait touchée. Tête, mains et corps protégés, les hommes de l'art entament leur mission. Derrière eux, Basile explore la Goldwing sous tous ses angles.

Henri a les yeux qui brillent.

– Magnifique, non ? C'est pas les Japonais qui l'ont construite, c'est le père Noël !

Pour la conception de cette moto, les ingénieurs ont d'abord pensé au passager et ont conçu le plus confortable des fauteuils, véritable pullman de luxe, avant d'imaginer autour la calandre, les caissons et la motorisation. Avec la plus précise des technologies. Basile sourit devant la passion démonstrative de son chef. Si Henri berce dans le lyrisme, lui reste pragmatique. Au milieu du guidon un écran de contrôle attire son attention.

– C'est un GPS. C'est une Goldwing 1 500 quand même, dernier modèle. *All inclusive*.

– C'est bon, ça.

– Avec la précision des Japonais, on devrait vite savoir quel était son dernier trajet. Au mètre près. Et à quelle date.

Pendant que les experts œuvrent, Basile se demande comment une femme peut canaliser un tel engin de plus de 400 kilos. Le regard d'Henri se durcit. Conduire une moto n'est pas une question de force physique, mais bien de pilotage, surtout une Goldwing, qui se manipule comme une trottinette. Avec son look et ses doigts boudinés, rien ne laissait penser que Basile pouvait être un fin mélomane. Pourtant il est bien premier prix du conservatoire de Bayonne et membre du groupe « Papa Juliette ». Le lieutenant préfère changer de sujet.

– Tu le connais, Malmaison ?

– Qui ça ?

– Le collègue de la division centre qui a balancé l'info à Lucie pour la Goldwing.

– Bons réflexes professionnels.

– C'est lui qui a fait le lien avec la Carlton en identifiant la bécane, quand

Battisteli lui a communiqué le numéro d'immatriculation.

Basile fronce les sourcils. Ce n'est pas la première fois que Saint-Donat remarque ce tic quand son collègue est perturbé.

– Pourquoi il l'a prévenue, elle ?

– Quoi ?

– Pourquoi Malmaison a prévenu Lucie ?

– On s'en fout, non ? L'essentiel, c'est que ça nous a permis de savoir que la Carlton était bien descendue à l'Intercontinental.

Urteguy prend sur lui, mais ne peut pas s'en empêcher.

– Quand même, un major en sécurité publique qui appelle directement une capitaine de la BRB. Tu crois qu'ils sont ensemble ?

Saint-Donat cesse d'admirer la Goldwing.

– Basile, si tu t'intéresses à Lucie, je vois qu'une solution...

Henri commençait à s'en douter, même si cela l'étonne, mais le jeune flic semble vraiment attiré par la capitaine au doux caractère.

– ... oublie que t'as aucune chance, fonce ! On sait jamais, sur un malentendu, ça peut marcher.

– *Les Bronzés* ? Mais c'est les années 70, ça ? T'as pas plus vieux comme référence ?

26

La réquisition est établie dans l'urgence. Les flics marseillais font appel à leur serrurier habituel, un génie du métier, surnommé affectueusement professeur Carouble. Un homme de l'art qu'ils préfèrent avoir dans leur camp que dans celui d'en face. En dix minutes, l'homme les a rejoints au troisième étage, où en expert il scrute les verrous. Ils ne devraient pas lui résister longtemps. Il attend le feu vert de Lucie.

– Hosni. Le serrurier est là. Ouvre, sinon on force ta lourde.

Aucune réponse, ça n'étonne personne. Le prof entre en scène. À peine glisse-t-il un tournevis dans la serrure que les pênes s'ouvrent. Carouble peste, déçu de ne pas avoir pu faire étalage de son talent.

– Ils attendent toujours le dernier moment.

Et prend soin de s'écarter. La porte libérée, les flics s'engouffrent dans l'appartement, déterminés. Le jeune homme qui vient d'ouvrir est mis à terre et menotté.

– J'ai rien fait, moi ! Chercher sa poubelle, c'est pas un délit !

Les policiers parisiens s'assurent que l'individu arrêté est bien Yassine Hosni. Il semble surpris. Et soulagé.

– C'est mon grand frère, Yassine. Moi, c'est Bilal. Bilal Hosni.

Les flics trouvent sa carte d'identité. Leur déception est aussi grande que celle de Lucie.

– On a serré le frangin, c'est ça ? Mais alors il est où, Yassine ?

Bilal n'a pas de nouvelles de son aîné depuis plus de trois mois. Il ne sait pas où il se trouve, peut-être du côté de Paris. Depuis le départ de ses parents pour le bled et la détention de Khaled aux Baumettes, il n'y a personne d'autre que lui, ici.

– Et la came, tu l'as mise où ?

Bilal ne comprend pas. Mais de quoi parle cette femme ? De drogue ? De cannabis, ou pire de cocaïne ? Jamais de la vie il ne toucherait à ce type de produits, c'est trop dangereux. Lucie lui désigne son front.

– Et là, c'est écrit grosse conne de la PJ ?

Bilal ne comprend pas cet acharnement. C'est Yassine qu'ils veulent. Pourquoi ils lui cherchent des poux dans la tête ? Et cette flic, elle cherche quoi ? Le provoquer ? Il se tourne vers les policiers qui l'entourent, s'étonne qu'ils se fassent diriger par une « gonzesse ». Les policiers ont beau être habitués à ce type de propos, ils sont excédés par l'attitude de Bilal. Dans le même élan, Labord et Forest appuient sur les menottes qui enserrent ses poignets dans le dos. L'effet est immédiat et douloureux. Il se tait, enfin.

Lucie finit par trouver la poubelle avec laquelle Bilal est remonté. Elle ouvre le couvercle. Vide. Le silence de Bilal est de courte durée.

– Y'a rien chez moi, je vous l'ai dit. Vous n'avez pas le droit de fouiller partout. Je me plaindrai à mon avocat.

Les flics parisiens, dans la même osmose, appuient sur les menottes à chaque fois qu'il répond. Lucie a conscience du soutien de ses collègues, lequel conforte sa pertinacité.

– Je te promets qu'on va la trouver.

L'air imbécile qui se veut insolent de Bilal Hosni l'excite encore plus. Elle ne fait qu'une bouchée de l'appartement, qu'elle retourne. Il transpire le vide, la saleté et la tristesse. Pas une couleur pour apporter un peu de goût ou une touche de gaieté.

Elle éventre le canapé élimé et vide les tiroirs de cuisine. Dans les chambres, elle jette les draps au sol, vide les cabas, mais ne trouve rien. Ces recherches vaines la rendent dingue, sûre que l'homme transportait de la came dans sa poubelle. Il l'a planquée chez lui. C'est pour ça qu'il a mis du temps pour ouvrir.

27

Les responsables sécurité de l'Intercontinental interdisent l'accès au garage. Ils protègent les experts à l'œuvre sur la Goldwing et évitent ainsi toute mauvaise publicité pour leur établissement. Henri et Basile ne sont pas dupes, mais n'ont cure de cette attitude, habitués à travailler à l'abri des regards. Urteguy lit de nouveau la fiche SIV de la moto.

– Octave de Gounod, 2 septembre 1998 à Annecy. Il n'a pas encore 20 ans, Octave.

À l'énoncé de ce prénom, Henri a un trouble, à peine perceptible. Urteguy ne s'en rend pas compte, il continue. D'après la fiche, le gamin habiterait 18 place de la République, à Saint-Rémy-de-Provence.

– C'est quoi, cette adresse ?

– Faut vérifier, c'est pas si loin, Saint-Rémy.

– Tu te fous de mes vieilles références cinématographiques, le geek, et t'es pas capable d'utiliser Google Maps ?

Urteguy vérifie en deux clics. Son visage se détend, ses yeux se mettent à briller.

– Un sacré phénomène, la Carlton.

Le commandant découvre ce qui provoque l'étonnement de son collègue.

– L'adresse de l'hôtel Gounod, en centre-ville de Saint-Rémy, où Charles Gounod a séjourné et composé son opéra en cinq actes : *Mireille*. « Mireille de Gounod », on comprend mieux, maintenant.

Les experts rangent leur poudre magique et leurs écouvillons. La limousine à deux roues est disponible. Henri rentre dans le système de navigation et découvre la dernière destination enregistrée. Il essaye de comprendre. Impatient, Basile se penche sur l'écran.

– Rond-point de Vaucanson. Qu'est-ce que ça veut dire ?

– C'est où ?

– Dans le 9e. L'entrée de la Cayolle.

– La cité de Lucie ?

– Oui, celle où elle planque avec les Parisiens.

Dubitatifs, les deux flics se regardent. Mais qu'allait faire la Carlton dans cette cité ?

28

Les recherches de Lucie ont provoqué un tsunami dans l'appartement de la famille Hosni. La capitaine n'abandonne jamais.

– Je te jure qu'on va la trouver, cette putain de came.

Depuis une dizaine de minutes, l'homme a demandé à fumer une cigarette. Pour le calmer, les flics ont accepté.

– Vous trouverez rien, y'a rien chez moi.

Il ne fallait pas dire ça à Lucie la teigneuse. Elle continue de plus belle. Placards, matelas, vide-ordures, tout y passe. Sur le balcon, elle regarde par-dessus la rambarde et ne voit que ses collègues qui assurent la sécurité du bâtiment. L'un d'eux lui fait signe de se dépêcher. La surprise passée de voir débarquer les flics, les jeunes de la cité viennent les harceler. Savoir que le temps presse énerve encore plus Lucie et décuple son imagination. Elle lève les yeux au ciel et réalise. Ils sont au dernier palier. C'est quand même sympa les cités où les immeubles ne font pas quinze étages. Elle se précipite et ouvre la porte de la cage d'escalier menant sur le toit.

Labord et Forest la regardent étonnés. Bilal Hosni devient livide. Quelques secondes après, les trois hommes l'entendent marcher au-dessus, avant de l'entendre hurler « *Bingo !* ». Labord se tourne vers Bilal.

– Je l'aime bien, cette gonzesse. Au premier abord, elle n'est pas facile, je te l'accorde, mais elle lâche rien. Ça fait tout son charme.

– Et elle tient ses promesses. Elle a trouvé, t'as perdu !

Ils conduisent Hosni sur le toit, où Lucie, mains croisées sur la poitrine, les attend devant un sac de voyage d'où sortent des pains de résine de cannabis.

– Pas mal, depuis le balcon, un joli shoot à l'envers pour atteindre le toit.

Lucie enfile des gants de protection, secoue le sac, s'étonne de la marque, puis compte les pains de cannabis, avant de les replacer dans leur cabas de luxe. Malgré son apparente solidité, il est éventré.

– Ça ne l'a pas arrangé, ce petit saut avec 12 kilos de came à l'intérieur.

L'homme regarde les trois flics. Cette drogue n'est pas à lui, il n'a rien à voir avec tout ça. L'air confiant des policiers ne le pousse pas à insister. Il connaît la musique qu'il a à jouer. Il sera temps, plus tard, avec son avocat, d'assurer sa mélodie de défense.

29

Le retour à l'Évêché est plus détendu. Ils ont un gardé à vue, des éléments et quelques certitudes. Dans la famille Hosni, ils espéraient Yassine, ils ont le petit frère, Bilal. Loin d'être un ange, son palmarès judiciaire est éloquent. Quarante rôles au TAJ depuis sa majorité. Et il n'a que 21 ans. En matière de délinquance aussi, la valeur n'attend pas le nombre des années.

Les policiers parisiens ont la priorité. Ils veulent entendre le jeune homme sur les relations qu'il entretient avec son frère Yassine. Quand Bilal ne fait pas preuve de mauvaise foi, il est de mauvaise volonté. Avec morve, il consent à peine à reconnaître que Yassine est un de ses frères, de deux ans son aîné, qu'il n'a pas vu depuis au moins trois mois, ou quatre, ou cinq... il ne sait pas. Ne connaît pas l'emploi du temps des membres de sa famille.

– Allez vous faire foutre avec vos questions à la con, je vous emmerde tous.

La sagesse de Labord tempère la rage de son jeune collègue. Forest s'est dressé devant le gardé à vue qui le toise, prêt à lui donner une leçon, très physique. Le brigadier retient à temps le bras vengeur du lieutenant. Une gifle, même éducative, les conduirait à plus de problèmes que de solutions et pourrait ruiner l'enquête comme leur carrière.

– Franchement, il ne le mérite pas.

Petit sourire narquois de l'homme, qui n'a pas le courage de leur cracher dessus et le fait par terre. Les esprits se calment, Labord jette un œil à son portable et pâlit.

– Je crois qu'on va s'arrêter là.

Forest lit à son tour le message que vient de recevoir son collègue, il blêmit.

– Qu'est-ce que ça veut dire ?

Lucie a dû sentir que l'audition se terminait, elle frappe à la porte.

– Vous avez fini, les gars ? C'est mon tour ?

Les deux flics parisiens acquiescent, plient leurs affaires sans un mot. Avant de sortir, Lucie les arrête.

– Le directeur vous cherche. Je sais pas pourquoi, un truc important. Je vous laisse vous démerder, vous connaissez la maison maintenant.

Ils quittent Lucie en lui souhaitant bonne chance avec le gardé à vue. Forest redresse sa tenue. Labord rentre ses pans de chemise dans son pantalon. Avec ce qu'ils viennent d'apprendre, ils devinent la raison pour laquelle le directeur veut les voir.

30

Il n'y a que deux sortes d'hommes, ceux qui disent la vérité et les autres. Bilal Hosni fait partie des autres. Et ça ne le dérange pas, par atavisme, par éducation, presque par culture. Nier jusqu'à l'évidence lui permettra de toujours jeter un doute sur sa culpabilité et restera un moyen de prouver qu'il n'a rien lâché devant les « keufs ».

Même quand les prélèvements effectués sur le film plastique entourant les pains de cannabis trouvés sur le toit de son immeuble mettent en évidence son profil ADN. Le Fnaeg a établi cette vérité scientifique. Les 12 kilos de cannabis trouvés sur le toit de la Cayolle ont été manipulés par Bilal. De l'inconvénient d'avoir déjà été serré par les flics et d'avoir son ADN enregistré.

Pour la énième fois, Lucie lui désigne la photo prise par l'identité judiciaire, où l'on voit la besace de voyage et les douze pains de résine trouvés sur le toit de l'immeuble.

Elle lui demande s'il reconnaît le sac et la came comme étant les siens. Il nie tout en bloc, de toute son âme.

Leur jeu se répète *ad libitum*. Jeu de dupe, jeu de menteur, jeu de tricheur.

Lucie bâille, regarde de plus près la photo de l'IJ*. Les caractéristiques de cette besace mafflue l'étonnent. Plutôt ovale, elle est plus large d'un côté que de l'autre. Forme étrange, ne correspondant à aucun modèle standard.

– C'est un vrai ?

Bilal ne comprend pas.

– C'est un vrai Vuitton ?

Le gardé à vue hausse les épaules.

– Si c'est un vrai, on saura vite qui l'a acheté. Ce n'est pas un modèle courant. Tout le monde ne peut pas s'offrir un sac Louis Vuitton sur mesure.

Bilal frémit. Comme s'il prenait conscience qu'il avait fait une erreur. Lucie veut profiter de son avantage et le conduire à la faute, quand une sonnerie de deux-tons éclate dans la cour de l'Évêché. Elle se penche à la fenêtre, la sirène émane de la voiture des policiers parisiens coincée par un fourgon « police ». Quand la voie est libérée, le silence reprend ses droits.

---

* IJ : identité judiciaire.

– Vous partez sans me dire au revoir, les gars ?

Labord et Forest cherchent d'où provient la voix de Lucie. Forest veut gueuler quelque chose, mais Labord lui fait signe d'être discret. Il s'approche au plus près de la fenêtre d'où Lucie a crié.

– On a retrouvé Yassine.

– Quoi ?

– Il est mort !

– Pardon ?

– Laval nous a envoyé un message. Il n'arrivait pas à nous joindre, il a prévenu Saint-Donat.

– Saint-Donat ? Pourquoi il m'a rien dit ?

– On pouvait pas t'en parler devant Bilal.

Perdu dans ses pensées, Bilal ne prête aucune attention à l'échange de la capitaine avec son collègue.

– Ils ont repêché un cadavre hier matin dans l'Yonne, près de Montereau. Un mec dans une bâche en plastique, deux balles dans le corps. Ça pue le règlement de comptes. L'ADN a matché ce matin : Yassine Hosni.

– C'est quoi, cette histoire ?

– Forcément, ça change la donne. Plus besoin du petit frère. On fonce à Melun.

Et, dans un grand sourire, il salue la capitaine, sans omettre de la remercier pour son accueil inoubliable.

31

Lucie en veut à la police entière. Quels que soient les grades. Aux collègues de Melun qui partent en lui laissant un gardé à vue sur les bras, au directeur qui l'ignore et à Saint-Donat, informé de la découverte du cadavre de Yassine et qui ne lui dit rien. Elle a la désagréable sensation d'être prise pour la débile de service et déteste ça.

Les Parisiens partis, le directeur intouchable, il ne lui reste que le commandant de la Crim' pour exprimer sa colère. Elle dépose Bilal Hosni en cellule, pas mécontent d'en terminer avec cette policière qui ne lâche rien et qui commençait à lui poser des questions délicates. Elle part à la recherche d'Henri. Une explication s'impose. Et pas question de se laisser embobiner. Qu'il ait eu son père comme chef ou mentor ne change rien. Sur un truc similaire, son « paternel », malgré ses énormes défauts, n'aurait pas agi de la sorte. Il aurait eu la courtoisie de l'aviser. En premier, et non pas comme la dernière des connes.

En marchant dans les longs couloirs de l'Évêché, elle rumine sa colère. Dans cet état, personne ne prend le risque de lui adresser la parole. Ses traits se durcissent et ses yeux jettent des éclairs. Les collègues qu'elle croise s'écartent, ne tentent même pas une vanne facile. Lucie a cette capacité incroyable de monter en pression toute seule. Un trouble obsessionnel du comportement, comme si une vis sans fin de questions sans réponses se mettait à tourner dans son cerveau.

En furie, elle débarque devant le bureau de Saint-Donat. Décidée à obtenir des explications sur la découverte de Yassine Hosni, elle en oublie les règles de politesse, sans frapper elle ouvre la porte, entre et gueule.

– J'suis pas un lapin de six semaines, Henri...

32

Saint-Donat ne s'y fait pas. Si son bureau est neutre, celui d'Urteguy est un capharnaüm musical et informatique. La table de travail est envahie d'ordinateurs éventrés, de disques durs ouverts et de câbles épars. Le tout mêlé à des instruments de musique, guitares sans cordes, violons sans manche, et un accordéon sur lequel il manque des touches. L'ensemble trône au milieu d'outils, de tournevis de toutes tailles et de petits marteaux. Au mur, des affiches indiquent des dates de concert du groupe « Papa Juliette ». Quelques photos de Basile, tenant une guitare devant un micro ou jouant du piano, finissent d'agrémenter la décoration.

Chaque fois qu'il rentre dans cet antre particulier, Saint-Donat a un mouvement de recul. Urteguy lève à peine la tête, plongé dans l'étude d'un ordinateur portable. Cheveux en bataille, regard concentré, il marmotte :

– Un MacBook Pro 13″ Core i5 2,5. Dernière génération. Elle s'emmerdait pas, la Carlton.

– Il était où ?

– Dans son sac récupéré à l'hôtel. Y'avait ça aussi.

Il désigne un téléphone portable à côté de l'ordinateur. Un iPhone 5 S, sans détails particuliers, protégé dans un sachet plastique.

– T'inquiète, chef. Le sac a été ouvert après examen par l'IJ. À part les paluches* de la Carlton, y'avait rien dessus. Ils ont fait des prélèvements « bio » aussi, mais ça donnera rien.

Le sac de la Carlton est posé sur la chaise en face du bureau. Henri jette un regard à l'intérieur. Sous-vêtements, chemisiers, tee-shirts et jupes de marque y sont jetés en vrac. Urteguy voit la moue de son chef.

– Au départ, tout était bien rangé. Après le passage de l'IJ, j'allais pas tout replier.

– Cool, ton explication, sinon on aurait pu croire que t'étais particulièrement bordélique.

Le commandant enlève le sac de la chaise et remarque qu'il est de belle qualité.

– C'est un vrai ?

– Un Vuitton ? J'en sais rien. Mais ça serait bien son genre, à la Carlton.

Henri pose le sac par terre, entre un lot de cédéroms et des cordes de guitare, et s'assoit en face de Basile.

– Et sinon, il dit quoi, cet ordi ?

---

* Paluche : expression argotique policière, signifiant « empreinte ».

33

La voix de Lucie résonne dans le vide. Saint-Donat n'est pas dans son bureau. Elle trépigne, passe sa main sur sa tête, ce qui n'arrange pas sa coupe, ses cheveux sont déjà défaits par la colère. Elle attrape un chewing-gum, ouvre avec rage l'emballage, le gobe. Recommence avec un deuxième, puis un troisième. Au cinquième, elle arrête. Mâchouiller l'apaise, légèrement. Elle retombe en tension.

Se retrouver seule dans le bureau de Saint-Donat l'oblige à reprendre son souffle. Elle regarde les posters de Paris, de la Goldwing. Malgré ces touches de vie, elle trouve ce lieu très impersonnel. Une image lui revient, celle d'Henri pétant les plombs quand elle avait fait bouger son sous-main en cuir, faisant apparaître des documents.

La tentation est trop grande. Selon son père, pour les flics, la curiosité est une qualité professionnelle. Elle soulève le sous-main. La photo est un peu vieillie, mais l'image est nette. Le visage rieur d'un enfant d'une dizaine d'années lui apparaît.

Cheveux bruns tirant sur le roux, petit nez en trompette, taches de rousseur, sourire malin. Aucun doute, la forme des lèvres, cette lueur d'espièglerie dans les yeux, les mêmes qu'Henri.

Lucie regarde plus attentivement le cliché. Elle ne l'avait pas tout de suite remarqué, mais le jeune garçon tient dans sa main une barre en fer, en haut de laquelle se trouve une poche contenant un liquide. Un tuyau en sort et vient se fixer dans son bras. Lucie ne comprend pas. Octave ? Le fils d'Henri ? Il est malade ?

Depuis qu'il est arrivé à la DIPJ, Lucie n'a jamais croisé le fils d'Henri, ni même ceux de ses autres collègues. Sait-elle seulement s'ils en ont ? Dans un réflexe naturel, elle pose ses mains sur son ventre. Toujours plat. À 37 ans, pourquoi n'a-t-elle pas de môme ? Elle a déjà croisé des mecs, mais n'a pas encore rencontré celui qui pourrait être le père de son enfant. Elle hausse les épaules. Trouve des explications. Les services de police en général et ceux de la PJ en particulier ne sont pas des lieux pour les gamins. On peut y croiser n'importe qui. Des victimes en pleurs, des témoins en sang, des mis en cause qui hurlent. Et des flics qui portent sur l'humanité qu'ils protègent un regard désabusé, cynique parfois, sceptique souvent. Des tranches de vie, des lieux, des hommes, à ne pas mettre sous des yeux d'enfant. Et elle sait de quoi elle parle. Depuis toute petite, elle baigne dans cette ambiance. Elle la connaît par cœur. C'est peut-être pour ça, aussi, que son ventre est resté vide. Paradoxe.

Lucie sort de sa réflexion et retrouve un peu de lucidité. Elle est quand même en train de fouiller le bureau d'un collègue, presque une perquisition illégale. Elle repose la photo d'Octave, remet tout en place, ouvre la porte. La voie est libre, elle s'engage dans le couloir, avant de s'arrêter net.

Pourquoi cette photo ? Pourquoi Henri conserve-t-il, secrètement, ce cliché de son fils encore enfant ? 10, 11, 12 ans tout au plus ? Quel âge peut-il bien avoir aujourd'hui ? Et surtout, pourquoi la photo de son fils malade ?

34

Urteguy fait la moue. Le MacBook de la Carlton n'est pas bavard. Dans le disque dur, rien trouvé de personnel, que du général. Son attention a juste été retenue par une consultation assidue des sites de la Fédération française de football. Pas de boîte mail, pas de page Facebook, aucun réseau social à son nom ou à celui de ses alias.

– Le néant, quoi !

Il désigne le téléphone placé dans son sachet plastique.

– Pour le portable, c'est pareil. La puce est un toc*, enregistrée au nom de Mireille de Gounod. Mais aucun contact ni trace d'appels. Le vide intégral.

– Les « fadettes** », ça donne quelque chose ?

---

* Toc : expression policière pour désigner des téléphones portables achetés sous de fausses identités.

** Fadette : raccourci policier signifiant « facture détaillée ».

– C'est un téléphone dédié, en contact avec un seul numéro. Un autre toc, plutôt rigolo, identifié à Maria Castafiore.

Il insiste pour faire comprendre l'allusion à son chef.

– Maria Castafiore. Ça a aussi un lien avec Gounod, le compositeur.

À la mine de Saint-Donat, Urteguy voit que son chef n'a pas compris la référence.

– C'est Gounod qui a composé l'*Air des Bijoux*, chanté par Maria Callas, caricaturée par Hergé dans *Tintin*, sous les traits de la Castafiore. D'où le toc à ce nom.

– Ah oui, quand même...

– La seule chose qu'on a, ce sont des messages entre Gounod et la Castafiore, à intervalles réguliers, avec seulement un code : un chiffre et une lettre accolée ; une nouvelle lettre, avec un ou deux chiffres. Bien sûr, jamais les mêmes.

Henri essaye d'analyser ce que vient de lui annoncer son subordonné.

– Ça veut dire quoi ?

– Faut demander à la Castafiore.

– Son téléphone est toujours actif ?

– Eh non, portable coupé depuis la mort de la Carlton. La Castafiore a cessé de chanter.

– Comment on va faire, alors ?

– J'en sais rien : c'est toi, le chef.

Henri se revoit jeune inspecteur au « 36 », quand il n'était encore que le 3e ou 4e de groupe, obéissant aux instructions de son supérieur hiérarchique, le CID Louis Clert. Même s'il lui arrivait de proposer des axes d'enquête, il n'avait pas de décisions à prendre, juste à exécuter. Les temps ont changé, il a acquis de l'expérience et est devenu numéro un de groupe. C'est à lui que revient la responsabilité de décider des actions. Quand toutes les issues semblent fermées, il aimerait bien, un instant, que ses anciens chefs lui donnent des directives, ne plus être celui qui décide, redevenir celui qui exécute.

Son regard se pose sur une affiche de « Papa Juliette » annonçant leur prochain concert à la salle de réception du cercle militaire de Marseille, au fort Ganteaume. Le concert sera donné en hommage aux policiers blessés ou morts en service.

– Basile, c'est à cette occasion que le père de Lucie sera décoré ?

Le lieutenant n'a pas le temps de répondre, la porte s'ouvre avec énergie. Lucie, la fille de Louis Clert, entre.

35

Les deux policiers ne s'attendaient pas à cette entrée et Lucie ne pensait pas trouver Henri ici. Elle est troublée, elle souhaitait discuter de Saint-Donat avec le jeune lieutenant. Il est celui qui le connaît le mieux. Peut-être s'est-il déjà confié sur son fils, sur sa maladie ?

Elle cherchait surtout un prétexte pour avoir un peu d'intimité avec Urteguy, un moment de répit, en tête à tête, sur un sujet ne relevant pas des enquêtes en cours.

– Ça va, Lucie ? Un problème ?

La présence d'Henri agace la capitaine. Elle reste muette.

– T'as besoin d'un coup de main avec ton gardé à vue ?

Après avoir été si remontée contre le commandant, elle sent sa colère retomber. Mais elle n'est pas femme à lâcher le morceau.

– T'aurais pu me prévenir, Henri.

Henri ne tient pas compte de la réaction de la capitaine.

– T'as vu, Lucie ? La PJ de Melun a identi-fié Yassine Hosni. On le cherche à Marseille et on le retrouve dans l'Yonne.

– Henri ? Pourquoi tu m'as pas donné l'info en premier ?

– ... ?

– J'en ai marre d'être prise pour une conne, Henri.

Basile, surpris, intervient.

– Quoi, Yassine Hosni a été retrouvé ?

– Oui, mort. Deux balles dans le buffet, enroulé nu dans une bâche plastique et jeté dans l'Yonne.

– Sans déc ? Mais c'est énorme.

– Je te le fais pas dire.

Basile cherche à comprendre la raison de la colère de Lucie. Elle a vu trop de voyous morts pour s'apitoyer sur leur sort.

– Il est où, le problème ?

– Je ne sais pas, demande à Lucie.

La capitaine, furieuse, s'avance vers Henri pour lui demander des comptes, quand elle voit le sac de la Carlton au pied du bureau.

– C'est quoi, ça ?

– Un sac Louis Vuitton. Une folie à 30 000 euros. Pour me faire plaisir. Ça va très bien à mon teint.

– Arrête de déconner, Basile. T'as trouvé ça où ?

Lucie n'apprécie pas à sa juste valeur l'humour de Basile.

– C'est le sac de la Carlton. La seule chose qu'elle a laissée dans sa chambre. Avec des fringues, un ordi, quelques bricoles à l'intérieur.

Lucie est obnubilée par ce qu'elle vient d'apprendre. Elle se penche, ramasse le sac. Le regarde sous toutes les coutures. Confirme ses formes étonnantes.

– Putain, le même. Exactement le même.

Le changement d'attitude de leur collègue étonne Henri et Basile. L'excitation gagne Lucie. Elle s'énerve, obligée de leur expliquer : en perquisition au domicile de la famille Hosni, ils ont trouvé de la came sur le toit, jetée depuis le balcon par Bilal, glissée à la hâte dans un sac.

– Le même sac, avec les mêmes formes, les mêmes coutures. Vous voyez bien que c'est pas un modèle courant, c'est un truc fait sur mesure, ça !

– Désolé, on est plus « Prisu » que « Vuitton ».

Le ton perfide de Basile n'atteint pas Lucie. Elle soulève le sac par les anses, le soupèse, le tourne dans tous les sens, l'expose devant les yeux d'Henri.

– Les valises de la Goldwing !

Saint-Donat arrache le sac des mains de Lucie et le scrute à son tour. Il plonge ses bras dedans, lui redonne tout son volume et l'exhibe fièrement.

– Il a les mêmes dimensions que les caissons latéraux de la Goldwing. Les valises contre la roue arrière. Il est conçu pour se glisser à l'intérieur.

Basile lance un clin d'œil pernicieux à Lucie.

– Comme papa dans maman, quoi…

Henri, dans l'excitation de sa découverte, continue.

– D'où ses dimensions particulières. Elle se refusait rien, la Carlton, des sacs sur mesure pour sa moto chez Louis Vuitton.

– Ça a dû lui coûter une blinde !

– Et vous avez trouvé le même chez Hosni ?

Lucie quitte le bureau en courant. Les deux hommes, habitués aux éclats de la capitaine, se regardent, dubitatifs. Lucie les surprendra toujours. Elle est de retour avant qu'ils aient le temps de commenter son attitude, avec le sac trouvé chez Hosni, qu'elle exhibe avec fierté à ses collègues. Elle le place à côté de celui qui contenait les affaires de la Carlton. Le doute n'est pas possible. Si celui trouvé chez Hosni est un peu abîmé, les deux sont identiques.

Deux sacoches sur mesure, deux valises arrière pour la Goldwing de la Carlton.

36

Après l'effervescence, le silence règne. Henri s'est assis de nouveau sur sa chaise, à l'écart. Le jeune lieutenant s'est rapproché de la capitaine, côte à côte ils contemplent les deux sacs. Lucie rompt la réflexion. Basile lui répond.

– Putain, ça pue...

– Le mot est faible.

– Comment une gonzesse comme la Carlton a pu être en contact avec la famille Hosni ?

– C'est toute la question.

– C'est quoi, le lien entre cette femme qui fréquente l'Intercontinental et ces petits voyous de la Cayolle ?

– On se le demande.

– C'est la lutte des classes chez les voyous ?

– Ça y ressemble.

Cette tentative de rapprochement de Basile vers Lucie n'échappe pas à Henri. Habituellement si prompt à dégainer une vanne légère ou à faire preuve d'esprit mordant, Urteguy ne trouve pas d'autre solution pour séduire Lucie que d'abonder en tous points à ses propos. Saint-Donat se dit qu'être doué en musique n'est pas un gage de réussite en amour. Si tous les deux étaient plus simples dans leur relation à l'autre, ils feraient un beau couple. Comme pour lui donner tort, les deux officiers se collent presque. Il hésite avant de casser l'intimité qui se crée entre eux.

– Vous êtes mignons, les minots.

La capitaine et le lieutenant s'écartent l'un de l'autre, gênés, comme s'ils étaient pris en train de discuter en classe. Basile retourne triturer son ordinateur, pendant que Lucie pousse une guitare pour s'asseoir. Henri continue d'être professionnel.

– Avant les interrogations, les faits. Un sac appartenant à la Carlton est retrouvé au domicile d'Hosni. Elle est donc en lien avec cette famille. Fait confirmé par le GPS de sa Goldwing : le dernier trajet effectué par sa moto indique qu'elle s'est rendue à la Cayolle...

– Quoi ? Et vous m'avez rien dit ? Vous attendiez quoi ?

– De te voir. Jusqu'à maintenant on n'a pas vraiment eu le temps.

La capitaine grogne, bien obligée de reconnaître qu'Henri a raison. Les événements qui se sont déroulés depuis vingt-quatre heures ne l'ont pas laissée souffler.

– À Marseille, on découvre le cadavre de la Carlton dans un barbecue. À Paname, les collègues identifient Yassine Hosni, Marseillais d'origine, comme étant l'un des auteurs d'un braquage de fourgon et d'un flingage sur une malheureuse passante. Ils le retrouvent mort dans des circonstances s'apparentant, là aussi, à un règlement de comptes. D'où les questions : ces règlements de comptes sont-ils liés ? Si oui, pourquoi ?

Basile, comme un môme, tend la main pour prendre la parole.

– La bagnole cramée dans laquelle a été retrouvée la Carlton a été volée à la Soude. 800 mètres à vol d'oiseau de la Cayolle.

– Lien indirect, mais lien tout de même. Un point pour toi.

– La Carlton est une pro du braquage d'envergure et Yassine Hosni, avant d'être retrouvé mort, est identifié sur un vol à main armée commis par des pros.

– Deuxième point pour toi.

Le silence se fait. Lucie semble n'avoir rien à ajouter. Elle se passe la main dans les cheveux, réfléchit, avant de se faire l'avocat du diable :

– En même temps, chez les Hosni, c'est Bilal qui est trouvé en possession du sac de la Carlton, pas Yassine.

– « Si ce n'est lui, c'est donc son frère… »

Lucie jette un regard noir à Basile. Il y a deux minutes, il acquiesçait à tout ce qu'elle disait, maintenant il se moque ? Basile rougit, regrette déjà son mot d'esprit. Henri ne perd pas la spirale d'idées.

– Remarque pertinente, Lucie. Il faut vérifier si la Carlton était en lien avec Bilal ou Yassine.

– Ou les deux. Elle était peut-être en affaires avec les deux frangins.

Le caractère impétueux de Lucie n'empêche pas son professionnalisme. Bien la fille de son père, pense Henri. Le silence reprend ses droits dans le bureau.

37

Depuis cinq minutes, les policiers réfléchissent devant les sacs de la Carlton. Henri le sait, après la synthèse et les questions vient le temps des directives.

– C'est moi le chef. Mais chacun peut y aller de sa proposition. Je vous écoute.

À tour de rôle, les deux autres policiers énumèrent ce qu'ils doivent faire. Les idées fusent.

– Vérifier auprès de l'usine Vuitton qui a fait faire les sacs. Une commande comme celle-ci doit laisser des traces.

– Je prends.

– Analyser la vidéosurveillance des caméras de la ville le soir du vol de la Picasso ayant brûlé avec la Carlton.

– OK.

– Pareil avec la vidéosurveillance de l'Intercontinental, savoir si la Carlton a eu des visites durant son séjour.

– C'est pas encore fait, ça ? En toute urgence.

– Secouer Bilal Hosni en garde à vue pour savoir s'il connaît la Carlton.

– En urgence aussi.

Petit moment de répit. Chacun réfléchit aux enquêtes en cours. L'émulation monte entre les deux officiers.

– Établir la chronologie des morts. Qui est mort en premier, la Carlton ou Yassine Hosni ?

– Pourquoi ?

– Si ces affaires ont un lien, quelle mort a entraîné l'autre ? C'est le principe des règlements de comptes, non ?

Henri félicite Lucie pour cette proposition. Le point sera fait après les autopsies. Basile ne veut pas être en reste.

– Identifier Maria Castafiore ?

Saint-Donat lui demande comment il compte s'y prendre. Lucie s'étonne : qui est cette femme ? Henri le lui explique : le seul contact avec qui la Carlton échangeait avec son téléphone portable. Un toc, qui communiquait avec elle par messages, en énumérant des lettres et des chiffres.

– Un code à déchiffrer, quoi.

– Mais encore ?

– Faire les fadettes de ce téléphone ainsi que la triangulation téléphonique dans le secteur de la Cayolle, du lieu de découverte du corps de la Carlton, de l'Intercontinental...

– Et du lieu du braquage du fourgon des Parisiens, ainsi que du lieu de découverte du corps de Yassine Hosni. Avec un peu de chance, on aura peut-être des numéros qui carillonnent sur ces mêmes points.

Henri sourit devant cette saine concurrence d'idées. Les deux officiers se complètent bien, en tout cas professionnellement.

– Le fichier Mercure* nous sera pratique pour ça. Rien d'autre ? On a fait le tour ?

Lucie et Basile pensent avoir tout énuméré. Il y a du pain sur la planche, mais ils savent où aller. Ils ont un certain nombre de portes à fermer ou derrière lesquelles fouiller. Ils se lèvent, prêts à lancer leurs investigations. Henri stoppe leur élan.

– Encore deux-trois petites choses à noter.

Basile et Lucie sont étonnés, persuadés d'avoir fait le tour des actes d'enquête.

– Premièrement, Lucie, tu prends rendez-vous chez ton coiffeur, et tu te rases la tête. T'as perdu ton pari. Les deux affaires ont un lien.

La capitaine lâche un juron encore plus grossier que d'habitude. Par réflexe, elle passe la main dans ses cheveux. Basile

---

* Fichier Mercure : fichier d'exploitation des factures détaillées de téléphone.

lui assure que sa beauté naturelle ne sera pas altérée par ce dépouillement capillaire intempestif. Cette réflexion ne l'apaise pas. Elle continue de bougonner.

– Deuxièmement, on appelle les collègues de Melun, et on se met d'accord avec eux pour former une équipe commune d'enquête, après en avoir avisé le magistrat instructeur. Lucie, tu t'en occupes. Troisièmement, on rend compte au directeur. Je m'en charge.

– Pourquoi toi ?

– Basile nous l'a rappelé : je suis le chef !

Urteguy prend l'air contrit et se met à distance. Avec deux stylos, il tape en rythme sur son écran d'ordinateur. Henri jette de nouveau un œil à l'affiche du groupe « Papa Juliette » annonçant le concert au fort Ganteaume et demande à Lucie si c'est bien au cours de la cérémonie qui précède que son père sera décoré. Lucie acquiesce. Pour l'ensemble de sa carrière, Louis Clert va recevoir l'ordre national du Mérite.

– Tu seras magnifique, tête nue !

Ce sarcasme ne fait pas sourire Lucie. Elle devient grave, l'air ailleurs. Henri le remarque.

– Si ça t'emmerde tant que ça, t'es pas obligée. Ça peut attendre.

Lucie, vexée, se lève, quitte le bureau de Basile avant le commandant en lui claquant la porte au nez. Henri se tourne vers le lieutenant, il était moqueur mais bienveillant, qu'a-t-il encore dit pour provoquer l'ire de sa collègue ? Basile, stylos en l'air, s'est arrêté de battre le rythme. Il regarde, interdit, le commandant, se demande si la démonstration de la forte personnalité de Lucie l'effraie chaque fois un peu plus ou le séduit davantage. Il ressent juste l'envie furieuse de serrer cette femme dans ses bras. L'amour a ses raisons que le sale caractère ignore.

38

Il est arrivé avant les trois autres, s'est assuré que le bar était vide de toute menace. Rien qui de près ou de loin puisse ressembler à un condé. Il appelle encore les flics ainsi, même si ce n'est plus d'actualité. Il n'a jamais été du même camp que les poulets, mais a toujours considéré que, dans son système où l'illégalité est la règle, les flics sont un mal nécessaire, et qu'ils ne méritent certainement pas les insultes que certains n'hésitent pas à leur adresser. Question de respect. Et de génération.

En rentrant dans le rade où il a donné rendez-vous à ses potes, il jette de nouveau un regard suspicieux à l'intérieur. Un établissement d'un autre temps, à la décoration surannée, couleur rougeâtre aux murs, vieilles affiches de films, photos en noir et blanc d'acteurs dont les noms ont été oubliés depuis la fin de la guerre mondiale. La première, pas la seconde. L'ensemble respire la transpiration et ne pousse pas à la consommation. Il a bien choisi, les flics ne s'aventurent plus depuis longtemps dans ce type d'établissement.

La salle est clairsemée. Deux éternels pochtrons, déjà présents à l'ouverture de ce bistro du 18e arrondissement de Paris, ont pris possession du comptoir. Ils tiendront ainsi tant que leur cirrhose leur permettra d'être accrochés au bar, sachant que l'alcool finit toujours par vaincre l'alcoolique. Le patron, souffrant de rosacée, visage émacié, calé derrière le comptoir, essuie nonchalamment quelques verres, avec un torchon devant également lui servir de serpillière.

L'homme qui vient d'entrer salue d'un geste vague le gérant, qui ne bouge que d'un cil. Il ne s'étonne plus de rien depuis longtemps et surtout pas de la présence d'un client inhabituel. Ce dernier, pourtant, avec son physique de basketteur américain blanc, ne passe pas inaperçu. Ce n'est pas pour rien que dans le milieu, sans beaucoup d'originalité, on le surnomme le Grand. Mais le barman s'en fout. Comme il se fout de tout. La vie s'est chargée de lui rappeler qu'il n'a plus rien à en attendre, sinon la mort. Ici, maintenant, demain ou ailleurs, quand il sera l'heure. Parfois il se dit même que le plus tôt serait le mieux, et si un basketteur blanc de presque deux mètres, au visage peu engageant et au flingue dans le dos à peine dissimulé, pouvait lui faire gagner du temps sur son crédit horaire, il ne lui en voudrait pas.

L'homme s'installe au fond de la pièce, cale ses deux mètres entre la banquette et la table, dos au mur, à quelques pas de l'issue de secours, prêt à bondir. Depuis sa position stratégique, il commande au patron une pression et regarde sa montre. 18 h 50. Les autres ne vont pas tarder. Ils ont l'habitude d'être ponctuels. C'est aussi pour ça qu'il les a choisis.

C'est lui qui a provoqué cette réunion. Depuis la découverte des corps de Yassine Hosni et de la Carlton, il était urgent de voir toute la bande et de décider de la suite des opérations. Le souvenir de Nathalie Fournier, alias Mireille de Gounod, noue sa gorge. Pas de quoi provoquer un sanglot, mais un vrai haut-le-cœur, titillant ses glandes lacrymales. Il n'est pas habitué à ce genre de réaction. Quand on a commis autant de saloperies que lui, on a perdu l'habitude de chialer. Et vu sa taille, c'est mieux pour tout le monde. S'il se met à pleurer, ça pourrait vite se transformer en averse tropicale.

Mais depuis l'annonce de la mort de la Carlton, chaque fois qu'il pense à elle, une émotion inconnue l'étreint et le met dans un état de rage. S'il attrapait à ce moment-là le salaud qui l'a butée, l'homme passerait le pire moment de sa vie, avec délectation de supplices en prime. Et en la matière, son sens de l'imagination dépasse largement celui du quidam moyen.

Depuis qu'il a appris son décès, il se pose la question en boucle : pourquoi la Carlton ? Pourquoi avoir tué cette femme, dotée d'une sacrée paire de couilles ? Ce n'est pas incompatible. Capable de monter sur des braquages de haut vol et de se taper des jolies filles avec liberté et envie. En s'en foutant du qu'en-dira-t-on. Ce n'était pas sa petite amie, encore moins sa maî-tresse, surtout pas son épouse, c'était juste la grande, la belle, la talentueuse Carlton, ayant réussi l'improbable : se faire un nom de femme dans ce milieu d'hommes, un sur-nom de légende dans ce monde de réalités. Des salopards l'ont butée. S'il découvre qui, ils vont passer un mauvais quart d'heure. Le dernier.

Il n'est pourtant pas du genre à encen-ser les frangines. Il a même toujours pensé que leur place était au fond du lit, le sien de préférence. Dans son monde, il leur réserve une activité très personnelle, dénu-dée et physique. Histoire de leur rappeler qu'en termes de sexualité c'est toujours lui qui propose, dispose et explose. En tout cas dans sa vision limitative de la femme, dont la Carlton bien sûr ne fait pas partie. Et dans cette matière aussi, son sens de l'imagination dépasse largement celui du quidam moyen.

Il hausse les épaules, avec la Carlton, il ne se serait même pas permis d'imaginer le début du commencement d'un chaste baiser. Il descend d'une traite la pression que vient de lui servir le cafetier. Alors, le reste, il n'en a jamais été question, même en rêve ou dans le plus furieux de ses délires.

La porte du bistro s'ouvre. Le décès de la Carlton aura au moins permis ça : revoir ses vieux potes. Ponctuels, comme toujours. Teddy, le boxeur, Willy, l'acrobate, et Fred, le tatoué, le physique de chacun étant aussi significatif que son surnom. Les trois hommes, sans aucun regard pour les pochtrons affalés au comptoir, le rejoignent. Il les serre dans ses bras. Leur murmure : « Legio Patria Nostra. » Le Grand se sent déjà mieux. Il commande au patron une tournée générale de bière.

Entouré de ses frères d'armes, à l'engagement et à la détermination sans faille, il peut enfin sourire. Les autres n'ont qu'à bien se tenir. Les salauds qui l'ont butée

169

au match aller ont oublié ce détail : la Carlton ne jouait pas seule, elle était entourée d'une équipe. Ils n'auraient pas dû s'en prendre à elle. Les quatre hommes réunis sont prêts pour le match retour. En levant leurs verres, ils se le promettent : il y aura une revanche, sans place pour une « belle ».

39

La cour de l'hôtel de police grouille. Les uns et les autres se saluent. Les mêmes blagues du matin retentissent le soir. Certains sont pressés de rentrer chez eux. D'autres proposent d'aller boire un verre, prolonger la journée, se raconter leur dernière interpellation, prévoir les prochaines, avec moult anecdotes et beaucoup de mousse de bière. Henri a démarré sa moto et laisse ronronner le moteur, pour faire monter l'huile en température. Pas question de déroger à cette règle. Il enfile son casque et voit passer Lucie, étonné qu'elle quitte le service si tôt, ce n'est pas dans ses habitudes. Elle ne prête aucune attention à l'agitation qui règne dans la cour de l'Évêché. La relève assure un taux de remplissage élevé du parking. La police veille 24/24. Les lumières ne s'éteignent jamais à l'Évêché.

Son air égaré intrigue Henri. Elle porte en elle un côté enfantin. Une douce inquiétude perce sous la rebelle. Il enfourche sa Goldwing, fait le tour du parking, franchit la barrière et retrouve Lucie, qui partait à pied. Il l'appelle. Prise dans ses tourments, elle ne le reconnaît pas. Le commandant soulève sa visière, lui sourit. La capitaine reste stoïque, comme si elle ne pouvait toujours pas mettre de nom derrière ce casque. Saint-Donat l'enlève pour qu'enfin elle percute.

– Désolée, Henri, j'étais ailleurs.

– Ça ne va pas, Lucie ?

La capitaine hésite, mais coupe court, reste professionnelle.

– J'ai repris Bilal Hosni en audition. Il ne veut rien savoir. Il ne connaît pas la Carlton, n'a jamais entendu parler d'elle. Le sac Vuitton qui transportait la came, il ne sait pas d'où il vient. Selon lui, il n'est pas seul à habiter à cette adresse. Ce sac peut être à ses frangins, Yassine ou Khaled, ou à sa mère.

– Tu t'attendais à autre chose ?

Depuis presque quinze ans qu'elle est flic, Lucie ne désespère pas un jour de trouver un peu de bon sens chez les voyous. Espérer que l'évidence les conduise à la vérité. Ce n'est pas Bilal Hosni qui lui donnera raison.

– Dès que je lui ai posé des questions plus précises, il a fait valoir son droit au silence. Il a refusé d'y répondre.

– « On a beau dire, on a beau faire, le cul du berger sentira toujours le thym. »

Lucie sourit à l'évocation de ce proverbe provençal.

– Il a un bon baveux* ?

– Maître Juan Marco Fernandez. Un spécialiste de la voyoucratie locale.

Henri sent que Lucie ne lui dit pas tout et se raccroche à ce qu'elle sait le mieux faire : parler boulot.

– De toute façon, on le tient sur les stups. Il a beau chiquer**, y'a son ADN dessus. Il devrait partir au ballon pour ça. Ça nous donnera le temps de continuer à gratter sur sa relation avec la Carlton. Les Stups reprennent le dossier sur le trafic, on s'occupe du reste.

Le regard profond d'Henri met mal à l'aise la capitaine. Elle fait semblant de s'intéresser à l'enquête en cours.

– Et vous, ça a donné quoi ? La vidéo-surveillance de l'hôtel ? Le téléphone de la Carlton ?

– Un bordel. Ils ont au moins vingt-cinq caméras à l'Intercontinental. On a pu bloquer les images, Basile bosse dessus.

---

* Baveux : expression argotique pour désigner les avocats.

** Chiquer : « nier », en argot.

Mais c'est du boulot. Et on a fait partir en urgence les « réquises* » aux opérateurs de téléphonie. Si tout va bien, on aura les réponses demain.

Lucie ne sait pas comment relancer la discussion et n'a surtout pas envie de la poursuivre. Mais Henri ne la lâche pas des yeux. La capitaine lui sourit, s'apprête à le saluer, mais il la devance.

– T'es pas obligée, Lucie, mais si t'as un souci, tu peux m'en parler.

Lucie n'a pas l'habitude de discuter de ses problèmes personnels avec ses collègues. Ce n'est pas une coutume professionnelle de la BRB. Se mettre en colère, balancer des vannes, parler stratégie ou procédure pénale, elle sait faire, mais se confier, pas le genre de la maison. Elle n'a pas été élevée comme ça. Par son père, par ses collègues et par orgueil, s'étant persuadée qu'une femme dans la police devait encore moins que les hommes montrer ses faiblesses. Elle ne s'étale jamais sur sa vie privée et les inévitables soucis qui peuvent en découler.

– On a franchi la barrière de sécurité, Lucie. On est dans la rue, pas au bureau. Tu peux te lâcher.

---

* Réquise : raccourci policier signifiant « réquisition ».

Pour Lucie, c'est l'effet Kiss Cool. En souriant, elle fond en larmes.

– C'est papa.

– Qu'est-ce qu'il se passe ?

– Son état s'est aggravé.

Lucie comprend qu'Henri n'est pas au courant.

– Il t'en a jamais parlé, c'est ça ? Têtu comme une bourrique. Et ça ne s'arrange pas en vieillissant.

– Quel âge il a, ton père ?

– 74 ans. Mais avec sa maladie il en fait dix de plus.

– Alzheimer ?

– Ça y ressemble. La démence à corps de Lewy. Une dégénérescence neurologique qui provoque d'importants troubles moteurs, cognitifs et psychiatriques. Il perd l'équilibre, fait des dépressions.

– C'est le métier, ça. Trente-cinq ans de police, ça laisse des traces...

Lucie sourit. Jaune.

– Peut-être, mais pas que. Petit à petit il perd son autonomie. Les médecins disent que c'est irrémédiable. Ça s'est aggravé ces derniers temps. Y'a huit jours, je l'ai retrouvé à moitié nu dans sa résidence. Aujourd'hui les pompiers l'ont récupéré boulevard Michelet, portant juste un maillot de l'OM sur lui. Rien en dessous.

Il voulait entrer au Stade-Vélodrome. Et tu le connais : pour jouer, pas pour être spectateur.

Henri ne peut pas s'empêcher de sourire. L'amour du foot chez Louis Clert a toujours été prégnant, pas étonnant qu'il ait décidé de prendre sa retraite sur les bords de la Méditerranée, où règne l'un des clubs les plus titrés de France.

– Ils l'ont conduit à la Timone, je partais le voir.

C'est donc pour ça qu'elle quittait le service plus tôt. Henri ne lui laisse pas le choix et décide de l'accompagner. Elle tente bien de s'y opposer. Mais Saint-Donat insiste. Il sort un casque de sa valise arrière et finit par lui avouer que c'est là aussi où il se rendait.

Lucie enfourche la moto, et quand Henri démarre, elle passe ses deux bras autour de sa taille. La scène n'échappe pas à Basile, qui sort de l'Évêché. Cette situation l'agace et sa réaction encore plus, il a bien conscience qu'elle est ridicule et a du mal à accepter que sa jalousie l'emporte sur sa raison.

40

Lucie est bercée par la douce conduite de Saint-Donat. Surprise de constater que la Goldwing est un véritable paquebot sur roues. Casque sur les oreilles, elle se laisse porter par l'ambiance, le doux ronronnement du moteur et les trajectoires parfaites du pilote. Elle ferme les yeux et lâche prise. Comme si le fait de ne pas voir son interlocuteur l'aidait à s'épancher.

– Tu te rends compte, Henri, papa a deux fois mon âge. J'en ai 37, il a 74 ans. Il avait mon âge quand je suis née...

Saint-Donat acquiesce du casque. Le moment est rare, presque précieux. Pas question de troubler les confidences de Lucie.

– Et moi, au même âge, j'ai toujours pas de mec... Pas de mec et pas d'enfant.

Perdue dans ses pensées, Lucie ne se rend pas compte qu'à ses mots la moto fait un léger écart de côté.

– Avec les mecs, je n'ai toujours eu que des histoires merdiques. Des plans cul, des histoires sans lendemain. Ce n'est pas faute d'avoir cherché le bon, celui qui pourrait être le père de mon fils. Je me suis toujours imaginée maman d'un petit garçon.

Lucie ne se rend pas compte qu'Henri évite de justesse une voiture qui déboule devant lui.

– Quand j'étais avec Malmaison, je pensais avoir trouvé le bon. Un mec précis, sérieux, un putain de bon flic, je me suis dit « ça y est, c'est le bon », il a toutes les qualités. Un peu plus âgé que moi, mais pas trop. Méticuleux, ne laissant rien au hasard. Avec sa maturité, il ferait un super papa. Tu parles, un triste cul, intéressé que par la gestion de son pognon. Pour être précis, il était précis. Mais chiant. Impossible d'imaginer avoir un môme avec un mec radin.

Même si le boulevard Baille devant lui n'est pas complètement dégagé, Henri accélère. En même temps que les propos de Lucie augmentent en intensité.

– Mais tu vois, Henri, en cherchant comme ça, d'histoire en histoire, de mec en mec, on se retrouve vite sans rien. Sans amant, sans mari, sans personne. On se retrouve juste avec le temps qui file et son père qui vieillit. Maman est partie si tôt. Il ne me reste que lui, papa. Le super-méga-casse-couilles chef inspecteur divisionnaire

Louis Clert, que j'aime par-dessus tout et qui me casse les pieds encore plus, mais c'est mon p'tit papa, mon héros. Et si ça se trouve, avec cette putain de maladie, je n'aurai même pas le temps de lui montrer son petit-fils. Mon père qui a tout fait pour moi, jusqu'à me filer son job et ce putain de sale caractère.

Le feu orange à l'angle des boulevards Baille et Sakakini oblige Henri à stopper. Lucie ne peut pas voir ses yeux rouges. Enfermée dans son discours, elle ne se rend pas compte qu'Henri n'est pas dans son état normal. Quand le feu passe au vert, la Goldwing ne redémarre pas. Les voitures la doublent en klaxonnant.

– Henri, c'est vert. Tu peux y aller.

Ces propos le sortent de sa léthargie, il relance son engin. Cet arrêt prolongé n'a pas stoppé le soliloque de Lucie, au contraire, et comme si elle souhaitait donner plus d'importance à ses paroles, elle tape rageusement sur la veste de motard de Saint-Donat.

– Tu comprends, Henri, pendant ce temps, mon horloge biologique, elle tourne, putain. Elle tourne sans s'arrêter, et bientôt, moi, je pourrai plus avoir d'enfant.

Henri freine plus qu'il n'aurait dû. Malgré son état, il maîtrise sa bécane. Ils sont

179

arrivés devant le service des urgences de la Timone. Pas question de montrer quoi que ce soit à Lucie. Il garde son casque sur la tête, invite sa passagère à descendre et lui précise qu'il la rejoint. Le temps de trouver un endroit sûr où stationner sa Goldwing.

Et de sécher ses larmes.

41

Henri retrouve ses esprits et la chambre de Louis, où Lucie a déjà pris place au chevet de son père, placé sous perfusion. Le potentiel de son caractère semble intact.

– Henri ? Je vais bien ! Tu vas pas t'inquiéter chaque fois que je vais au Vélodrome. Tu le sais, s'il n'en reste qu'un, je serai celui-là.

– Même si l'OM joue en première série, tu seras encore supporter !

– Le dernier.

– Le seul…

Les deux hommes sourient de leur complicité, sous l'œil bienveillant de Lucie. Louis attrape le bras de son ancien subordonné et lui demande à l'oreille.

– Comment elle se débrouille, la gamine ?

Lucie a entendu la question. Elle connaît son père par cœur : malgré ses quinze ans de métier, son grade de capitaine, les nombreux voyous à son tableau de chasse, il sera toujours inquiet de savoir si elle est un bon flic.

– Bon sang ne saurait mentir.

Le visage du vieil homme s'illumine, il se tourne vers sa fille, souriant.

– Je n'en ai jamais douté. Mais, dans ce job de dingues, il ne faut rien lâcher. Jamais. La persévérance est la clef du succès.

– Papa ! Tu radotes.

– Sois pas inquiet, Louis. Elle a touché la part principale de son héritage.

Sous le sourire de Louis, une ride de douleur traverse son visage. La crainte se lit dans les yeux de Lucie et Henri.

– Ça va. Faites pas ces têtes. Je serai en forme pour ma remise de médaille. Pas question que je meure avant de les avoir revus. Lulu, Marcel, Guy, Félix. Si je pars avant eux, ils seraient encore capables de se foutre de moi !

À l'évocation des prénoms de ces illustres anciens de la PJ, que Lucie a connus enfant et Henri jeune flic, ils se regardent. Admiratifs du lien qui les unit encore, même à la retraite. Les deux policiers encore actifs se regardent, sauront-ils entretenir cette amitié après avoir rendu leur arme et leur carte ? La police judiciaire, devenue parfois si administrative, leur permet-elle encore de créer de tels liens ? La présence d'Henri dans la chambre de son ancien chef de groupe est un début de réponse. Tous les deux le sentent : tant qu'ils partageront les mêmes aventures, leur solidarité sera assurée. Dans ce métier, l'humain prendra toujours le pas sur l'administratif. C'est cet esprit qu'ils doivent préserver.

Lucie s'affaire auprès de son père en silence. Henri glisse sa main dans sa poche de pantalon et triture l'objet qu'il a glissé à l'intérieur. L'heure avance, il ne va plus pouvoir reculer. Il se l'est promis il y a des années, quand il était encore en poste au « 36 ». Il se rendait plusieurs fois par semaine à l'hôpital Necker, il a poursuivi à la Timone en arrivant à Marseille. Même si l'approche de ce moment le glace d'effroi, il sait que l'instant qui suit donne du sens à sa vie. Et que ce moment douloureux lui est devenu nécessaire. Il se décide, embrasse Louis et sa fille, et quitte le service des urgences.

Ses pas le conduisent dans une autre aile de l'hôpital, où il a ses habitudes. Des infirmières, des médecins le reconnaissent et le saluent. Il serre encore plus fort cette petite boule de plastique au fond de sa poche. Certains lui glissent un sourire, d'autres le remercient de sa présence. Tous ne savent pas le courage qu'il lui faut pour pousser la porte du service pédiatrique.

42

Ils sont quinze, parfois vingt. En fonction de la disponibilité laissée par leurs soins, les enfants malades vont et viennent devant la troupe des « Nez rouges ». Henri n'a jamais osé demander l'âge du plus jeune. Tous n'ont pas pu se rendre dans la salle où se joue le spectacle. Certains ne peuvent pas quitter leur chambre. Parmi les enfants présents, quelques-uns ont entre 3 et 8 ans, les plus vieux ont entre 9 et 12. Après cet âge, on change de catégorie, la préadolescence a parfois du mal avec des types maquillés et affublés d'un nez rouge. Il faut trouver autre chose pour les distraire.

Presque tous sont vêtus d'une simple blouse, certains ont la tête rasée, d'autres tiennent entre leurs mains des déambulateurs sur lesquels sont fixées des perfusions. Devant eux Henri a enfin sorti son nez de clown du fond de sa poche. Il s'est rapidement maquillé et a pris sa place dans la troupe. La compagnie de musiciens, de comédiens et de bénévoles comme lui, s'évertue à faire rire son public. Le but de l'association des « Nez rouges » est simple et ne vise qu'une chose : distraire les enfants malades.

Henri est méconnaissable. Ce n'est pas le maquillage et l'accessoire au bout de son nez qui le rendent ainsi. D'habitude posé, réfléchi, il est transfiguré et dispense une énergie phénoménale. C'est ce que pense Lucie quand elle le découvre assis à même le sol, jambes repliées, devant un garçon âgé de 10 ou 12 ans maximum. Le flic et l'enfant discutent à bâtons rompus. Lucie les regarde, gênée et étonnée tout à la fois.

Quand il se rend compte de sa présence, Henri est à peine surpris. La capitaine n'a pas pu s'empêcher de vérifier où il se rendait après avoir quitté son père. Louis Clert n'a pas de raison de s'inquiéter, sa fille est un excellent flic. Elle vérifie tout, toujours. Juste pour comprendre le monde qui l'entoure et les gens qui l'habitent. Henri l'invite à s'asseoir à côté de lui et lui tend un nez rouge. Le petit garçon se tourne vers Lucie, qui tente de lui renvoyer un sourire bienveillant.

– Elle est trop canon, ta copine, elle est flic aussi ?

Henri assure les présentations.

– Lucie, je te présente Édouard. Dit « Doudou ». Doudou, je te présente Lucie.

La capitaine de police Lucie Clert. Oui, elle est flic, comme moi, mais non, ce n'est pas ma copine…

– Dommage. Elle est trop belle.

Édouard se tourne vers Lucie.

– C'est vrai, toi aussi t'es flic ? À la PJ comme Henri ?

Lucie, pas complètement à l'aise, se contente de hocher la tête.

– Et t'es où ? Aux mœurs, à la financière ?

Henri se tourne vers Lucie et, comme pour excuser le gamin, lui dit :

– Il est fan de la police, depuis tout petit.

– Il est pas bien grand.

– Il connaît tout sur tout. Il risque de te scotcher.

Comme pour lui donner raison, le petit Édouard persiste dans son interrogatoire.

– C'est quoi, ton poste ?

– Cheffe de groupe à la BRB.

– La BRB, mais c'est pas pour les femmes, ça !

– C'est quoi, ces préjugés, Doudou ? En 2018, dans la police, y'a pas de postes réservés aux hommes ou aux femmes.

La glace est rompue, la discussion roule. Henri lui a dit vrai, Doudou ne manque ni de culture policière, ni de sens de l'humour. Il interroge Lucie sur son métier et lui parle d'affaires policières qu'il a suivies à la télé.

Le gamin n'a peur de rien, et surtout pas de leur différence d'âge. Il lui demande si être aussi jolie dans la police est un atout ou un avantage. Devant ce numéro improbable de séduction, Lucie explose de rire. Henri ne se souvient pas de l'avoir vue comme ça, naturelle. Ses joues sont aussi rouges que son nez, et ses yeux brillent d'un éclat qu'il ne lui connaissait pas. Doudou en profite, sent que c'est le moment et pousse son avantage. Il est très inquiet et voudrait savoir si elle a un amoureux. Ou plusieurs. Et que, dans tous les cas de figure, il tient à la prévenir, lui n'est pas jaloux et est d'accord pour être son petit ami. Lucie ne peut pas se retenir, elle le prend dans ses bras et le serre très fort.

La capitaine se laisse porter par l'ambiance particulière du lieu et du moment. Celui où les maux et la souffrance disparaissent derrière les rires des enfants. Elle ne pose même pas la question de la pathologie d'Édouard. Tous oublient l'endroit où ils se trouvent et ne pensent pas à demain. Il sera toujours temps de se préparer, après, plus tard, un autre jour, aux transfusions, aux opérations ou aux départs.

Lucie et Henri, silencieux, errent dans les couloirs de la Timone. Perdus dans leurs pensées, ils cherchent la sortie, tout en se foutant de la trouver rapidement. Ils finissent par s'orienter et atterrissent sur le parking. Sans un mot, Henri recommence ses gestes mécaniques pour démarrer sa limousine sur deux roues. Il tend un casque à Lucie, mais la jeune femme décline. Elle souhaite rentrer seule, besoin de s'aérer le corps et l'esprit.

– Tu habites où ?

– Au Vieux-Port, sur mon voilier. Quatre kilomètres, max. Même pas une heure de marche.

Lucie a les moyens de se défendre. Henri monte sur sa moto et s'apprête à partir. Lucie pose sa main sur son bras.

– Henri. Merci.

Saint-Donat hausse les épaules.

– Merci à toi.

– C'était donc ça ?

– Quoi ?

– Toutes les fois où tu t'absentes de l'Évêché, c'était pour ça, pour eux. Les enfants malades, Doudou… et les autres ?

– Le cul, c'est plus de mon âge. Faut bien que je m'occupe.

– C'est pour Octave, aussi ?

À l'énoncé de ce prénom, Henri cale. Il essaye de redémarrer, mais n'y arrive pas. Il n'insiste pas, enlève son casque. Le moment est venu. Il ne peut plus reculer.

– On n'a pas trouvé de donneur compatible. Il nous a quittés. Il y a dix ans.

Lucie n'est pas sûre de comprendre.

– Mais ?

– Je ne m'étale pas sur ma vie privée. Pour les collègues, mon fils est majeur. Il poursuit ses études ou bosse quelque part.

Pour Lucie, c'est la soirée des découvertes et des émotions. Elle danse d'un pied sur l'autre.

– Désolée, Henri, je n'étais pas au courant.

– En même temps je fais tout pour ne pas en parler.

– Qu'est-ce qu'il s'est passé, Henri ?

Henri retient ses larmes. La douleur est encore si vive. Les années qui passent n'effacent rien. Bien au contraire. Son psy le lui a assez répété : elle sera toujours là, prégnante, comme un couteau qui s'enfonce dans la chair chaque jour un peu

189

plus profond. Elle ne deviendra acceptable que lorsqu'il arrivera à mettre des mots sur sa souffrance.

– C'est difficile, Lucie. Je n'en ai jamais parlé. Octave était plein de vie.

À ces mots, Henri fond en larmes. Il secoue la tête, se mouche bruyamment, essaye de ne pas sombrer complètement.

– Excuse-moi. Elle est tellement con, cette expression. Bien sûr qu'il était plein de vie, il avait 13 ans. Comme tous les enfants de son âge, il avait une énergie débordante. Mais il fatiguait plus vite que les autres, il vomissait, avait mal au ventre à se tordre de douleur. Ça a inquiété notre médecin traitant, qui lui a fait une kyrielle d'examens. Et le verdict est tombé, sans appel.

Lucie a arrêté de tanguer sur ses pieds, suspendue aux propos d'Henri. Elle lui attrape les mains, les serre fort dans les siennes.

– Insuffisance cardiaque. Un cœur trop gros pour son petit corps. Il ne pouvait pas suivre le rythme qu'il lui imposait. On n'avait pas le choix, c'était la transplantation ou... Mais on n'a pas trouvé de donneur. L'attente a duré onze mois. Il s'est battu tant qu'il a pu, avec toute son énergie d'enfant de 13 ans. Mais sa force et notre amour n'ont pas suffi. Il a fermé les yeux et ne les a plus jamais rouverts, il y a dix ans.

Les larmes d'Henri repartent de plus belle. Pour Lucie, tout s'éclaire, l'attitude du commandant quand elle a fait bouger son bureau, cette photo de son fils malade qu'il conserve, cet air absent qu'il peut avoir, comme si rien ne pouvait l'atteindre, cette absence de décoration personnelle dans son bureau et la conduite particulière de sa moto quand ils sont venus à l'hôpital.

– Les deux derniers mois, il était à l'hôpital Necker. Les membres de l'association « Les Nez rouges » passaient le voir régulièrement. J'étais tellement angoissé pour lui qu'Octave se marrait plus avec eux qu'avec moi. J'ai été étonné, puis j'ai compris. Je n'avais pas à lui faire supporter le poids de ma souffrance.

Henri essuie les larmes qui coulent sur son visage. Il tente d'afficher un timide sourire.

– J'ai adhéré aux « Nez rouges », et j'ai fait rire mon fils. Je l'ai fait rire jusqu'à ce qu'il nous quitte. Avant son départ, il m'a fait jurer de continuer à faire rire les enfants malades comme lui. Il m'a dit : « Tu comprends, ils ont pas tous la chance d'avoir un papa flic et clown. »

À ces mots, Lucie fond en larmes à son tour. Henri ne retient plus les siennes.

– Alors, Doudou et les autres, c'est douloureux, mais c'est vital pour moi.

Lucie sait qu'elle mettra plus d'une heure pour rentrer à pied au Vieux-Port. Il lui faut du temps pour digérer cette soirée. Henri prend sa moto, direction Cassis, en passant par le col de la Gineste. Pas question de prendre l'autoroute après tout ça. Il a besoin d'air, de solitude et de liberté.

44

La moto, la route, la beauté des paysages. Et le silence. Surtout en pleine nuit. Henri est usé. Jusqu'alors il voyait seul les enfants malades. Il ne partageait ce moment avec personne. Son jardin secret. Sa bulle protectrice. Celle qui l'oblige à se battre contre ses démons. Les évacuer, les exorciser avec un nez rouge sur le visage. Quitter son costume de justicier du quotidien et enfiler celui de clown. Pour faire sourire Doudou et les autres, et se sentir lui-même un peu plus vivant. Il n'est pas dupe. Sa participation à l'association relève d'une démarche égoïste. Tout un paradoxe. En donnant aux autres, s'oublier soi. Il sourit, jaune. Un peu comme son métier de policier. Flic, clown d'une société malade, chargé d'en assurer la sauvegarde. On en a toujours besoin, mais comment prendre au sérieux des hommes ou des femmes de 20 à 60 ans, qui jouent encore aux gendarmes et aux voleurs ?

Le col de la Gineste défile. Les idées se bousculent. Il n'arrive plus à en trouver le

sens. Pour la première fois, ce soir, il s'est
confié à quelqu'un du service. Cette trans-
parence lui a fait du bien, mais a ouvert
une brèche qu'il ne voulait pas montrer.
Depuis combien de temps n'avait-il pas
parlé d'Octave ? Pourquoi s'est-il confié à
Lucie ? Pouvait-il faire autrement ? Quand
le trop-plein du silence déborde, faut-il
nécessairement l'évacuer ?

En pilotant sa moto, il revoit Octave, il
entend son rire. Sa voix résonne en lui. Elle
résonnera toute sa vie, ancrée au plus profond de ses entrailles. Il a juste envie de lui
parler, le serrer dans ses bras. Comme dans
une chanson de Renaud revisitée, sauter
dans les flaques pour le faire marrer, et
s'asseoir sur un banc, encore cinq minutes
avec lui, lui dire que les méchants c'est les
autres. Il le sait, il est flic. Lui parler de ce
métier, si fort, si prenant, si douloureux.
Partager. Les rires, les jeux, les pleurs,
les câlins. Encore. Sa vue se brouille, ses
yeux débordent. C'est le moment. Il doit
s'arrêter, ne pas aller plus loin. Rejoindre
Octave, enfin.

Il vient de franchir Cassis, attaque la
route des Crêtes, les premiers passages en
douceur, en courbes fines et élancées, les
suivants un peu plus vite, et la lune qui l'accompagne comme inspiratrice magnifique,

ronde et lumineuse. Elle le guide jusqu'aux hauteurs des falaises. Le cap Canaille, vertigineux, se fait l'écho des démons qui le hantent, des souvenirs qui le détruisent.

Il stoppe sa Goldwing sur un parking naturel éclairé par cette lune sans tache. Il ôte son casque, suit le chemin tracé par ses rayons. Il a pris sa décision, il est presque apaisé. Aucune barrière ne pourrait le retenir. Le cap Canaille est libre de toute protection. Il a le choix. La vie ou retrouver Octave.

Il regarde la mer, 390 mètres plus bas. Attirante et sensuelle.

Drôle d'endroit pour mourir.

45

Marseille,
mercredi 11 avril 2018, 9 heures.

Francis Larrivée est agacé, c'est peu de le dire. Sa moustache se dresse toute seule. En invitant ses cadres à rentrer, il provoque leur surprise : la grand-messe du matin débute à l'heure. En se rendant dans son bureau, Lucie se glisse vers Julie, la secrétaire :

– Il n'a pas lu *L'Équipe* ce matin ?

Julie Montserrat, la cinquantaine clinquante, grande, sèche, connaît Francis Larrivée depuis trente-sept ans. Quand il est dans cet état, elle est la seule à lui tenir tête. Le prix de sa fidélité administrative, que lui concède Larrivée. Lorsque, jeune policier sorti de l'École nationale supérieure de la police de Saint-Cyr-aux-Monts-d'Or, formant les commissaires, il a intégré son premier service à la brigade criminelle du SPRJ d'Orléans, elle était déjà en poste. Elle a eu la prémonition que son nouveau patron, grand gamin aux allures de dandy anglais, avait une personnalité hors du commun et ferait une carrière exceptionnelle. Elle a décidé de lui lier la sienne.

Cette allégeance bureaucratique ne s'est jamais démentie et Julie a suivi Larrivée sur tous ses postes. Cela l'autorise à tenir tête au contrôleur général. Un vieux couple, sans aucune ambiguïté. Leur relation a été et restera professionnelle. Juste une forme d'admiration réciproque. Larrivée sait tout ce que sa secrétaire lui apporte, depuis la gestion des ressources humaines jusqu'au suivi des finances en passant par la tenue impeccable de son agenda. Et il a l'intelligence de ses débordements. Il a besoin d'elle lorsqu'il s'égare, tempête et hurle, pour lui rappeler qu'il est temps de revenir à la raison et à des propos plus mesurés.

Il y a plus de trente ans, Julie est tombée sous le charme singulier et intellectuel de ce jeune commissaire aux faux airs de Jean Rochefort. Le temps a donné raison à sa prémonition orléanaise. Le jeune commissaire du SRPJ d'Orléans a déroulé depuis une carrière remarquable. Le ministère de l'Intérieur parle de lui pour le plus haut poste de la police judiciaire, celui de directeur central. Diriger depuis Paris les quelque six mille flics de police judiciaire œuvrant sur le territoire national, zone

Antilles-Guyane incluse. Et ce ne serait que justice eu égard à son parcours exceptionnel. Et à l'investissement de sa secrétaire.

Julie aime bien Lucie. Les caractères semblables se reconnaissent. Elle lui confirme que Francis Larrivée est de mauvaise humeur, non seulement parce qu'il n'a pas lu *L'Équipe* pour cause de grève des ouvriers du papier, mais aussi parce qu'il vient d'apprendre que le poste de directeur central est en train de lui passer sous le nez.

– Ce n'est pas tant qu'il n'ait pas le poste, qui l'énerve. Mais c'est que celui qui est pressenti est un gamin. Enfin, pour lui. Un commissaire divisionnaire de dix ans son cadet, et qui à Bordeaux était un de ses subordonnés. C'est normal qu'il l'ait mauvaise. De toute façon, il est le meilleur pour ce poste.

Lucie n'en doute pas. Même si l'opinion de Julie envers son patron reste aussi subjective qu'aléatoire. La capitaine rentre dans le bureau de Larrivée, regarde les chefs de service présents en prenant place et percute. Elle se tourne vers la secrétaire.

– Appelez Urteguy. Je sais pas ce que fout Saint-Donat, il n'est pas là.

Julie s'exécute, et avant que tous n'aient le temps de s'installer, Basile Urteguy, cheveux en bataille et pantalon débraillé, se glisse dans le bureau.

– Le commandant Saint-Donat s'excuse, un problème avec sa bécane.

Résigné, le directeur l'invite à s'asseoir. Le laisser-aller vestimentaire du jeune lieutenant l'agace, mais c'est un bon flic. Et il faut croire que la mode n'est plus au costume en tweed anglais et cravate chic. La preuve, le jeune blanc-bec qui risque de devenir directeur central porte même des pantalons et des vestes non assortis. Sans parler de ses chaussettes. Orange. Crime de lèse-élégance. Tout se perd dans la boîte, il serait peut-être temps de raccrocher.

L'arrivée commence la réunion. Lucie capte l'attention de Basile et, par un jeu de regards, lui demande ce qui arrive à Saint-Donat. Une Goldwing ne tombe jamais en panne et en particulier celle du chef de la Crim'. Le mouvement fataliste des épaules de Basile ne la rassure pas. Il a menti au directeur. Lui non plus ne sait pas où est Saint-Donat.

46

La réunion s'éternise et ennuie Lucie. Elle est inquiète, Saint-Donat ne répond pas à ses messages. Elle s'impatiente. Jette des regards noirs aux différents participants et cherche à faire taire les beaux parleurs, soucieux de démontrer au directeur qu'ils maîtrisent l'affaire sur laquelle leur service travaille. Les thuriféraires l'emmerdent et lui font perdre son temps. Il y a urgence. Elle ne se gêne pas pour le faire remarquer. Ce qui n'échappe pas à Larrivée. Pourtant il ne fait rien pour accélérer les débats et semble même prendre un malin plaisir à ne pas lui céder la parole. Quand enfin il se décide.

– Mademoiselle Clert, tout vient à point à qui sait attendre. C'est votre tour.

Au ton employé par le directeur et à ce « mademoiselle » cinglant, Lucie sait qu'elle ne doit pas en rajouter. Pourtant elle n'hésite pas.

– Maintenant on a deux « macchab' » sur les bras, monsieur le directeur, sans compter le dommage collatéral de la pauvre femme tuée à bord de sa 307. La Carlton retrouvée aux Pennes-Mirabeau et Yassine Hosni, le braqueur fou de Melun, trucidé dans une bâche en plastique au fond d'une écluse de l'Yonne. À son « dom' », on a récupéré son petit frère Bilal avec 12 kilos de résine, qu'il transportait dans un sac Vuitton appartenant à la Carlton.

– Ça veut dire quoi, mademoiselle Clert ?

– Que la Carlton a rencontré les Hosni.

– Mais encore ?

– Que... que les deux affaires sont liées, monsieur le directeur.

– Et donc ?

Les autres intervenants ont compris où voulait en venir le DIPJ, certains commencent à sourire. D'autres soufflent la réponse à Lucie. Qui, lasse, finit par répéter :

– Que vous aviez raison, monsieur le directeur.

– À la bonne heure, capitaine. Ce n'est pas au vieux poulet qu'on apprend à tenir le poulailler. Il a encore de bons réflexes, le vieux coq. Ils ne savent pas ce qu'ils perdent à la direction centrale.

Il se frotte les mains. Et demande à Lucie de poursuivre ses explications.

– Le sac trouvé au domicile des Hosni à la Cayolle est le même que celui retrouvé à « l'Interco » contenant les affaires de la

Carlton. On a vérifié chez Vuitton, elle s'emmerdait pas, la Carlton. 90 000 balles les deux sacoches, faites sur mesure, celles des caissons d'une Goldwing 1 500, payées en espèces.

Elle se caresse les cheveux.

– Saint-Donat aussi avait raison.

Le directeur se tourne vers Urteguy.

– Des nouvelles de votre commandant ?

– Toujours pas, monsieur le directeur.

– Vous me tenez au courant.

Basile hoche la tête. Lucie s'autorise à continuer.

– Par ailleurs, monsieur le directeur, les collègues de Melun ont procédé à l'autopsie de Yassine Hosni. Le médecin légiste est formel. Sa mort remonte à fin mars.

– Et alors ?

– C'est plusieurs jours avant celle de la Carlton, qui s'est rendue à la Cayolle, la cité des Hosni, la veille de son décès.

– On le sait comment, ça ?

Urteguy intervient.

– L'exploitation du GPS de sa moto. On a retracé son itinéraire. Elle a fait l'Intercontinental-la Cayolle, en passant par le Vieux-Port, le quai de Rive-Neuve, la plage des Catalans, la Corniche, la Pointe-Rouge.

Le directeur impose le silence. Son front se tasse et ses doigts lissent sa moustache.

Urteguy regarde, un peu perdu, Lucie, qui lui fait signe de continuer. Il racle sa gorge avant de poursuivre :

– On a aussi procédé à l'exploitation de la tablette numérique retrouvée dans la chambre de la Carlton. Rien de personnel à l'intérieur, juste un truc étonnant : elle s'intéressait au championnat de France de foot. Elle était connectée sur des sites relatifs au calendrier des matchs de première division.

Le directeur semble surpris, mais pas plus que cela. Il est quand même le premier à suivre les résultats sportifs.

– Et on a exploité son téléphone dédié, avec lequel elle ne contactait qu'un seul numéro, attribué à Maria Castafiore.

– La Castafiore ? Elle ne manquait pas d'humour.

– Elle ne lui envoyait que des messages avec des chiffres et des lettres.

– Un code ?

– Certainement, monsieur. On ne l'a pas encore déchiffré. Par contre, on a les fadettes, avec la géolocalisation de ce téléphone.

Urteguy laisse le silence investir les lieux. Les doigts du directeur tirent encore plus sur sa moustache. Signe d'impatience.

– Et alors, Urteguy ? Il carillonne où, ce portable ?

– Sa dernière géolocalisation borne à proximité de Melun. Deux jours avant le braquage commis sur le fourgon blindé, où Yassine Hosni flingue un témoin.

– Nom de Dieu de bordel de merde, qu'est-ce que ça veut dire ?

La réaction outrancière du directeur surprend tout le monde. Sauf Lucie, heureuse de voir que le directeur connaît des jurons plus anciens que les siens, et de l'effet produit par ce *cliffhanger*.

– Eh bien, que de près ou de loin, la Carlton est aussi liée à l'équipe de braqueurs de Melun, celle de Yassine Hosni, qui a trouvé la mort dans un règlement de comptes onze jours avant qu'elle-même se fasse cramer, façon barbecue marseillais. Ça pue, monsieur le directeur, si vous m'autorisez l'expression.

– Vous n'attendez pas toujours ma permission, Lucie.

Le directeur regarde la capitaine, puis le jeune lieutenant Urteguy. Ils ont fait du bon boulot en peu de temps. Avec cette fièvre dans le regard, qu'il connaît par cœur, et qu'ils viennent de lui transmettre. Même s'il n'est pas nommé demain directeur central de la police judiciaire, il n'est pas encore prêt à lâcher ce job.

47

– C'est pas tout, mais, là, on a du taf, les enfants.

En l'absence de Saint-Donat, le directeur se plonge dans l'enquête commune de la BRB et de la Crim'. Il fait sortir les autres chefs de service et garde dans son bureau Clert et Urteguy, un peu impressionnés. L'ancien chef de la brigade criminelle au SRPJ d'Orléans qu'il était au début de ses jeunes années ressurgit. Cette attitude rassure Julie Montserrat, elle reconnaît bien là son patron, jamais abattu, toujours prêt à relever le défi. Une bonne enquête criminelle, des ficelles à tirer, des meurtres à élucider, et il repart. Loin du bureau du directeur central de la police judiciaire, au plus près de la réalité des enquêteurs.

Francis Larrivée n'a rien perdu de ses réflexes d'homme de terrain, il distribue sa liste de courses aux deux officiers. D'abord s'intéresser aux membres de la famille Hosni. Et à tous leurs proches. Il faut trouver qui a pu mettre en relation la famille Hosni avec la Carlton. Sur les trois frères connus, Yassine est décédé, Bilal et Khaled sont détenus à la maison d'arrêt des Baumettes. Il charge la BRB d'étudier toutes les affaires pour lesquelles les frères Hosni sont tombés.

– … avec leurs complices, les femmes, les maîtresses, les parents, les frères et sœurs de leurs complices. Vous me passez tout le monde au tamis. Je veux tout savoir sur eux.

Travail fastidieux de recherche sur la documentation criminelle, nécessaire pour mieux diligenter les investigations. Revenir aux fondamentaux, toujours. Vérifier ensuite quelles sont les personnes ayant demandé de visiter les frangins en prison.

– Au premier lascar suspect, on demande au juge de sonoriser le parloir.

Lucie lui propose de lister tous les braquages de transports de fonds s'étant déroulés sur la DIPJ au cours de ces derniers mois. Vérifier s'ils ne pourraient pas avoir un lien avec l'équipe ayant « tapé » à Melun.

– On va faire mieux que ça, capitaine. On va lister TOUS les braquages de fourgons s'étant déroulés sur l'ensemble du territoire national, au cours de ces TROIS dernières années…

Il poursuit son raisonnent et se tourne vers Urteguy :

– ... et on va les mettre en corrélation avec les fadettes géolocalisées du portable de la Castafiore. La Carlton communiquait par code avec le portable de la chanteuse lyrique. Si je ne me trompe pas, un ou deux jours après que ce portable dédié reçoit un message codé, on devrait trouver un braquage dans le secteur où il se trouvait.

Il réfléchit encore, puis poursuit :

– ... et chaque fois que le téléphone a carillonné avec le code reçu, il devrait y avoir à proximité un hôtel de luxe où la Carlton est descendue. Il ne nous restera plus qu'à vérifier si Mireille de Gounod a pris une suite dans ces établissements. Vous voyez autre chose ?

Basile, concentré comme un écolier, suce son stylo. Il lève son doigt, provoquant un sourire attendri de Lucie et amusé de Larrivée.

– On peut faire l'inverse, monsieur. Établir des réquisitions auprès des établissements de luxe et leur demander de nous préciser si Mireille de Gounod a réservé une chambre au cours de ces trois dernières années, et vérifier en fonction de la date de réservation s'il y a eu des braquages d'envergure dans le secteur.

Le directeur tape dans ses mains. Ce jeune lieutenant l'épate.

– Vous avez raison, Basile, ça marche dans les deux sens. On fonce, les enfants, on fonce.

Urteguy et Clert se lèvent tout sourire de cet entretien. Avant de sortir de son bureau, le directeur leur donne une dernière consigne :

– Tout ceci ne nous exonère pas de vérifier les vidéosurveillances de l'Intercontinental pendant le séjour de la Carlton, histoire de voir s'il n'y a pas des têtes connues qui ont fréquenté ce haut lieu hôtelier de Marseille pendant cette période.

Quand ils sortent, Julie Montserrat remercie les deux officiers. Cela faisait longtemps qu'elle n'avait pas vu Francis Larrivée dans cet état d'excitation. Elle jette un coup d'œil dans son bureau, le DIPJ est déjà concentré, occupé à déchiffrer le code employé par la Carlton et la Castafiore.

48

Dès qu'elle est dans le couloir, Lucie empoigne son téléphone. Malgré le moment qu'elle vient de passer dans le bureau du DIPJ, elle rumine.

– Qu'est-ce qu'il fout, bordel ? T'as des nouvelles, toi ?

Basile hausse les épaules. Le commandant ne l'a toujours pas contacté. Lucie a une idée, joindre sa femme, Isabelle. À la tête que fait son jeune collègue, elle comprend.

– T'as pas ses coordonnées, c'est ça ? Basile, Saint-Donat, c'est ton chef de groupe, et t'as même pas le téléphone de sa femme.

La discussion qu'elle a eue la veille avec Henri lui revient. Le commandant n'a rien fait non plus pour laisser transparaître des éléments de sa vie privée.

– C'est bon, j'y vais.

– Tu vas où ?

– Chez lui, à La Ciotat.

– Mais tu vas faire comment ? T'as pas son adresse.

Sa question-affirmation se perd en écho dans les couloirs de l'Évêché. Lucie part en courant.

– Au secrétariat, ils l'ont forcément. Tu sais ce que c'est qu'un plan de rappel ?

Ce plan permet de rappeler tous les effectifs de police en situation d'urgence, les obligeant à laisser leur adresse personnelle et des numéros de téléphone utiles. Ce que Basile ne sait pas, c'est pourquoi il se retrouve planté comme un con. Et quel lien entretient Lucie avec Henri, pour qu'il devienne ainsi la source principale de son inquiétude. Il aurait bien poursuivi ce moment avec Lucie, à parler de leurs affaires en cours. Ou passées. Ou à venir. N'importe quelle affaire, pourvu qu'elle lui permette de rester encore un peu avec elle.

Il serait peut-être temps qu'il suive les conseils des « Bronzés » et de Saint-Donat. Oublier qu'il n'a aucune chance et foncer. En ronchonnant, il rejoint son bureau. S'assoit devant son ordinateur, ouvre sa boîte mail et clique sur le lien du message qu'il vient de recevoir.

Une vidéo s'ouvre sur son écran. Il vérifie le nom de l'expéditeur : Robert Battisteli, de l'Intercontinental. Il sourit jaune en repensant au responsable marseillo-britannique de l'établissement de luxe, mêlant expression argotique locale et accent anglais, quand il ne fait pas l'inverse. Il regarde l'ensemble d'un œil léger, quand son attention est attirée par un détail.

– *What the fuck !*

Lui aussi maîtrise parfaitement les subtilités de la langue de la perfide Albion.

49

Malgré son gyrophare et la sirène hurlante, Lucie n'arrive pas à circuler dans les
embouteillages menant à La Ciotat. Déjà,
pour atteindre la sortie sur l'A50 menant
à l'ancien port maritime, elle a eu du mal
à se faufiler. Depuis qu'elle roule sur les
voies rapides desservant le centre-ville,
c'est pire. La circulation est en croix dans
les deux sens. Si elle avait su, elle serait
passée par le col de la Gineste et Cassis,
et aurait emprunté la route des Crêtes. Au
moins elle aurait surplombé la baie de La
Ciotat et admiré les paysages depuis le cap
Canaille, connu des voyous pour les règlements de comptes, des amants pour des
relations adultères, et des désespérés qui
cherchent un moyen définitif pour en finir
avec cette saloperie de vie.

Prise par son enquête et son inquiétude,
elle ne s'est pas branchée sur Autoroute
FM. Sinon elle aurait su qu'un mouvement social bloquait la circulation dans le
centre-ville de La Ciotat, qui se répercutait
jusque sur l'A50. Comme toujours quand

elle est seule en voiture, elle préfère écouter un vieux titre de Bob Dylan, *Hurricane*, qui sait calmer son anxiété. Ça l'a toujours étonnée : la chanson capable de soigner son angoisse est celle du chantre de la liberté dans laquelle il raconte pendant huit minutes de scansion l'histoire d'une erreur judiciaire. Où la police n'a pas le plus beau des rôles.

Bloquée dans la circulation, elle fait taire Dylan. Il faudra quand même qu'elle demande à son psy ce que signifie sa passion pour les titres libertaires. Elle branche la radio et prend enfin connaissance de la cause du blocage. Elle tape du poing sur le volant, la liberté de manifester de certains prend vite le pas sur la liberté de circuler des autres ! Elle enrage et appelle Basile.

– Des nouvelles de Saint-Donat ?

– Toujours pas. Et toi ?

– Si je t'appelle pour t'en demander, l'arpète, à ton avis ?

La réflexion vexe Urteguy. Il prend sur lui.

– En revanche, j'ai un truc pour toi.

– Balance.

– Non ! Tu m'emmerdes, Lucie. Tu me parles mal, tu me jettes, tu m'insultes. Si tu veux le savoir, t'as qu'à rentrer, la Vioque.

Il doit s'affirmer face à la capitaine. La
« Vioque » n'était peut-être pas nécessaire,
mais reste la juste réponse à l'« arpète ». Et
tant pis si ce n'est plus de l'humour.

Lucie se demande si c'était une bonne
idée de le traiter ainsi. Ses humeurs ne
doivent pas empiéter sur ses relations avec
ses collègues. Surtout avec Basile. Elle s'en
veut et tente de le rappeler, mais le jeune
lieutenant ne répond pas. Elle hésite, puis
se décide à lui envoyer un message d'excuses, plus facile à écrire qu'à prononcer.

La réponse ne tarde pas, son téléphone
sonne. Les policiers ne se perdent pas en
effusion. Professionnels tous les deux.

– Sur la vidéo de l'Intercontinental, pendant le séjour de la Carlton, j'ai trouvé un
truc intéressant.

– Je t'écoute.

– Un mec que j'ai déjà serré : Ernesto
Dominguez. Un escroc à la petite semaine.
Tchatcheur, hâbleur. Il connaît tout le
monde à Marseille. Des petits voleurs aux
braqueurs. C'est un malin. Jamais dans les
gros coups, mais jamais bien loin. On le voit
plusieurs fois entrer à l'Intercontinental.

La phrase de Basile se perd dans le brouhaha des moteurs qui redémarrent et du
concert de klaxons qui s'ensuit. Le mouvement social a fini d'exercer sa liberté et

autorise le reste du monde à retrouver la sienne. Le flux de véhicules repart. Lucie remercie Basile et raccroche. Sa priorité est de savoir ce qu'est devenu Saint-Donat. Elle replace le gyrophare, actionne la sirène et arrive enfin à se glisser dans la circulation. Pour se redonner de l'allant, elle remet la chanson de Bob Dylan. En arrivant dans le centre-ville, elle croise des manifestants, qui, à la vue de sa voiture, crient encore plus fort des slogans anti-police.

Il y a des jours comme ça, où il ne faut pas l'agacer. Sirène hurlante, gyrophare sur le toit, par la fenêtre ouverte qui diffuse la chanson de Dylan, elle leur fait un magnifique doigt d'honneur.

50

Seul devant son écran, Basile est perplexe. Il n'a pas eu le temps de tout dire à Lucie. Mauvaise idée que de s'attacher à cette femme. Il faut qu'il avance. Qu'il ne se laisse pas perturber. Il souffle, sifflote un air. Tapote machinalement sur son clavier. Sa messagerie professionnelle est pleine. Des tonnes de mails qu'il ne prend pas toujours le temps d'ouvrir : des propositions de stage, des notes internes, des circulaires ministérielles, des directives locales. Il n'a pas le cœur, ni l'envie, il saisit l'ensemble et clique sur la corbeille.

Puis il attrape la guitare qui traîne dans son bureau et balance quelques accords. Ils ne sonnent pas juste. Il tente un riff, même résultat. Il se concentre et, à l'oreille, tend les six cordes de son instrument, avant d'enchaîner des accords harmonieux. Il peut enfin s'évader et être sur la scène de l'Olympia, il est Téléphone à lui tout seul. « Je rêvais d'un autre monde... où la Terre serait ronde... »

Ça le détend, il joue de plus en plus fort. Entre chaque couplet, il retend les cordes. La guitare n'a pas servi depuis longtemps. Quand il se met à hurler « *dansent les ombres du monde, dansent les ombres...* », il frappe encore plus sur son instrument. Éreintée par tant de frénésie, sa gratte abandonne la lutte. Une corde casse. Celle du *si*. Basile est trop puriste pour continuer à jouer avec cinq cordes et l'image d'une guitare à l'abandon le désole. C'est dommage, il était en voix. Mais il ne peut pas jouer sans *si*.

Cette réflexion sonne à son oreille. Il la répète. Il ne peut pas jouer sans *si*. Lui, le musicien, se demande pourquoi il est touché par la mélodie de cette formule. Il la prononce encore. Jouer sans *si*.

Il se précipite, pose sa guitare, ouvre sa boîte mail et trouve ce qu'il cherchait : un message qu'il venait de jeter. L'expéditeur est le directeur du Château de Sancy, hôtel-restaurant 4 étoiles situé à Sancy-les-Meaux, en Seine-et-Marne. Il a d'abord cru à une publicité du service social de la police, proposant des tarifs préférentiels dans cet établissement, et a saisi ce mail avec tous les autres pour s'en débarrasser, puis sa guitare a abandonné la lutte et la corde de *si* a lâché. Sans si : il a fait le lien...

... avec le braquage de fourgon sur lequel la PJ de Melun a identifié Yassine Hosni. Au cours de leur séjour marseillais, le lieutenant Forest lui avait signalé que le flingage au cours duquel la dame âgée avait trouvé la mort s'était déroulé sur un petit parking, pas très loin de l'A4, le long d'une départementale menant à Sancy.

Ce nom de village avait fait sourire le premier prix de conservatoire. Il avait tenté un de ces jeux de mots pourris dont il a le secret, en leur disant que, quand on est musicien, on ne peut pas jouer sans *si*. Il avait fait un bide. Pas certain maintenant que ce « sans-*si* » ne les fasse pas marrer, quand il va leur expliquer ce qu'il vient de découvrir. Le directeur de l'hôtel-restaurant 4 étoiles le Château de Sancy est un des premiers à avoir répondu à sa réquisition. Leur établissement a eu l'honneur d'héberger madame Mireille de Gounod du 23 au 27 mars, soit dans la période où le braquage du fourgon et le flingage de la vieille dame ont eu lieu.

Francis Larrivée avait raison. Quand un braquage d'envergure avait lieu, la Carlton n'était jamais loin.

51

Le plan de rappel est à jour. Au fond de l'impasse des Vieux-Moulins, Lucie trouve le numéro correspondant à l'adresse laissée par Henri. Elle coupe la musique, se laisse envahir par le silence. Regarde l'ensemble du quartier, et particulièrement la maison des Saint-Donat. La villa est jolie, sans plus. Ni petite, ni grande. Une terrasse surplombe un jardinet, propre mais sans fantaisie. Rien ne trouble la quiétude des lieux. Elle ne voit ni voiture ni moto derrière le portail blanc menant au garage. Elle se décide. Elle est quand même venue pour ça. Elle sonne à la porte.

Une femme de 50 ans environ, élancée, à l'allure noble, l'invite à rentrer sans faire de bruit.

– Vous devez être Lucie, Henri m'a parlé de vous.

La capitaine la regarde, un peu décontenancée.

– Des années que je fréquente les flics. Henri est très fort dans la description de ses collègues. Isabelle, sa femme.

Lucie serre la main qu'elle lui tend et prend le temps de la regarder. Isabelle est une jolie femme, grande, mince, visage fin, nez aquilin, cheveux auburn, yeux clairs. Deux choses la troublent : aucune trace de maquillage n'est visible sur son visage et ses yeux sont cernés. Ils portent en eux la même infinie nostalgie que ceux d'Henri. Lucie n'a pas le temps de lui faire part de son inquiétude.

– Il va bien. Il dort. Ça lui arrive une fois par an. Il boit rarement, autrement. Sauf le 10 avril.

Dans un sourire triste, elle rajoute :

– Le lendemain, il faut qu'il récupère.

Lucie la regarde, étonnée. Elle ne comprend pas.

– Le départ d'Octave. C'est la seule fois de l'année qu'il s'autorise à boire autant. Et surtout n'importe quoi. On ne dirait pas comme ça, mais il est très fort dans les mélanges absurdes d'alcool.

Lucie se sent stupide. Henri ne lui avait pas tout dit hier soir. Ce n'était pas seulement un jour habituel de représentation des Nez rouges. Hébétée, elle ne sait pas quoi dire. Isabelle la regarde encore avec le même sourire triste, comme si elle avait tout compris de l'état de Lucie.

– Ne vous inquiétez pas, dès qu'il se réveille, je lui dis que vous êtes passée. Un message urgent à lui transmettre ?

Lucie reste muette. Urgent ? Que pourrait-il y avoir d'urgent maintenant qu'elle sait ? Maintenant qu'elle comprend ? Il n'y a plus rien. Plus rien d'essentiel, de vital. Les braquages, les meurtres, les Hosni, la Carlton ? Quelles foutaises, quelles conneries !

Juste laisser Isabelle et Henri. Ne pas les emmerder avec des histoires de voyous et d'enquête qui avance. Quelle importance ? Les grandes souffrances sont muettes. Et solitaires.

La seule urgence est de respecter leur silence et leur intimité. Il y a des endroits et des moments où l'homme ne peut pas, ne doit pas s'immiscer dans la sphère de l'autre. Les respecter, c'est se taire et partir.

En prenant congé d'Isabelle, Lucie n'enclenche pas le deux-tons, se passe du gyrophare. Elle coupe même la radio. Plus envie d'entendre Bob Dylan. Ne plus faire cœur avec la musique, juste faire corps avec elle-même. Pleurer d'abord pour tout vider. Hurler ensuite pour exorciser. Taper du poing sur le volant, le fauteuil, le tableau de bord. Taper sur n'importe quoi, mais fort. Pour sentir le sang affluer, circuler. Se faire mal pour se sentir bien. Vivante.

Souffler enfin, couper le téléphone, refuser d'aller vite, ne pas prendre l'autoroute, suivre les chemins de traverse. Savourer le temps et la route des Crêtes, surplomber la mer et le cap Canaille. S'arrêter, stationner sa voiture au plus haut de la falaise, s'avancer au plus près du précipice, humer l'air, la mer et le vide. Et hurler. Gueuler, chanter, aboyer. Et ne pas oublier la vie et l'amour.

Tout peut s'arrêter si brutalement.

52

Le Grand a tout prévu et a toute confiance dans les hommes qui l'entourent. Chacun est à sa place et connaît son rôle par cœur. Il n'a pas peur. La force de l'habitude et de l'entraînement. Il est juste déçu. La Carlton n'est pas à leurs côtés pour contempler leur œuvre. C'est elle qui lui avait communiqué ce coup. Lors de la réunion au bar, ils ont tous accepté d'en être. Pour elle, pour sa mémoire. Elle aurait dû les accompagner, parachever ce travail ensemble.

Jusqu'alors elle donnait le « top départ » ou au contraire annonçait le renoncement du braquage. Savoir abandonner est la clef du succès, répétait-elle. Sentir, deviner, appréhender le danger. Qu'il vienne des flics, des convoyeurs, voire des passants anonymes. Parfois même juste l'air du temps ou l'ambiance, un oiseau qui passe, le ballon d'un enfant, une moto pilotée par une femme. Un soir de confidences, elle lui avait raconté comment elle avait perdu l'amour de sa vie. Un braquage à bécane, place Vendôme. Un gérant qui revient de déjeuner plus tôt que prévu et qui tire dans le dos d'Elaia. L'imprécision, la toute confiance, le sentiment d'impunité et c'est la fin d'une carrière. La fin d'une vie. Depuis elle n'avait cessé de le lui répéter : pour durer, il faut savoir s'arrêter. Et c'est justement ce qu'elle s'apprêtait à faire lors de son séjour à Marseille. De rage, il tape sur son volant.

– Pourquoi ils l'ont tuée alors, ces enculés ?

Le fourgon entre dans l'enceinte protégée du stade. Dan regarde sa montre. Pile à l'heure. Il saisit sa radio.

– Tirelire en place. Préparez-vous.

Il a encore une pensée pour la Carlton, leur porte-bonheur. Il lui envoie un baiser imaginaire avant de démarrer sa Peugeot 607 et d'assurer les dernières vérifications. Le gyrophare est à portée de main sur le siège passager, juste à côté de la kalachnikov, le logo « Police » en place sur le pare-soleil. Il est prêt. Les autres aussi.

Douze minutes après être entré dans l'enceinte du stade, le fourgon blindé réapparaît…

– Ça sort, les gars. Top départ.

... et s'engage dans l'avenue principale, devant lui un camion-benne démarre et l'oblige à freiner. Le chauffeur tend son bras par la fenêtre pour s'excuser. Le conducteur du blindé lui répond par un appel de phare. Fred le tatoué, au volant, apprécie.

– Putain, les convoyeurs, quelle éducation !

Derrière, les transporteurs ne prêtent pas attention à la fourgonnette qui les suit, et encore moins à la Peugeot 607 qui s'aligne derrière eux. Le convoi ainsi constitué roule sur plusieurs centaines de mètres, avant que des cônes de balisage l'obligent à ralentir et à stopper.

Dans leur fourgon, le chauffeur et son passager pestent contre cet arrêt intempestif. Coincés dans la circulation et gênés par le camion, ils ne voient pas ce qui se passe devant. Dans sa cabine, Fred prend la radio et lance le signal.

– Go !

53

De la benne du camion, Willy l'acrobate surgit, encagoulé, ganté et armé d'une kalachnikov. Protégé par la ridelle arrière, il met en joue le chauffeur et son passager. Choqués, les convoyeurs hésitent, mais Willy et son fusil d'assaut sont très persuasifs. Les deux hommes se regardent, apeurés. Dans une chorégraphie parfaite, ils lèvent leurs bras au-dessus de leur tête. Ils se penchent en avant et posent leurs mains en évidence sur le pare-brise. Derrière, le troisième convoyeur s'inquiète, il leur demande ce qui se passe. Doucement d'abord, avant de se mettre à hurler.

Tourné vers l'avant, il ne voit pas Teddy enfiler sa cagoule et surgir de la camionnette située à une dizaine de mètres au cul du fourgon. Malgré ses énormes mains et ses 115 kilos, le boxeur est agile. Et professionnel. Il lui faut moins de 45 secondes pour positionner les pains de plastique sur le pourtour de la porte arrière. Le temps pour Fred de lâcher le volant du camion-benne et de le rejoindre, armé lui aussi d'une kalachnikov.

Tous deux se mettent en protection derrière la camionnette. Échange de regards, signe d'acquiescement, et Teddy appuie sur le détonateur. Les charges sont idéalement réparties. La porte ne résiste pas et le souffle de l'explosion secoue le convoyeur dans l'habitacle du fourgon.

Quand il reprend ses esprits, devant lui, un homme en tenue paramilitaire le menace de son canon et l'invite à sortir sans résister. Il ne joue pas les héros. Face à ce calibre de 7,62 mm, la sagesse l'emporte sur la riposte. Il lève les mains et sort. L'homme à la « kalach » l'empoigne, sort une paire de menottes et l'enferre à ce qu'il reste de la porte du véhicule blindé.

Devant, au moment de l'explosion, les deux transporteurs ferment les yeux. Quand ils les rouvrent, l'homme derrière la ridelle est toujours là, calme et menaçant. La même danse du canon leur ordonne de reposer leurs mains sur le pare-brise. Ils reprennent leur position initiale. La peur empêche toute réponse inappropriée.

Derrière, le rythme s'accélère. Depuis le début, Dan a positionné son véhicule de travers. Il se tient à l'extérieur de la voiture. Sa grande taille, l'arme qu'il porte à la main, la cagoule sur sa tête et le brassard orange siglé « Police » sèment le trouble dans l'esprit des riverains assistant atterrés à cette scène. Tout cela ne leur donne pas envie de s'approcher, ni même de prendre leur téléphone portable pour appeler les secours.

Deux allers-retours entre le fourgon éventré et la Peugeot 607 de Dan suffisent à Teddy et Fred pour charger les six sacs d'espèces. Le dernier posé dans le coffre de la voiture, Dan prévient Willy. L'acrobate acquiesce. D'un geste circulaire, il fait bouger le canon de son fusil en direction des convoyeurs. Par réflexe, les deux hommes ferment les yeux. Quand ils les ouvrent de nouveau, l'homme derrière la ridelle a disparu.

En moins de temps qu'un clignement d'œil, Willy rejoint ses complices dans la Peugeot 607. La voiture démarre en trombe. Teddy a pris le volant. Dan abaisse le pare-soleil « Police », pose le gyrophare sur le toit, et la voiture s'enfonce dans la circulation parisienne. Où, habitués et obéissants, les usagers de la route laissent passer ce véhicule d'urgence.

54

Fred, rigolard, enlève sa cagoule, se tourne vers Willy.

– J'adore quand un plan se déroule sans accroc !

– Ça nous change du dernier...

– Il nous manque pas, le baltringue marseillais.

– Quel gros con.

– Con et dangereux.

– Pléonasme !

Willy à son tour se détend, pose sa kalachnikov sur ses genoux.

– C'était une idée de qui, déjà, le « nique ta mère » provençal ?

– Mireille...

– La Carlton ? Putain, mais qu'est-ce qui lui a pris ?

Pour toute réponse, Willy n'obtient qu'un juron de Dan. Il est bien d'accord, c'était une mauvaise chose d'accepter la présence du Marseillais. Mais c'était une décision de la Carlton, rentrant dans le cadre de son vaste projet. Impossible de lui dire non. Il l'avait pourtant prévenue, que cela pouvait mal finir. La suite lui a donné raison. De bien triste façon. Il aurait préféré avoir tort.

Le silence s'impose dans la voiture, qui zigzague avec souplesse et autorité sur le périphérique. Chacun vogue sur ses pensées, qui deviennent sportives pour Willy.

– C'était quoi, le match hier, déjà ?

– PSG-Barça. Un match de gala.

– Paris a gagné, au moins ?

– Match nul, 2 partout.

– Le stade était plein ?

– Complet, pour voir jouer Mbappé contre Messi, ils se seraient battus. 47 929 places.

Fred siffle entre ses dents. Tente de faire un rapide calcul mental. Dan le coupe.

– Cherche pas, tous les spectateurs n'ont pas payé en espèces. Mais entre les recettes des buvettes, des guichets et autres conneries du même genre, la Carlton me l'a assuré : un coup à plus d'un million d'euros.

L'évocation de la Carlton provoque de nouveau le silence dans l'habitacle. Juste violé par les jurons de Teddy, quand un conducteur moins docile ou plus aveugle que les autres met du temps avant de s'écarter.

Ils sortent du périphérique, enlèvent le gyrophare. Plus la peine de se faire remarquer. Après tout ça, ce serait dommage.

La conduite du chauffeur devient discrète. Même vêtus de façon similaire, coincés dans leur berline sombre, ils passent inaperçus dans les embouteillages parisiens. Ils écoutent la radio en fond sonore.

France Info en boucle annonce qu'un spectaculaire braquage vient de se dérouler aux abords du Parc des Princes à Paris. Des malfaiteurs parfaitement organisés ont attaqué le fourgon blindé qui venait récupérer la recette du match de gala de la veille opposant le Paris-Saint-Germain à Barcelone. Une première estimation fait état d'un préjudice de plus d'un million d'euros. La brigade de répression du banditisme de la direction régionale de la police judiciaire de la préfecture de police de Paris est saisie.

55

Marseille,
mercredi 11 avril 2018, 19 heures.

« Je rêvais d'un autre monde, où la Terre serait ronde… »

« Papa Juliette » est au diapason. La reprise de la chanson de Téléphone sonne juste. Un bassiste de la Crim', un batteur de la financière, un chanteur de la BRB et Basile Urteguy à la guitare et au clavier, harmonie de la PJ réalisée dans un groupe de musiciens souriants, enjoués, dégoulinant de sueur. Ils y sont. Y croient à fond. Passionnés. Comme envoûtés.

L'estrade est installée au fond de la salle de réception, située au dernier étage du fort Ganteaume, face aux baies vitrées dominant le Vieux-Port et s'ouvrant en vision panoramique sur les lumières de Marseille. Le site est majestueux, il surplombe la Canebière de ses vieilles pierres. Les paroles de Jean-Louis Aubert résonnent jusqu'aux oreilles de la Bonne Mère, située à quelques encablures, qui en a entendu d'autres et ne s'étonne plus de rien. La foule se presse de plus en plus nombreuse. Des flics de tous âges s'y croisent. Après Téléphone, Papa Juliette entonne une parodie de *La Mama* d'Aznavour.

– Ils sont venus, ils sont tous là, y'a même les Catalans, et ceux de Menton... pour rendre hommage à la PJ de Marseille.

Le chanteur laisse volontairement traîner sa voix sur la dernière syllabe, plus que ne l'aurait fait le grand Charles lui-même. Personne ne l'a remarqué. Au début de cette soirée, après le moment solennel des remises de médailles, les invités n'écoutent pas encore les chansons proposées par « Papa Juliette ». Entre parodies et reprises, ils assurent le fond sonore de la fête et couvrent les tintements des verres et les éclats de voix des policiers.

Du plus jeune au plus ancien, ils se reconnaissent, s'embrassent, se charrient. Se racontent pour la énième fois leurs interpellations marquantes. Se mélangent dans leurs souvenirs, confondent leurs histoires, s'embrouillent dans leurs propos, avant d'éclater de rire. Tous unis par ce métier de dingues, qui les a rendus si différents du commun des mortels, et si semblables entre eux. Les verres et les vestes tombent. Les cravates disparaissent, les cols de chemise s'ouvrent. Plus que les aventures, ils se remémorent les petites anecdotes qui font les grandes affaires. La voiture qui ne démarre pas au top interpellation, le flingue qui tombe en sortant du « soum* », la ceinture de sécurité qui ne se débloque pas, la vieille dame qui traverse la route, les empêchant d'accélérer pour se coller aux fesses du voyou.

Éclats de rire, d'émotion et de larmes, à l'évocation de ceux partis trop tôt, trop vite. Les accidents de la vie, les suicides, les maladies, les interpellations ratées. Personne n'oublie. Personne n'est oublié. Tous se souviennent. Avec plus ou moins de précision, mais avec la même passion.

Louis Clert a tenu parole, il est venu. Les médecins de l'hôpital ont bien compris qu'ils ne pourraient pas l'empêcher de se rendre à cette cérémonie où il était mis à l'honneur. Quand vous êtes capable de vous balader à poil pour rentrer au Vélodrome filer un coup de main à l'OM en perdition, aucun cadre médical ne peut s'opposer à votre détermination. Et puis Serge Thalassadourian, l'organisateur, sans qui aucune soirée policière n'existerait à

---

* Soum : raccourci policier signifiant « sous-marin », véhicule discret de surveillance.

Marseille, a pris soin de passer deux-trois appels téléphoniques à des gens bien placés. Et comme personne n'échappe à sa volonté ni à sa bonne humeur, les autorités médicales ont accepté qu'il dépêche une ambulance prendre en charge le récipiendaire. Le chauffeur voulait faire monter Louis derrière, allongé sur son lit ambulant, mais le vieux flic a refusé, il a fait le trajet assis, devant, à la place du passager.

– Derrière, c'est le gardé à vue ou le mort. Je ne suis ni l'un ni l'autre, merci !

Dès son arrivée, ses anciens collègues, Guy, Félix et les autres, l'ont accaparé. Il n'a eu besoin de personne pour marcher, trop fier et heureux de recevoir l'ordre national du Mérite devant et avec ses collègues de toujours. Pas question de ne pas tenir debout, quand le DIPJ Francis Larrivée, avec sa verve, son humour et sa solennité, lui a accroché la « bleue » au revers du veston et l'a cité en exemple devant toute l'assistance, faisant de lui le policier le plus ému de la soirée.

Installé sur un des immenses toits-terrasses du fort Ganteaume, entouré de ses amis, il cherche du regard sa fille. Pour rien au monde, Lucie n'aurait manqué cet événement. Il s'en veut presque de ne pas avoir pris le temps de la serrer avant dans ses bras. Mais, trop pressé et un peu stressé quand même, il ne l'a pas appelée. Maintenant elle ne répond plus au téléphone.

– Félicitations, monsieur le chef inspecteur divisionnaire Clert.

Le timbre et les intonations de voix de sa fille le font sursauter, il se retourne, mais ne la reconnaît pas. Lucie n'est jamais apprêtée de la sorte, visage maquillé, lèvres rouges, robe-bustier et escarpins. Il ne l'avait jamais vue avec des talons et encore moins sans cheveux. Lucie a la boule à zéro et elle est magnifique. Louis est tout hébété. Il n'en croit pas ses yeux.

– Félicitations, papa, je suis si fière de toi.

Elle lui tombe dans les bras. Louis lui murmure à l'oreille à quel point elle est belle et qu'il est aussi fier d'elle. Puis il l'embrasse tendrement avant de l'écarter et de s'étonner.

– J'ai perdu un pari, p'pa.

Pour une fois, la rageuse Lucie Clert a été bonne joueuse. Elle a honoré le pari perdu avec Henri. Et ce qu'elle ne dit pas au héros de la soirée, c'est que ce look comme sa nouvelle coupe signifient qu'elle a pris de grandes décisions. En lien avec ses promesses faites en haut du cap Canaille.

Après avoir embrassé de nouveau son père, elle se dirige vers la salle où résonne la musique de Papa Juliette. Les autres flics se retournent derrière elle, des murmures, des sifflements, des questionnements. Certains la reconnaissent, n'osent pas croire qu'il s'agit de la capitaine Clert, se mordent les doigts de lui avoir parfois si mal parlé. Tous sont séduits par sa beauté. Et son originalité. Lucie ne fait pas attention à eux. Elle sait pourquoi elle est là. Elle entre dans la salle du concert. Les musiciens du groupe commencent un nouveau morceau. Elle sourit. Elle ne croit pas aux signes, pourtant celui-là est fort. Aux premières mesures, elle reconnaît l'air.

D'un pas décidé, elle se dirige vers l'estrade où Papa Juliette joue, mais en n'ayant d'yeux que pour le guitariste du groupe. Basile en a le souffle coupé. Cette femme improbable, magnifique, avec sa tête rasée et ses talons hauts, s'approche de lui. Il en jouerait presque faux. À deux mètres de lui, il la reconnaît enfin. Il balbutie un « mais » à peine audible, se trompe d'un temps, provoque un grincement de nez du chanteur et un délicat sourire sur le visage de Lucie.

– *Hurricane* de Dylan, ma chanson préférée.

Sans lui demander son avis, profitant qu'il ait les mains occupées par ses instruments, elle se penche sur lui et l'embrasse à pleine bouche. Enfin.

56

Méditerranée,
jeudi 12 avril 2018, 8 heures.

L'eau clapote délicatement contre le sloop. Le voilier *Tania* ondule au gré de la houle. Dans la cabine, Basile ne se lasse pas de caresser le corps nu allongé à côté de lui. La fatigue a fini par avoir raison de leurs envies. Épuisée, Lucie s'est endormie. Le visage reposé, un sourire sur les lèvres. Elle dort sur le ventre, la main sur le buste de Basile. Besoin de sentir sa peau sous ses doigts. Comme lui ne peut s'empêcher de faire glisser sa main depuis les douces rondeurs de ses fesses jusqu'au bas de sa nuque. Et de recommencer, en sens inverse.

Basile ne se souvient pas à quelle heure ils ont quitté le fort Ganteaume ni comment ils ont accédé au bateau de Lucie. Il se souvient juste de l'avoir suivie, le cœur battant, les doigts mêlés aux siens. En montant sur son voilier, il a été surpris par la taille du carré et de la cabine. De l'extérieur, il n'imaginait pas qu'il pouvait y avoir autant de place à l'intérieur. Si bien décoré. Élégant et sobre. Quelques touches de couleur sur le bois verni, où chaque affaire trouve naturellement sa place dans des caches aménagées. Et ce lit immense, véritable appel des sens.

À son tour, il l'a embrassée. Un baiser délicat, sans précipitation, où ses lèvres ont rejoint les siennes avec douceur. Comme une envie de gommer le temps, de ne pas laisser le désir qui les animait prendre le dessus. Laisser s'égrener les minutes pour en profiter, goûter à l'autre avec envie, gourmandise et patience. Sans oublier toute cette immense tendresse.

C'est le mot que Lucie cherchait. Elle en aurait pleuré. Tellement longtemps qu'un homme ne l'avait pas embrassée de cette façon, qu'un homme ne la considérait pas autrement que comme une possession, un trophée. Tellement longtemps qu'un homme ne cherchait pas à lui prouver qu'il était un homme. Viril, puissant, dans la performance, jamais dans le moment.

Dans un sourire adolescent, Basile lui avait demandé de ne pas rester au Vieux-Port. De ne pas stagner sous les bruits des drisses des bateaux se cognant sous l'effet du mistral. De ne pas s'éterniser trop près des quais de la nuit, où la foule, avinée, se laissait aller à des hurlements incompréhensibles. Même la Bonne Mère, malgré son habitude, commençait à en frémir et, si elle avait pu, leur aurait demandé de la fermer.

Il n'aspirait qu'à la plénitude du silence. Tellement de notes de musique résonnaient dans sa tête. Tant de mélodies enchantaient son cœur, il ne voulait pas que ce moment soit pollué par la vacarme.

Seul, avec elle, la mer et le silence. Lucie a adoré cette proposition. Elle est passée en un temps record de reine de soirée à navigatrice au long cours. S'est débarrassée de ses escarpins et de sa robe, avant d'enfiler un tee-shirt trop large et un short en jean. Avec juste ses boucles d'oreilles en or pour auréoler son visage, elle était encore plus désirable, plus vraie. Plus elle.

Il l'a admirée faire glisser le *Tania* entre les passerelles étroites du port. Il l'a admirée dominer la nuit et la mer. Il l'a admirée maîtriser la barre du voilier. Il l'a admirée les amener à l'endroit qu'elle avait choisi pour leur première fois. L'immensité de la mer comme projet furieux, la Méditerranée comme lit d'amour.

Basile s'est laissé envoûter par l'ambiance. La lune comme guide, les clapotis

des vagues sur les flancs du voilier, l'ondu-
lation du bateau et Lucie à la barre. L'œil
attentif mais le visage heureux. Détendue
et libre. Quand elle a jeté l'ancre, ils étaient
au milieu de nulle part.

Elle l'a rejoint à la proue du bateau, s'est
penchée sur lui et l'a embrassé de nouveau.
Il s'est laissé faire, avec ce même goût de
tendresse. Lucie lui a pris la main et l'a
invité à la suivre. Jusqu'à sa cabine. Il était
temps.

La fougue et le désir les ont rattrapés.
Dès que leurs peaux se sont touchées, leurs
sexes se sont trouvés, et leur union a été
parfaite. Le grand lit n'a pas suffi à leurs
échanges. Basile a goûté plusieurs fois à
l'étroitesse de la cabine. Il s'est cogné la
tête contre les murs. Leurs rires se sont
mêlés à leur plaisir. Intense, vrai, sincère.
Et ils ont recommencé.

57

Le soleil commence à illuminer la cabine. Comme un papillon fragile, un rayon vient se poser sur le dos de Lucie, laissant une trace de lumière entre ses fesses et sa tête nue. Instant fugace de beauté totale.

– C'est peut-être ça, le bonheur, pense Basile, avant que son téléphone ne résonne.

Sa main abandonne avec regret les caresses. Il cherche dans le capharnaüm de leurs vêtements où peut bien se trouver son portable. Voit le nom qui s'affiche à l'écran, décroche en sortant à l'air libre.

– Saint-Donat, mais t'étais où ?

Il n'écoute pas la réponse, ébloui par le soleil et la beauté de l'endroit. Lucie a jeté l'ancre sous une falaise immense, dans une baie magnifique. La plus belle du monde selon plusieurs agences de voyages. Entre Cassis et La Ciotat. Plusieurs centaines de mètres de roches les dominent. Lucie les a conduits sous les hauteurs du cap Canaille. La voix caverneuse d'Henri résonne.

– Tu déboules vite, Basile, y'a du nouveau. Les braqueurs de Melun ont retapé à Paris, la recette du Parc des Princes. On a rendez-vous avec la BRB du « 36 » et les collègues de la PJ de Melun. Réunion au sommet à Paris.

– Quoi ?

– Enfin, pas Paris exactement. Un petit village sympa à une centaine de bornes. Ça devrait te rappeler des souvenirs.

– Quel village ?

– Tu verras quand tu y seras.

Basile est sur le point de raccrocher, encore sonné par sa nuit, son réveil et ces nouvelles.

– Basile ?

– Oui ?

– Tu sais où est Lucie ? Personne n'arrive à la joindre.

Basile hésite.

– On lui a laissé des messages sur son portable. Si tu la vois, n'hésite pas, embrasse-la pour moi.

Lucie sort nue du carré. Les yeux encore remplis de sommeil, aveuglée à son tour par le soleil. Elle se colle à Basile. Fait glisser ses mains sur son dos, descend jusqu'à ses fesses, lève son visage sur le sien. Le jeune lieutenant n'en demandait pas tant. Il l'embrasse.

– Un ordre est un ordre.

– Quoi ?

– Non… rien.

Lucie découvre à son tour le paysage qui l'entoure.

– C'est magnifique.

Basile hoche la tête, l'embrasse de nouveau. Et confirme.

– Magnifique.

Lucie aurait aimé que cet instant dure. Son bateau, la mer, une nuit d'amour, un réveil délicieux, un homme tendre. Quand elle s'aperçoit qu'il a son portable à la main.

– C'était qui ?

– Un revenant.

– Saint-Donat ?

– Lui-même.

– Et ?

– Rendez-vous au sommet. Les braqueurs de Melun ont retapé à Paris. Création d'une cellule de crise et tout le toutim. Y'a urgence. On est attendus. Tout le monde te cherche.

Lucie regarde intensément Basile. La vie vient de lui rappeler qu'il faut savoir profiter du moment présent, et le cap Canaille lui murmure qu'elle s'est promis de s'y tenir. Elle lui attrape la main, jette son portable dans le carré et l'invite à la suivre dans sa cabine. Elle le pousse sur son lit, se jette sur lui. Ses lèvres se posent sur les siennes, descendent sur son buste. Basile frémit de

plaisir. Avant d'aller plus loin, Lucie s'arrête, le regarde droit dans les yeux.

– Tout le monde attendra. On n'est plus
à une demi-heure près.

– Une demi-heure ?

– Le temps qu'il faudra...

– Un ordre est un ordre.

58

C'est Lucie qui accompagne Henri à Paris, volonté du DIPJ. Francis Larrivée souhaitait que Basile reste à Marseille et se charge des vérifications sur Ernesto Dominguez, antécédents, relations, affaires marquantes, « tombées* » possibles. Nul doute aussi que Larrivée, qui ne pouvait ignorer le baiser échangé entre Basile et Lucie au fort Ganteaume, dans un souci de management approprié, souhaitait séparer les jeunes tourtereaux. S'assurer qu'ils soient tout à leur tâche et n'envisagent pas d'autres activités.

Urteguy fait la gueule. Pour une fois, ça l'emmerde, qu'un ordre soit un ordre. Il se sent des velléités de désobéissance. Alors que son histoire commence à peine avec Lucie, Larrivée lui coupe les ailes. Il est furieux. Il avait plutôt envisagé d'accompagner Saint-Donat et Lucie à la réunion parisienne. Il avait même espéré y aller seul avec

---

* Tombées : expression policière signifiant « points de chute ».

la capitaine et n'avait pas hésité à faire cette proposition au directeur. Au sourire poli et au refus de Larrivée, Henri s'est douté qu'il avait raté quelque chose. Au regard que Lucie a lancé à Basile, il a eu une synthèse de l'épisode qu'il venait de louper. Grand seigneur, il a voulu les laisser monter seuls à Paris, mais le discours de Larrivée, insistant sur sa connaissance des flics parisiens, a coupé court à toute revendication. Dans la voiture, il a supporté une Lucie silencieuse, collée à son portable, qui n'a pas cessé d'envoyer des messages à Basile, pour calmer sa fronde révolutionnaire.

Lucie a pâli quand elle a su où la réunion au sommet était prévue : l'École nationale supérieure des officiers de police à Cannes-Écluse. Perdue au milieu de nulle part, entre champs de betteraves et vols de corbeaux. Certes, depuis qu'ils avaient quitté cette école, des centres commerciaux et des pizzerias avaient vu le jour, faisant diminuer la fréquence des vols de choucas en Seine-et-Marne et chuter la production de betteraves.

Si ce lieu rappelait de bons souvenirs à Henri, il n'en était pas de même pour Lucie. Elle avait vécu ses dix-huit mois de formation comme une corvée. Trop éloignée de Marseille et du terrain, de ce que son père avait pu lui raconter et de l'égalité hommes-femmes, qui n'était pas encore de mise. Sans parler de la délicatesse des élèves policiers, qui n'avaient pas arrêté de la draguer lourdement. Elle avait détesté cette période.

Henri avait intégré l'École au milieu des années 80. Il y avait tout appris de ce qui allait être son futur métier. Il avait adoré. En y retournant plus de trente ans après, il avait été surpris de constater qu'elle était restée dans son jus d'origine. Les six bâtiments de couchage entourant la cour d'honneur n'avaient pas changé, ni le confort des chambres, avec douches et W-C à l'étage. À l'intérieur du réfectoire, les mêmes tables et chaises moulées en plastique, dans les couleurs improbables des années 70. Le mess, avec son immense comptoir en formica, était toujours ancré au sol. Seul avantage, le prix des bières n'avait pas augmenté et restait accessible à toutes les bourses.

59

Henri connaît tous les policiers présents autour de la table. Apanage de l'âge, du grade et de ses trente ans passés au Quai des Orfèvres. Son ancien adjoint, Martin Laval, ses deux enquêteurs, Forest et Labord, de la PJ de Melun, mais aussi le commandant Christian Chaize, chef de groupe à la BRB de Paris, à la voix tonitruante et à la carrure d'un troisième ligne, son adjoint le capitaine Antoine Bonifay, dit Tony, fan également de rugby, de taille et d'esprit plus proches de celui d'un demi de mêlée. Les deux s'entendent comme larrons en foire. Chaize, en tête de gondole, couvre tous les fronts, quand Bonifay, avec malice, assure les arrières et l'emballage des procédures judiciaires. Leur groupe est saisi du braquage du fourgon du Parc des Princes.

Les uns comme les autres n'auraient jamais cru qu'ils se retrouveraient ici des années après leur formation initiale, l'époque insouciante où ils rêvaient leur métier. Aujourd'hui assis sur les mêmes chaises orange et marron, ils sont au cœur de l'action, heureux de se retrouver. Les plus anciens, Chaize, Bonifay et Laval, font le show, se racontent leurs guerres, pendant que les plus jeunes, Forest et Labord, les regardent, moqueurs et un peu envieux. Lucie constate qu'elle est encore la seule femme. La police a pourtant évolué depuis quinze ans qu'elle est flic, mais il lui reste encore quelques progrès à faire. Elle se touche les cheveux qu'elle n'a plus. Se rappelle la promesse qu'elle s'est faite et tente de faire contre mauvaise fortune bon cœur. Elle a du mal à se concentrer, envoûtée par sa nuit de navigation et d'amour.

Après les vannes traditionnelles sur la prise de poids des uns, la perte de cheveux des autres, le manque d'activité sexuelle de chacun, Saint-Donat ouvre les débats. Tous savent pourquoi ils sont là. Partager leurs éléments sur des malfaiteurs spécialisés dans les braquages d'envergure, mêlés de près ou de loin à trois homicides, celui de Nathalie Fournier, alias la Carlton, de Yassine Hosni, jeune voyou marseillais, et de la vieille dame à bord de sa 307 Peugeot, victime malheureuse. Le but étant de définir une stratégie commune d'action. Chaize, fidèle à sa légende, n'y va pas par quatre chemins :

– Sur le braquage du Parc des Princes, on a une info de première bourre. Un indic de Tony qui balance une équipe de mercenaires. Des anciens légionnaires qui organisent des braquages millimétrés. D'après le tonton*, ils auraient une dette envers un Marseillais, surnommé le Chacal. Un ambitieux qui veut prendre la main sur tout Marseille.

L'information prend de court Lucie. Pendant douze secondes, elle arrête d'envoyer des messages à Basile. Bien qu'elle soit en poste depuis longtemps à Marseille, ce surnom de Chacal ne lui dit rien.

– Il te dit quoi de plus, ton tonton ?

– Rien d'autre. Une équipe de braqueurs, tous d'anciens légionnaires, avec un mec de grande taille comme chef. Un géant, type basketteur. Ils se donneraient rendez-vous dans un rade pourri du 18e. On a vérifié et récupéré quelques clichés de la vidéosurveillance du coin. On a identifié un certain Daniel Rabutin, inscrit au bottin mondain des braqueurs.

Saint-Donat percute.

– Rabutin ? Je le connais. Deux mètres, cent vingt kilos. Aussi haut que large. On

---

* Tonton : expression policière signifiant « indicateur ».

l'a fait tomber pour un braquage de bijouterie en 89 ou 90.

— Il est sûr, ton tonton ?

La question de Lucie tombe comme un
cheveu sur la soupe. Et en plein décalage.
Un informateur est par définition un voyou
qui balance pour se protéger, défendre les
siens ou prendre le marché de ceux qu'il
donne à la police. Tony toise Lucie.

— C'est un indic. Avec sa part de véri-
tés et de mensonges. Et de manipulations.
Pour l'instant, il ne nous a jamais déçus.
Maintenant, si t'as mieux, tu poses ton portable et t'abats tes cartes.

L'heure n'est pas à la guerre des ego
ni des polices. Lucie s'étonne juste de la
façon dont le nom de Rabutin arrive dans
la conversation. Elle se replonge dans la
lecture de ses messages. Chaize poursuit :

— Avec un physique pareil, il ne passe pas
inaperçu, le mammouth. Sur le braquage
du fourgon, les témoins nous signalent un
golgoth, avec un brassard « police ». On en
a quelques-uns en stock comme ça, à la
BRB. On a sorti les archives, secoué nos
indics, et un vieux gérant de bar du 18ᵉ a
craché qu'il avait reçu quelques jours avant
le braquage du fourgon du Parc un géant,
avec un flingue dans le dos, et trois de ses

potes, aux physiques et tatouages impressionnants. Le vieux les a entendus se saluer en disant « Legio Patria Nostra ».

– On a vérifié : Rabutin a fait cinq piges au 2e REP* à Calvi. Sous le blaze de Philémon Legrand. Adjudant-chef Philémon Legrand, ça claque, non ?

Lucie semble se désintéresser de la conversation. Pourtant, la tension monte d'un cran. Surtout quand Laval précise :

– Sur notre braquage, les convoyeurs signalent aussi un braqueur au physique impressionnant. Ça peut coller avec Rabutin. Tous les témoins disent qu'ils étaient super organisés. Un véritable commando militaire. Sauf un, qui paraissait plus jeune, agité comme un puceau entrant pour la première fois à la Jonquera.

– Yassine Hosni ?

– Qu'est-ce qu'il foutait là, le merdeux, au milieu de ces pros ?

Même signalement d'auteurs, même organisation militaire, même mode opératoire. Ça commence à sentir « bon ». Seule cette étonnante présence de Yassine Hosni qui interpelle.

---

* REP : acronyme de régiment étranger de parachutistes. Le 2e REP est un régiment de légionnaires basé à Calvi (Corse).

– Ça n'explique toujours pas pourquoi on le retrouve au fond de l'Yonne, à poil, troué de part et d'autre, dans une bâche en plastique ? demande Laval.

Le duo Chaize-Bonifay recommence son numéro de claquettes.

– Chaque chose en son temps.

– Un temps pour chaque chose.

– On met la main sur Rabutin...

– ... et compagnie.

– Et on leur demande comment ils ont fait pour emballer le petit Hosni...

– Façon rôti !

Saint-Donat sourit. À tout hasard leur demande s'ils n'ont pas oublié le b.a.-ba du métier.

– Sur le rade de votre tonton, vous avez pensé à la téléphonie ?

– Tu nous prends pour des bleus ?

Chaize plonge sa main dans son vieux sac en cuir. En sort deux clefs USB. En distribue une aux enquêteurs de Melun, une autre aux flics marseillais.

– Dessus, y'a un fichier de 753 pages de listing téléphonique. Un vendredi soir entre 19 h 30 et 20 heures, vous ne pouvez pas imaginer le nombre de Parisiens qui s'appellent dans le 18ᵉ. Pour l'instant, en l'état, c'est inutilisable. Mais si on peut les croiser avec d'autres, avec Mercure, ça peut matcher !

– À Marseille, vous avez quoi ? interroge Bonifay.

Saint-Donat se tourne vers Lucie, qui n'a aucune envie de prendre la parole. Il assure la réponse.

– On a retrouvé une valise de la Goldwing de la Carlton au « dom' » de la famille Hosni. Grâce au GPS, on sait qu'elle s'est rendue chez eux, la veille de se faire flinguer. Pour le reste, on n'a pas grand-chose. On a identifié un certain Ernesto Dominguez, présent à l'Intercontinental en même temps qu'elle. La panoplie complète du petit Marseillais. Tout à la tchatche, jamais sur des gros coups.

– Et alors ?

– C'est tout ?

– Ça prouve rien...

Le téléphone de Lucie résonne. Elle a reçu un message. Elle le regarde, sourit amoureusement. Tony Bonifay, excédé, la branche.

– Dis-moi, Yul Brynner... on t'emmerde ou quoi ?

Lucie met du temps avant de comprendre la métaphore cinématographique. Caresse sa tête lisse, prend son temps, sourit. Se souvient de sa promesse, mais « chassez le naturel, il revient au galop ».

– Yul Brynner, c'est les années 30, ça ? Les tractions avant, les brigades du Tigre... ta génération.

– Fais attention à ce que tu dis, quand même.

– On se calme...

D'un coup, Lucie se redresse, exhibe son portable devant l'assemblée et lit à haute voix le message de Basile qu'elle vient de recevoir.

– Trois nouvelles. Primo : Ernesto Dominguez a été vu à l'Intercontinental en train de discuter avec la Carlton, Battisteli confirme.

– Battisteli, c'est le groom en chef de l'Intercontinental, précise Saint-Donat.

– Deuzio : Ernesto Dominguez a demandé un parloir à Bilal Hosni.

– Le grand frère de Yassine.

– Ils sont vieux, mais pas à ce point, ils ont compris. Et tertio : Ernesto Dominguez est originaire de la Soude.

– La Soude ?

– Une cité du sud de Marseille, pas très loin de la Cayolle d'où sont issus les Hosni.

– C'est aussi la cité où a été volée la Scenic dans laquelle la Carlton a été transformée en barbecue... Alors, les tontons flingueurs, elle se défend pas mal, la nouvelle génération, non ?

L'ambiance autour de la table prend une nouvelle tournure. En effervescence, ils lissent leurs divergences. Ils analysent ce que signifie cet élément. Ernesto Dominguez était en lien avec la Carlton et semble parfaitement connaître la famille Hosni. Laval ajoute :

– On a vérifié les infos d'Urteguy, la Carlton a bien séjourné au Château de Sancy au moment du braquage, sous le nom de Mireille de Gounod. On a récupéré les vidéos internes de l'hôtel. Elle avait rien perdu de sa superbe et elle n'était pas toute seule.

Il étale devant lui des photos noir et blanc, de qualité moyenne, tirées de la vidéosurveillance de l'hôtel.

– Votre clown marseillais, Ernesto Dominguez, il aurait pas ce physique avantageux ?

Saint-Donat scrute les photos, on y voit un jeune homme de 25/30 ans, de petite taille, mais longiligne et mince, légèrement courbé au niveau des épaules, casquette à l'envers, cheveux frisés dessous, de type méditerranéen, porteur d'une parka un peu trop grande et d'une paire de baskets un peu trop voyante. Sourire en coin, le commandant concède :

– Il a le potentiel.

Au même moment, le portable de Lucie sonne de nouveau. Bonifay fait la moue. Chaize le calme. Lucie savoure le moment. Elle vient de recevoir un nouveau message de Basile, accompagné d'une pièce jointe. Elle arrache la photo que tient encore dans ses mains Saint-Donat. La présente à tous de sa main droite pendant que, de sa gauche, elle leur affiche le cliché qu'elle vient de recevoir : la fiche anthropométrique d'Ernesto Dominguez. La ressemblance est totale, jusque dans les détails : la dernière fois qu'il s'est fait « serrer », le jeune Marseillais portait déjà la même parka et les mêmes baskets.

60

Marseille,
vendredi 13 avril 2018, 5 h 50.

La voiture circule avec fluidité, le gyrophare sur le toit et la plaque police dégageant la route. À 5 h 30, les Marseillais n'ont pas encore réussi à créer des bouchons. Les quatre occupants trouvent facilement l'adresse qu'ils recherchent, à l'angle de la rue d'Endoume et de la rue Sainte, au-dessus d'une des plus vieilles boulangeries de Marseille, dont les spécialités sont connues dans le monde entier, les navettes. Rue d'Endoume, une porte permet d'accéder aux étages surplombant le commerce. Dans le hall d'entrée, ça sent bon le pain chaud et les réveils gourmands.

En silence, les policiers montent les marches les uns derrière les autres. En l'absence de Saint-Donat, Basile a pris la direction de l'intervention. Quand le boulanger, homme de 60 ans, goguenard, dégarni, porteur d'un marcel blanc et d'un tablier autour de la taille, sort dans le couloir en sifflotant, il tombe nez à nez avec le dernier flic de la colonne, arme à la main. La surprise se lit sur son visage. Le policier lui montre son brassard et pose un doigt sur sa bouche. Malgré ce geste explicite, le boulanger veut parler, mais le flic l'en empêche. Résigné, il hausse les épaules, regarde les flics accéder aux étages.

Au troisième, du rap qui se veut être de la musique sort d'une porte entrouverte. Basile reconnaît le titre et le chanteur.

– P'tain, Jul ! Goût de chiottes, Ernesto.

Il fait signe à ses trois collègues de baisser d'un ton, leur désigne la porte entrouverte et décompte sur ses doigts.

Trois, deux… un. Ils se ruent dans le studio d'où émane les rimes du rappeur marseillais.

L'endroit est dévasté. Le canapé est éventré, couettes et draps déchirés, des plumes d'oreiller jonchent le sol. Des tasses dans l'évier sont remplies d'un mélange douteux eau-bière-cendres. Des bouteilles d'alcool traînent sur le ridicule espace de travail. L'appartement est vide. Ernesto Dominguez n'est pas là.

Le silence plombe l'intervention policière, seul le rappeur « survêt-chaussettes » gesticule en rythme sur l'écran de télévision. Au milieu du capharnaüm, un policier trouve la télécommande et fait taire les trémolos asthmatiques de l'artiste. Un autre hausse les épaules.

– Pourquoi tu l'arrêtes ? Jul, c'est l'enfant du pays. Quand il chante, au moins, on ne voit pas ses fautes.

Basile, flingue à la main au milieu du bordel ambiant, est désabusé. Même si la propreté n'est pas la qualité première des lieux, il y règne un désordre inhabituel. La serrure de la porte ne tient que par une vis, l'effraction ne fait pas de doute.

D'autres sont passés avant eux.

Déçus, les policiers descendent l'escalier, enivrés par la puissante odeur du pain chaud. Ils croisent de nouveau le boulanger, au sourire béat.

– Vé, les condés, vous êtes rigolos. Vous parlez jamais entre vous ?

Basile s'étonne.

– Pardon ?

– Pute vierge, j'ai essayé de vous le dire, avant de me faire rabrouer. Mais y a une équipe qu'est déjà venue le chercher hier soir, le petit tox…

– Dominguez ?

– Le fada du dernier, oui. Toujours en train de barjaquer, encore plus que ma pauvre belle-mère, peuchère. Prêt à tout pour grappiller quelques navettes. Vos collègues, ils étaient quatre, tout comme vous, brassards, flingues, toute la panoplie des cow-boys. Oh, les condés, vous devez sérieusement avoir envie de lui parler, pour venir le chercher deux fois.

DGSI*, sécurité publique ou même section de recherches** ? Ernesto Dominguez est typiquement le genre de client dont raffolent les services d'investigations. Contrairement à ce que pense l'artisan, ça ne serait pas la première fois que des unités différentes tentent d'interpeller le même individu. Le boulanger jubile. Il s'imagine déjà à l'heure du pastis, au bar de la Marine, en train de raconter cette histoire de flics qui envoient deux équipes en moins de douze heures chercher le même bonhomme. Succès assuré pour des années.

– Oh, les condés, vous savez qu'on est au XXIe siècle ? Celui d'Internet. « Face de bouc », « As ta gramme », ça vous parle ? Ou vous en êtes encore au sémaphore et aux téléphones à trous ?

Moquer est sa nature. Brocarder, son talent. Ce n'est pas un quatuor de policiers

---

* DGSI : Direction générale de la sécurité intérieure.

** Section de recherches : service d'investigations judiciaires de la gendarmerie nationale.

irrités qui va calmer ses ardeurs gogue-
nardes. Malgré leur déconvenue, il arrive
même à faire sourire les policiers.

– À quoi ils ressemblaient, nos collègues ?

– Vé, à des condés, comme vous. Même
brassard, même pétard, mêmes têtes d'in-
telligents. Ça puait le flic à vingt mètres.

Basile s'irrite, mais insiste :

– Ils avaient des signes particuliers ?

– Bonne mère ! J'les ai pas reluqués, vos
collègues. Il fait pas toujours bon de vous
regarder pleine face, les flics.

Sans rancune, Basile et ses collègues
quittent l'artisan. Avant de partir, il rentre
dans sa boulangerie et leur offre un énorme
paquet de navettes.

– C'est le cœur qui parle. Vé, ça me
revient, y'en avait un, il passait pas sous
la porte d'entrée. Il devait mesurer plus de
deux mètres. Il a dû tomber dans la mar-
mite de navettes quand il était petit. Il devait
peser 150 kilos.

L'étonnement se lit dans les yeux de
Basile.

61

Entre ronronnement du moteur et infos de la radio, Lucie somnole. Saint-Donat prétend qu'il ne s'endort jamais quand il conduit, son cerveau est en ébullition, l'asphalte qui défile lui permet de mettre ses réflexions en perspective. Ils ont quitté Cannes-Écluse à l'heure où Urteguy s'est levé pour tenter d'interpeller Ernesto Dominguez, 5 heures. Le jeune policier a déjà envoyé plusieurs messages doux à Lucie, qu'elle a lus et relus. Apaisée, presque souriante, elle se dit que le bonheur est parfois simple comme un mot de Basile.

Elle regarde Saint-Donat, un pincement au cœur. Le commandant est concentré, ses traits sont tirés. Conduire doit être un prétexte pour oublier. Depuis sa réapparition, il a pris un coup de vieux. Comment pourrait-il en être autrement, après ce qu'il a vécu ? Ce qu'il vit depuis dix ans, à la même période de l'année. Des souvenirs enfouis, des souvenirs présents, des souvenirs sans fin.

Henri a lancé la Ford Mondeo sur l'auto-route A6. Toujours étonné que, malgré son âge, cette voiture tienne si bien la route. À hauteur d'Auxerre, Lucie rêve de voilier, de guitare et de corps nus, la sonnerie de son téléphone la ramène à la réalité, qu'elle espère douce. Mais elle déchante vite, Basile lui demande de mettre son portable sur haut-parleur. Il a une mauvaise nouvelle. Dominguez a disparu. Enlevé par des individus dont le signalement communiqué par le boulanger laisse peu de place au doute.

– Rabutin ? Qu'est-ce qu'il vient foutre là ?

– Pourquoi il s'en prendrait à Dominguez ? Ça ne tient pas la route, lance Saint-Donat.

Et sans attendre les explications de Basile, il lui donne ses instructions.

– Tu visionnes la vidéosurveillance du quartier, tu fais la triangulation téléphonique et tu fais passer l'IJ chez Ernesto. En urgence. Faut identifier ces mecs.

Il avait raison, conduire à grande vitesse favorise ses capacités de concentration. La réponse de Basile les surprend.

– C'est fait, Henri. Aucune trace chez Dominguez. Mais on a une caméra rue d'Endoume, qui les chope en sortant de chez lui. C'est fugace. Mais on reconnaît Rabutin. Je vous envoie la photo. Par ailleurs, six minutes après, on a une vidéo quai du Rive-Neuve qui repère une 607 avec cinq mecs à l'intérieur. Un modèle identique à celui utilisé sur le braquage du fourgon à Saint-Denis. La vidéo est partie en urgence au labo pour analyse. Lucie ? Tu me manques !

Lucie a la banane. Il apprend vite, son amoureux, et n'a pas peur de se dévoiler. Il est gonflé et ça la fait encore plus sourire. Avec lui, elle n'a pas envie de se cacher. Son téléphone sonne, un nouveau message d'Urteguy, avec une photo tirée d'une vidéosurveillance. Un homme de forte corpulence, cheveux courts, sort d'une porte d'entrée d'immeuble en tenant quelqu'un de petite taille sous son bras. Elle se tourne vers Henri, c'est bien l'ancien légionnaire qui a enlevé Dominguez. Henri tape du poing sur le volant.

– Rabutin qui chope Dominguez. Pourquoi ? Il vient de piquer un million d'euros et il joue au cow-boy à Marseille ?

Cette nouvelle booste ses réactions. Il attrape le gyrophare, le place au milieu du pare-brise et actionne la sirène. Il fait dégager une voiture prenant toutes les voies de l'autoroute pour son lit personnel et appuie sur l'accélérateur, avant de taper encore plus fort sur le volant.

– C'est bien le messager !

Lucie a pris conscience de la vitesse à laquelle roule Henri. Elle est blême, Henri ne s'en rend pas compte, continue sa réflexion.

– Ernesto, c'est le lien entre la Carlton et les Hosni. Yassine ou son frère Bilal ! Hosni et la Carlton sont en affaires et Dominguez assure la liaison. Pas de téléphone, pas de contact direct, juste Ernesto. Meilleur moyen de ne laisser aucune trace écrite ou informatique.

Lucie n'est pas du genre à avoir peur, pourtant elle est accrochée à sa poignée. La Ford file à plus de 200 km/h. Elle regarde Henri, presque suppliante.

– Tu ralentis, s'il te plaît ?

Henri obtempère en s'excusant. Retrouve une allure supportable pour Lucie, qui reprend son souffle.

– Dominguez, le messager, mais de quoi ?

– J'sais pas exactement. Mais si Rabutin enlève Dominguez, c'est qu'il n'avait pas le contact avec lui et encore moins avec ceux qui l'envoyaient auprès de la Carlton. Et à mon avis, il a la ferme intention de le lui demander. Parce qu'il pense que le meurtrier de la Carlton n'est pas loin de lui, ou d'eux.

Il tape encore du poing sur le tableau de bord.

– Ernesto, c'est le paravent et Rabutin veut savoir qui se cache derrière !

– Comme nous !

Lucie n'a pas tort. Henri souffle, énervé, presque furieux. Et légèrement désabusé.

– C'est ça. Mais ils l'ont eu avant.

En silence la Ford continue sa course sur l'autoroute. Pouilly-en-Auxois, Beaune, Châlon-sur-Saône. Ils regardent les paysages défiler, mais n'ont pas l'esprit à les admirer. Au péage de Villefranche-sur-Saône, dans un ensemble parfait, ils réalisent.

– Ils l'ont pas buté sur place...

– ... parce qu'ils le voulaient vivant.

Ils échangent un regard inquiet. Ils connaissent les capacités imaginatives de l'homme pour faire souffrir son prochain. Vivant, parfois, n'est pas une situation enviable.

62

Le major René Malmaison est encore bien emmerdé. Pourquoi ce genre de situation n'arrive qu'à lui ? Il aurait préféré ne jamais recevoir cet appel des gardiens de la paix du car police-secours. Dans les parkings souterrains de la gare Saint-Charles, ils ont trouvé une Peugeot 607 avec une plaque d'immatriculation à l'avant qui pendait. Ils ont vite compris qu'ils avaient affaire à une doublette*.

Malmaison va finir par croire qu'il est chat noir. Dans un service de quart, il y en a toujours un qui porte la poisse et récupère toutes les sales affaires. À la division centre, il est sûr d'être le « scoumounard » en titre. Conséquence de sa séparation amoureuse, Lucie et la chance l'ont quitté.

---

* Doublette : expression policière désignant une voiture volée supportant la plaque d'immatriculation d'un autre véhicule, non signalé volé, mais ayant exactement les mêmes caractéristiques – marque, type, couleur…

Le major est trop ancien dans la boîte pour ignorer que cette découverte n'augure rien de bon, si ce n'est une succession d'emmerdes qui décidément volent bien en escadrille. Chirac avait raison. Et la première et non des moindres, cela va l'obliger à passer un autre appel à Lucie.

Devant la découverte de cette voiture, et les décisions qu'il a prises, il n'a pas le choix. Il doit laisser ses émotions de côté. Il compose le numéro, retient sa respiration et attend.

– Le célèbre major René Malmaison de la « div' centre », lui-même ? J'y crois pas.

Formule usuelle de Lucie quand elle répond. Elle trouve ça drôle. Il ne s'y fait pas. La voix de Lucie, même fatiguée, réveille toujours les mêmes souvenirs mal cicatrisés. Il fait abstraction de tout et, l'entrain en moins, reprend à son tour sa tournure de phrase traditionnelle.

– La douce et charmante Lucie Clert qui décroche, j'y crois pas non plus.

– Ça y est, t'es RULP ?

– Te fous pas de moi, Lucie. Une 607 sous surveillance par la BRB du « 36 ». Ça t'intéresse ?

Engoncée dans son fauteuil, Lucie se redresse. Fait signe à Saint-Donat : elle a un appel de première importance. Henri baisse le son de la radio.

— Elle vient d'être découverte par la PS*, à la gare Saint-Charles. Doublette parfaite, mise sous surveillance par la BRB du « 36 » pour le braquage du fourgon au Parc des Princes.

— T'as prévenu les collègues de la PJ ?

— Je suis en train de faire quoi, là, Lucie ?

La capitaine réalise. Pour le major, l'appeler, c'est aviser la PJ.

— OK, tu touches à rien, l'IJ sera là dans dix minutes.

Un temps long. Trop long. Lucie s'inquiète, comprend.

— Putain, t'es rentré à l'intérieur ? T'as pas pu t'en empêcher, René. T'es allé foutre tes grosses paluches pleines de doigts dans la caisse.

Comme si, en entendant son ancien compagnon, elle retombait dans ses vieux travers, elle monte dans les tours.

— T'as pas fait une connerie pareille ? Sur un truc comme ça, on ne touche à RIEN, René, à RIEN, putain ! Ça fait combien de temps que t'es OPJ** ? Le b.a.-ba, merde, t'es chiant.

---

* PS : abréviation policière de « police secours » (en l'espèce, le car de police secours).

** OPJ : officier de police judiciaire.

– Lucie ?

– Une super affaire pourrie par ta connerie.

– Lucie ?

– C'est à cause de mecs comme toi que la police se meurt. Ceux qui croient tout savoir sur tout et qui font n'importe quoi. Révise tes classiques !

René est presque obligé de hurler pour se faire entendre.

– Lucie, on a récupéré leurs odeurs.

Lucie en reste coite. Elle s'en veut de s'être laissé rattraper par son passé. Elle s'était pourtant promis de ne plus sombrer dans ces phases colériques, qui alimentent sa réputation. Et elle connaît Malmaison, grognon, pingre peut-être, mais bon flic, il n'aurait jamais commis une telle erreur. Penaude, elle tente de s'excuser auprès du major, qui la coupe.

– Quand j'ai vu que la bagnole était mise sous surveillance par la BRB de la PJPP*, je me suis douté qu'on avait affaire à des pros. Ils n'ont pas dû laisser de traces. Je me suis dit qu'un moyen de les accrocher, c'était de récupérer leurs odeurs. Avec les bandelettes prévues pour ça. Et on a

---

* PJPP : police judiciaire de la préfecture de police (de Paris).

respecté la procédure d'odorologie*, on les a laissées sur les fauteuils de la bagnole pendant plus d'un quart d'heure avant de les placer dans les bocaux placés sous scellés. Un pour chaque place dans la voiture. Cinq en tout.

– Pourquoi cinq ?

– Sur la banquette arrière, la place du milieu était enfoncée. On a récupéré cinq signatures olfactives. L'argent n'a pas d'odeur, mais le cul du braqueur sentira toujours la peur.

Devant tant d'application et de citations, Lucie s'incline.

– Au fait, Lucie, sauf erreur de ma part, l'odorologie se fait avant le passage de l'IJ. On a terminé, tu peux envoyer tes experts, la voiture est à leur disposition.

Il raccroche, laissant son ancienne compagne figée. Lucie et la chance l'ont quitté, mais il a gardé sa fierté et son professionnalisme.

---

* Odorologie : science des odeurs, technique judiciaire reposant sur l'analyse des odeurs par des chiens spécialement formés.

63

Henri et Lucie retrouvent l'Évêché grouillant de bruits et de d'odeurs. Ils ne peuvent pas profiter de la brise marine se mêlant aux effluves d'essence, Francis Larrivée les réunit avec les enquêteurs de la BRB et de la Crim'. Basile et son sourire ne passent pas inaperçus. Il est aux anges. Il a retrouvé Lucie, et même s'il n'a pas eu le temps de l'embrasser comme il en rêvait, il a pu la serrer contre lui. Quelques secondes à peine, suffisantes pour savoir qu'elle n'avait pas changé d'avis. Ni d'envie. Un regard rempli de promesses, une pression de main, il n'a besoin de rien d'autre. Et le délicat « tu m'as manqué » glissé dans son oreille a comblé ses attentes.

Ce qu'il vient de trouver en épluchant pour la énième fois les procédures accentue ce sourire béat qui ne le quitte pas. Même les propos de Julie Montserrat n'entament pas sa bonne humeur.

– Ne vous fiez pas à son air calme, le directeur est énervé. On approche de la fin, il ne tient pas à la rater. C'est le moment d'affûter vos arguments. Il ne vous lâchera pas... On ne le changera pas maintenant. Et c'est tant mieux.

Dans son bureau, Larrivée prend son temps. Seul le tapotement de ses doigts trahit sa nervosité. Les traits de son visage sont impassibles, mais ses yeux circulent d'un visage à un autre à grande vitesse. Julie Montserrat connaît bien son patron. Derrière son apparence posée, un volcan gronde.

– Le voyage à Paris a été positif, on dirait. Des légionnaires défroqués qui braquent les fourgons. Pourquoi pas ? Les mêmes qui viennent à Marseille enlever Ernesto Dominguez. Dont acte. Dominguez, le seul lascar qui permettait de faire le lien avec la Carlton.

Ses doigts cessent leur mouvement incessant.

– Vous pouvez me dire où on a merdé, alors ?

Personne n'ose prendre la parole. Seul Basile ne se départ pas de son sourire. Même quand Larrivée surprend tout le monde, tape un coup sec sur son bureau et hausse le ton.

– Parce que, pour l'instant, on n'a arrêté personne. Ni Rabutin. Ni Dominguez. Ni le 2e REP. On est sur des suppositions. Que dis-je, des suppositions ? Des supputations. On sent des choses, on devine des trucs, on tourne autour du Vieux-Port... mais on n'a aucune réponse à la question essentielle : qui a tué la Carlton ?

Il prend ses lunettes, les essuie lentement, prolonge ce geste machinal. Son regard est encore plus tranchant sans ses loupes.

– Commandant Saint-Donat, vous m'expliquez la stratégie ?

Henri en a vu d'autres, même s'il reconnaît que le directeur maîtrise son art.

– Monsieur le directeur, pourquoi croyez-vous que le lieutenant Urteguy a la banane ?

À la vitesse de l'éclair, Larrivée se tourne vers Basile. Cette réaction surprend le jeune lieutenant. Mais la main de Lucie qu'elle pose sur son genou lui redonne immédiatement le sourire.

– Alors, Urteguy, l'objet de votre ravissement ?

Basile aurait bien aimé lui répondre : « Lucie », mais le moment n'est pas à la boutade légère.

– Grâce aux collègues parisiens, on sait que Rabutin était bien en contact avec la Carlton avant chaque braquage de fourgon. Et grâce à leurs indications, on a trouvé... monsieur le directeur.

Basile ménage une longue pause. Les doigts du directeur recommencent leur musique d'impatience.

– Vous avez trouvé quoi, LIEUTENANT ?

Urteguy lui tend une clef USB et l'invite à la brancher sur son ordinateur. Sur son écran s'affichent cinq dossiers, aux noms évocateurs : « PSG », « OM », « Vélodrome », « La bible de l'opéra » et « Képis blancs ».

– Et alors, ça signifie quoi, URTEGUY ?

64

Allongé dans l'herbe, il a froid. Il a chaud. Il a la chair de poule et dégouline de sueur. Il ne comprend pas ce qu'il ressent. Comment le définir ? Y a-t-il des mots pour ça ? Il voudrait savoir l'heure. Mais pour quoi faire ? Il ne connaît pas le jour. Il n'arrive pas à ouvrir les yeux. Ses paupières, closes et lourdes, ne lui obéissent pas. Éblouies par le soleil et les coups qu'elles ont reçus, impossible de les bouger. Son esprit lance des ordres dans le désordre. Comme s'il voulait reprendre possession de son corps.

Il tente de faire appel à ses souvenirs pour commander ses membres. Le bras droit, la main gauche, la jambe, le mollet, le pouce. Il n'y arrive pas. Il évolue dans une tempête de nuages. Se demande si c'est ça, la mort. Une absence totale de réaction. Seul son cerveau, en mille neurones éparpillés, cherche des connexions. Il n'est que désolation et se confond avec la terre. La conclusion qui l'effraie, c'est que son esprit s'est désolidarisé de son corps. Et s'il est dans cet état, c'est qu'il est mort.

La preuve, il est nu.

Cette réflexion le rassure. Ressentir la souffrance, avoir conscience de sa nudité, il est vivant. Mais, dans son état, la mort ne serait-elle pas préférable ? Son bras touche la peau de son ventre, ses doigts se heurtent aux crevasses et cicatrices. Il ne se souvient pas de son prénom. N'imagine pas avoir un nom. À force de persévérance, il réussit à ouvrir son œil droit, à moitié, car l'autre n'est qu'un hématome noirci. Le soleil est au zénith. Lui brûle le peu de rétine qu'il offre au jour. Le bleu infini du ciel lui explose la cervelle. Il n'est que souffrance.

Sans savoir qui il est.

Il se dresse dans un gémissement. Devant lui un autre bleu, celui de la mer. Les rimes d'une vieille chanson se bousculent dans son esprit. « La mer, qu'on voit danser le long des golfes clairs. » Il arrive à se mettre debout, chancelant sur ses appuis. « La mer a des reflets d'argent. » Pourquoi les paroles de Trenet viennent-elles heurter son réveil douloureux ? « La mer, des reflets changeants, sous la pluie. » Son sexe pend tristement entre ses jambes frêles, ses testicules le brûlent. « La mer, au ciel d'été, confond ses blancs moutons… » Il fait quelques pas, s'arrache la plante des pieds sur la falaise. « … avec les anges si purs ». Il avance les bras en croix, offerts au vide. Des centaines de mètres plus bas, elle l'attend, la mer, « bergère d'azur, infinie ».

Il lève sa jambe avant de la reposer brusquement. D'où vient cette atroce musique qui l'empêche de soulager sa souffrance ? Derrière son œil mi-clos, il cherche l'origine de ce son strident, qui l'empêche de profiter de la chanson de Trenet que lui fredonnait sa mère. Sa mère, son premier vrai souvenir. Il ouvre son deuxième œil, avant de le refermer, ébloui par le mélange rouge, blanc et bleu que projette à quelques mètres de lui un fourgon. Instinctivement, il sait qu'il doit éviter les hommes en uniforme, comme on le lui a toujours appris. Fuir devant la police est son deuxième souvenir. Ce sera son dernier. Il se retourne de nouveau, ferme les yeux et avance d'un pas en murmurant « maman », qu'on voit danser le long des golfes…

65

Dans le bureau du directeur, la tension est montée d'un cran. Basile a intérêt à ne pas se planter. Jouer avec le directeur n'est pas recommandé, c'est un doux euphémisme. Pourtant il s'y autorise. L'arrogance de son âge et sa découverte lui arrogent ce droit.

– C'est d'une facilité enfantine, monsieur le directeur. « PSG » est le listing téléphonique du soir où Rabutin et ses complices se sont rencontrés dans le bar du 18ᵉ à Paris. 753 pages. « OM », c'est celui du jour où Ernesto Dominguez a été enlevé. 1 223 pages. À la parlotte : victoire des Marseillais sur les Parigots.

Dans le regard du directeur se lit toute la limite de sa patience.

– « Vélodrome », c'est le mélange des deux : le match « OM-PSG ». Il se joue forcément au Vélodrome. Les numéros similaires qu'on retrouve sur ces deux listings, Paris et Marseille.

Le directeur ouvre ce fichier, trois numéros surlignés apparaissent.

– On avait donc trois utilisateurs de portable dans le secteur du bar du 18e à Paris le soir de la rencontre de Rabutin et ses légionnaires, qui étaient également présents le jour où Dominguez s'est fait enlever rue d'Endoume ?

– Les hasards de la vie.

– Vous avez fait identifier ces numéros, Urteguy ?

– Le quatrième fichier, monsieur le directeur : « La bible de l'opéra ». Un nom devrait vous chanter, si j'ose dire...

Le DIPJ retourne sur son ordinateur et clique sur l'icône « La bible de l'opéra ». Trois noms apparaissent.

– On peut en éliminer deux. J'ai vérifié, vraies identités, personnes inconnues de nos services, on n'est pas sur des TOC. Le dernier, par contre...

Le directeur a compris. Il change de visage. Ses yeux brillent, le contentement l'envahit. Les autres enquêteurs s'impatientent. Le directeur ne s'en rend même pas compte.

– La bible de l'Opéra ! Tellement dans la logique de la Carlton.

Ce sont maintenant les regards des policiers autour de la table qui vont à toute vitesse du directeur à Basile, de Basile à Lucie, de Lucie à Henri. Quel nom vient de lire le directeur ? Quelle identité d'abonné de téléphone portable Basile a-t-il mise en avant dans ce fichier ? Le directeur perçoit l'attente de ses subordonnés.

– La ligne est identifiée à Maria Callas, la « bible de l'opéra », comme l'appelait Leonard Bernstein. La plus grande cantatrice du XXe siècle. Une vraie diva !

66

L'homme nu tente de fuir policiers et pompiers. Il n'a pas le temps de lancer sa jambe dans le vide. Quand Jérémy Lafont, jeune ADS* du car police secours, trois-quarts de rugby à ses heures sportives, voit l'individu s'approcher en flageolant du bord de la falaise, il fonce. Lancé, il l'enlace au niveau de la taille et accompagne sa chute au sol. Un plaquage dévastateur, bien dans les règles, enseigné dans toutes les bonnes écoles de rugby. Son éducateur de l'époque aurait été fier de lui. Aujourd'hui il ne s'agit pas d'un jeu, mais d'une réalité plus violente. Il vient de sauver d'une mort certaine un suicidaire ou un fou délirant.

Quand Jérémy se relève, son chef de brigade, plus âgé, plus lourd et moins véloce, le félicite.

– Pour le concours, ça va te faire gagner des points !

_____

* ADS : adjoint de sécurité, emploi jeune dans la police.

Réussir son intégration dans le corps des gradés et gardiens n'est pas sa principale préoccupation. Jérémy se relève, renfile son polo dans son pantalon. Les pompiers les ont rejoints et procèdent aux premiers soins. Hagard, l'ADS regarde l'individu se faire soigner. Du haut de ses 20 ans et de la découverte de son métier de policier, il se demande comment cet homme a pu se retrouver dans cet état. Au-delà de sa nudité, les hématomes et cicatrices qu'il porte ne peuvent pas être les seules conséquences du plaquage qu'il vient de subir. Surtout les traces de pinces laissant des traînées bleutées sur ses deux testicules. On ne lui avait pas tout dit au cours de sa formation initiale.

La main de son chef de brigade se pose sur son épaule.

– T'es pas responsable, gamin. Ils sont tous dingues. Les gens, la vie, la société. Et notre job à nous, poulets, c'est de canaliser cette dinguerie.

L'ADS fait semblant de comprendre. Mais pas sûr qu'il termine son concours de gardien de la paix. Au rugby, au moins, les coups distribués ne sont qu'un jeu où à la fin les gagnants font une haie d'honneur aux perdants. Il regarde l'homme transporté sur un brancard, enroulé dans une couverture chauffante, des perfusions d'urgence dans les bras, encadré par quatre pompiers. Les haies chez les voyous ne sont pas d'honneur.

À l'écart, il entend son chef passer un appel.

– Le quart ? Tu me passes l'OPJ ? La mission, route des Crêtes. L'homme à poil qui voulait se jeter dans le vide. Oui, on est arrivés juste à temps. Non, on sait pas qui c'est. Complètement à poil, j'te dis. Et il a morflé, le zig. Des traces de coups partout. Même sur les couilles. Ils l'ont pas raté, ceux qui l'ont dérouillé. Actes de torture et de barbarie, si tu veux mon avis... Eh, c'est qui de permanence ?

Il attend la réponse, qui le fait sourire jaune.

– Sans déc ? Il va pas être déçu...

67

– Et dans « Képis blancs », Urteguy, on trouve quoi ?

Basile est aux anges, le directeur est entré dans son jeu.

– Je vous laisse le découvrir, monsieur le directeur. Vous ne devriez pas être déçu.

– Je l'espère, lieutenant.

Un rayon de soleil lance ses éclats réfléchissants sur la table de travail. Basile y voit un signe. C'est son heure de gloire. Il y a encore quelques jours, il était l'arpète, le freluquet, l'intermittent musical. Il est en train de montrer à tous ce qu'il sait faire. Heureux surtout de voir les yeux de Lucie se poser sur lui et ne plus le quitter. Le directeur le laisse dérouler son petit jeu, même si lui aussi a hâte de connaître la suite. « Képis blancs » contient un listing et l'identification de trois numéros de téléphone.

– On se trouve face à des hommes de goût, monsieur le directeur.

– Des braqueurs, peut-être des tueurs... Vous avez des goûts douteux, lieutenant.

Même détendu, le directeur aime rappeler qu'il reste le patron. À trop jouer le malin, Basile risque de perdre sa crédibilité.

– Des mélomanes, monsieur.

– Mais encore ?

– « Képis blancs », c'est la fadette de la ligne utilisée par celui ou celle qui se fait appeler Maria Callas, selon moi Daniel Rabutin...

– On l'avait compris, lieutenant. Avec la Carlton, il avait un abonnement au nom de la Castafiore. Depuis sa mort, il a changé de ligne et se fait appeler Maria Callas.

– Et comme le montre sa fadette, c'est un téléphone dédié, en lien uniquement avec trois autres numéros...

– Que vous avez fait identifier ?

Un nouveau temps long, qui titille Larrivée. Il lit sur son écran les fichiers mis à jour dans « Képis blancs ». Un sourire accompagne un hochement de tête. Les regards des enquêteurs sont tous dirigés vers lui.

– Allez-y, Urteguy, vos collègues ont hâte que vous terminiez votre petit numéro.

Basile jubile, c'est maintenant. Il prend son temps. Articule.

– Maria Callas est en lien avec Luciano Pavarotti, Roberto Alagna et Enrico Caruso.

Même si les policiers ne sont pas de fins connaisseurs de musique lyrique, tous ont déjà entendu chanter au moins une fois les trois ténors, même Caruso. Basile conclut :

– Maria Callas, alias Daniel Rabutin, est en lien avec trois ténors, ses trois complices braqueurs, ses frères d'armes. Ceux que le gérant du bar du 18e a entendu se dire « Legio Patria Nostra ». Des légionnaires.

Il savoure encore.

– Des képis blancs.

Un brouhaha se fait entendre. Chacun commente cette découverte. Le directeur lui-même semble ravi. Lucie résume le sentiment général.

– Maintenant, on a les numéros qu'utilisent les légionnaires chaque fois qu'ils veulent se rencontrer. Reste plus qu'à les mettre sur écoute.

– Et à déchiffrer leur code, précise Saint-Donat.

Il a pris connaissance du dossier « Képis blancs » et notamment de la facture détaillée du téléphone de la Callas, en lien avec Pavarotti, Alagna et Caruso. Elle ne mentionne pas de conversations téléphoniques entre les ténors et la diva, uniquement des échanges de SMS. Du même type que ceux que la Carlton échangeait avec la Castafiore : un chiffre puis deux lettres, suivies à nouveau d'un ou plusieurs chiffres. Le débroussaillage ne fait que commencer.

68

Les mouches n'ont pas changé d'âne, se dit Malmaison. Mais pourquoi les affaires bizarres arrivent-elles toujours quand il est de permanence ? En trente et quelques années de carrière, il n'avait encore jamais connu ça. Les effectifs de police secours viennent de retrouver un homme nu vagabondant à proximité de la route des Crêtes, au bord de la falaise, dont le corps n'est plus qu'un territoire de cicatrices et d'hématomes. Sans fringues et sans mémoire. Incapable de dire quoi que ce soit, juste de chantonner en boucle *La Mer* de Charles Trenet.

Encore un frappadingue ou un camé, pense Malmaison. Mais qu'allait-il faire à poil dans le parc national des Calanques ? Le major connaît bien le secteur pour s'inscrire chaque année au semi-marathon Marseille-Cassis. Lorsqu'il était en couple avec Lucie, il a battu ses records personnels. C'était l'époque où la chance et l'amour l'accompagnaient. Depuis, même s'il termine cette course mythique, ses temps dépassent largement les deux heures.

Il faudra quand même qu'il arrête de penser à Lucie s'il veut rester dans un chrono acceptable.

Il se dit que, sans le courage et la réactivité de l'ADS Jérémy Lafont, ce n'est pas un amnésique à poil qu'il serait dans l'obligation de traiter, mais un cadavre nu au pied d'une falaise de la grande bleue. Finalement, un peu de chance dans tout ce pandémonium.

Le fada a été transporté aux urgences de la Timone. Malmaison se présente à l'accueil, accompagné d'un jeune ASPTS*. Le major connaît les règles de base de son métier. Le b.a.-ba en cas de découverte d'un amnésique est de prélever ses empreintes, histoire de vérifier s'il ne serait pas connu des fichiers, permettant de mettre un nom derrière cette nudité, de corps et de mémoire.

Le jeune homme allongé sur un brancard, sous perfusion, est endormi. Pour vérifier l'état du blessé, Malmaison soulève le drap rêche couvrant son corps inerte. Jamais de sa vie de flic, il n'aurait pensé voir un sexe de la sorte. Le pénis est à peine visible, caché par les deux testicules

---

* ASPTS : agent spécialisé en police technique et scientifique.

hypertrophiés, qui portent des traces de griffes. Malmaison n'est pas voyeur, mais son métier l'oblige à être curieux. Même s'il ne fait aucun doute que sa préférence sexuelle est féminine, il prend pourtant soin de préciser à l'ASPTS :

– Si tu me prends en photo maintenant, je te fais bouffer ton Nikon et sa pellicule.

Le jeune agent aurait bien aimé lui rappeler qu'ils sont au XXIe siècle, et que depuis plus de vingt ans, même dans la police, pour faire de la photo, on a abandonné l'argentique pour le numérique. Il sent que ce n'est pas le moment de mettre en exergue leur différence d'âge, mais trouve quand même la suggestion de Malmaison intéressante. Il pianote discrètement sur son portable pour choisir le bon angle et attend le moment idéal pour prendre en photo Malmaison, la tête baissée à trois centimètres du sexe de l'homme endormi. On ne sait jamais, ce type de clichés peut toujours servir. Dans une carrière, il y a des photos qui peuvent rapporter gros et faire marrer un service pendant des années.

Religieusement, il écoute alors Malmaison commenter ce qu'il voit.

– Ils lui ont mis des pinces sur les testicules. Y'a encore la marque. Ils ont ressorti la gégène, ces tarés.

Par réflexe, il pose sa main sur la braguette de son pantalon.

– Tu m'étonnes qu'il ait perdu la mémoire.

Le reste du corps ne vaut pas mieux. Traces de coups au visage, yeux boursouflés, ongles arrachés, hématomes sur les bras et le buste, cicatrices au niveau des poignets. Malmaison n'en peut plus. Il se tourne vers le jeune ASPTS, qui a à peine le temps de ranger son portable.

– Vas-y, relève ses paluches, qu'on dégage de là.

Dès leur retour au commissariat, l'ASPTS scanne les empreintes digitales sur la borne reliée au FAED*, la machine est rapide et formelle. Elle ne met pas longtemps pour identifier l'amnésique, avec plus de quinze points de corrélation sur le pouce gauche. Si le suicidaire de la route des Crêtes a perdu la mémoire, celle du TAJ est particulièrement vive.

Principe de précaution et réflexe professionnel, il passe l'individu au FPR**. Il

---

* FAED : Fichier automatisé des empreintes digitales.

** FPR : Fichier des personnes recherchées.

aurait dû s'en douter : il va devoir de nouveau passer un appel dont il se serait bien
passé. Ce n'est pas encore cette année qu'il
va gagner Marseille-Cassis.

À l'euphorie de la découverte de Basile succède la déconvenue. Saint-Donat l'a rappelé, il ne suffit pas d'avoir les coordonnées des voyous, encore faut-il décoder leurs messages. Et quand ils se limitent à des chiffres et des lettres, ils peuvent signifier tout et n'importe quoi. Il leur faudrait un détail, même infinitésimal, qui leur ouvrirait la porte de la compréhension. Pour l'instant, à part le fait qu'ils ont affaire à d'anciens légionnaires, fans d'opéra, ils n'ont rien. C'est à la fois énorme et insuffisant. Tout est permis. Des connotations historiques, dates de victoires ou défaites de la Légion ou de succès mythiques de la Callas, voire de ses séparations amoureuses. L'imagination au pouvoir.

Le DIPJ est passé de l'agacement à l'excitation. Comme si les éléments apportés par Urteguy avaient réveillé l'enquêteur qui somnole en lui. Il s'autorise quelques facilités de langage et rappelle au groupe que ce n'est pas à deux mètres du bol de sangria qu'on abandonne l'apéritif.

– N'hésitez pas, tentez tout. Souvenez-vous du code qu'utilisaient les braqueurs de la Dream Team.

Le directeur parle d'une époque où tous les SRPJ de France et de Navarre traquaient des malfaiteurs autoproclamés la Dream Team. Une équipe composée entre autres d'anciens sportifs de haut niveau, prêts à tout, comme braquer un Airbus sur l'aéroport de Rivesaltes, pour dérober 4,2 millions de francs transportés en soute.

Avant chaque braquage, les malfaiteurs communiquaient entre eux par messages, envoyés sur des « tam-tams », petits boîtiers électroniques portés à la ceinture, permettant de recevoir une série de chiffres. Avant l'ère des téléphones portables, ils étaient utilisés pour contacter une personne et lui demander de rappeler le numéro qui s'affichait. L'équipe de la Dream Team avait détourné cette utilisation. Le chef envoyait à tous un code composé de trois séries de chiffres.

Légende ou réalité, les policiers n'auraient jamais réussi à le déchiffrer, mais, bien des années après, l'un des voyous impliqués aurait fini par en donner la clef. La première série de chiffres donnait la date du rendez-vous, la deuxième, une page du guide Michelin de l'année en cours, la troisième, le paragraphe de cette page qui renvoyait à un restaurant faisant l'objet d'une critique.

Moyen original de se donner rendez-vous dans un restaurant sans inviter le ban et l'arrière-ban de la police judiciaire, afin d'y organiser en toute discrétion le prochain braquage.

Les policiers écoutent religieusement Larrivée raconter ses souvenirs. Chacun essaye de voir comment mettre en parallèle le code de la Dream Team avec celui utilisé par les légionnaires. Au fur et à mesure, les réflexions fusent.

– Les légionnaires, ça bouffe pas dans des gastros.

– Ils carburent à la binouze.

– Avec Internet, ils ont pas besoin de guides.

– Ils ont déjà le manuel du petit braqueur illustré.

– ... et celui du règlement militaire.

– Ça a peut-être un lien avec la partition de la Callas quand elle a chanté *La Walkirie* de Wagner.

– C'est qui, Wagner ?

– C'est quoi, *La Walkirie* ?

– Ou alors ils utilisent un roman historique à la gloire de la Légion.

L'humour potache de la PJ prend souvent le dessus dans ce genre de débats. L'arrivée tape du poing sur la table pour rétablir le silence. Les flics ont l'humour léger, mais le sens de la hiérarchie.

Une sonnerie de téléphone résonne. Les regards se tournent vers Lucie, qui lâche précipitamment la main de Basile pour éteindre son portable. Quand elle voit le nom de Malmaison s'afficher, elle hésite, mais, si son ancien compagnon l'appelle, c'est qu'il a encore du nouveau.

– Major, je vous écoute.

Malmaison se doute que Lucie doit être occupée pour lui parler ainsi. Tant mieux, rester sur le terrain professionnel, c'est ce qu'il maîtrise le mieux. Ce qu'il a à lui dire tient en deux phrases.

Lucie s'étonne, le fait répéter, le remercie et raccroche.

Tous sont suspendus à ses lèvres. Elle reprend son souffle, regarde Basile, tente un sourire timide, jette un œil à Henri, prend sa respiration avant d'annoncer qu'Ernesto Dominguez vient d'être retrouvé par les effectifs de la sécurité publique, divaguant nu à proximité de la route des Crêtes, après avoir subi des actes de torture et de barbarie. Il a perdu la mémoire et a été conduit aux urgences.

Larrivée réagit le premier. Il leur ordonne de foncer à la Timone et d'aider Dominguez à retrouver la mémoire au plus vite.

70

Saint-Donat a beau connaître le CHU de la Timone, chaque fois qu'il arrive aux urgences, il ressent la même chose. Entre pleurs et complaintes, les patients venus pour traiter une bobologie légère ou des traumatismes lourds l'angoissent. L'effort déployé pour la qualité de l'accueil ne change rien à cette sensation. Il n'en peut plus des couloirs imprégnés d'éther et de ces corps en souffrance.

Les couleurs de sa carte professionnelle lui permettent rapidement de rencontrer l'interne. Lequel le prévient tout de suite : Ernesto Dominguez est dans l'incapacité de répondre aux questions. Sous sédatif, il ne peut pas réagir. Ernesto a reçu des décharges électriques, des pieds à la tête en passant par les parties génitales, ayant occasionné des séquelles irréversibles sur ses neurones.

Avec Lucie, il accède au box où le blessé reçoit ses soins. Sous perfusion, celui-ci est allongé sur le lit médicalisé, recouvert d'un drap verdâtre. Son visage émacié est

marqué d'hématomes. Sa bouche boursou-
flée porte des traces de saignement. Ses
yeux sont gonflés, rougis par les coups et la
chaleur. Son attitude ne laisse aucun doute.
Il est ailleurs, comme s'il vivait encore et
toujours les tortures qu'il a subies.

Lucie a du mal à supporter la vision
de cet homme à peine reconnaissable.
Pourtant elle est entrée dans la police
pour arrêter les individus capables de commettre de telles atrocités. Paradoxe de son
métier résumé dans le visage tuméfié de
Dominguez, délinquant notoire ; elle va
tout faire pour trouver les auteurs de ces
actes de torture et de barbarie.

Henri note les traces de coups visibles.
Les autres lui seront communiqués sur le
certificat médical. En même temps, il parle
sans discontinuer au blessé. Il ne sait pas
s'il l'entend, mais tente, malgré l'éloigne-
ment psychologique, d'établir un contact.
Une façon de le mettre en confiance.
L'habituer à sa voix, à son timbre, à son
rythme.

Lucie le prend pour un dingue, pourtant
Henri ne se trompe pas. Ce mouvement des
lèvres, ce positionnement de la bouche, la
langue qui cherche son chemin, Ernesto
veut parler. Saint-Donat se penche sur le
corps meurtri. Colle son oreille au plus

près du visage de Dominguez, qui murmure deux syllabes en boucle :

– Hos... Ni...

Ernesto ne peut rien dire d'autre. « Hos,
ni » en boucle, comme un leitmotiv. Lucie
se penche à son tour sur lui.

– Quoi, Hosni ? Il a donné l'ordre de te
faire ça ? Mais il peut pas, Hosni, il est en
prison... Putain, dis-nous...

Henri lui demande de se calmer. Comme
une furie, elle tourne en rond dans la
chambre. Saint-Donat l'oblige à l'attendre
à l'extérieur. En sortant, la capitaine se
retient de claquer la porte.

71

Henri retrouve Lucie adossée à leur voiture. La nuit est tombée sur le parking du CHU. Il n'a rien pu obtenir d'autre de Dominguez. La capitaine a allumé une cigarette et souffle longuement entre chaque bouffée. Henri fait de même, savoure la nicotine qui prend possession de ses poumons. Même si Lucie ne l'a jamais vu fumer avant, cela ne l'étonne pas. Certains soirs, l'envie de s'intoxiquer prend le pas sur tout le reste. Dans les volutes de fumée, ils tentent d'oublier au plus vite le visage mutilé de Dominguez. Et l'odeur exécrable régnant dans la chambre du torturé.

Même si les découvertes de Basile leur ont permis de progresser, avoir retrouvé Ernesto dans cet état leur donne la désagréable impression d'avoir toujours un train de retard.

– T'as des nouvelles de Basile ?

– Toujours avec le dirlo. Ils cherchent le code des képis blancs. Tant qu'ils auront pas une solution, Larrivée ne lâchera rien.

– Il est pas couché !

Lucie n'a qu'une hâte, retrouver Basile sur son bateau. Ce n'est pas pour tout de suite.

– Tu crois qu'il parlait de quel Hosni, tête de bec Bunsen ?

Henri ne sourit pas à l'humour vachard de la capitaine.

– J'en sais rien. Yassine est mort et Bilal est à la rate. Ce ne sont pas eux qui l'ont enlevé, on est bien placés pour le savoir.

Ils sont surpris par une ambulance qui s'arrête devant eux. La vitre du passager arrière descend et une tête d'enfant en sort.

– Alors, la police, on bronze ?

Henri reconnaît le minot qu'il rencontre lors de ses visites avec les « Nez rouges ».

– Doudou... qu'est-ce que tu fais là ?

– C'est moi qui pose les questions, commandant Henri, c'est mon terrain de jeu, ici !

– Ça y est, tu peux sortir ?

– Juste aujourd'hui, une permission de deux heures, accompagner papa acheter nos billets pour le dernier match de l'OM. On ne le manquera pas. La trente-huitième journée au Vélodrome !

Par la fenêtre, il exhibe fièrement ses billets. En voyant ce môme, sans cheveux, garder toute cette énergie malgré la maladie qui le ronge, Lucie est émue. Elle

s'avance à son tour vers la voiture. Édouard
la reconnaît, se tourne vers Henri.

– Je croyais que c'était pas ton amoureuse ?

– C'est pas elle. Je te l'ai déjà dit, je suis
marié !

– Côte à côte en train de fumer la même
cigarette, ça veut dire quoi alors ?

– On est fatigués de travailler sur une
grosse affaire.

– Je peux vous aider ?

En parlant, dans l'excitation, Édouard
laisse tomber ses billets, que ramasse Lucie.
Elle les lui tend avant de s'arrêter net. Un
détail a attiré son attention. Elle scrute à la
loupe les billets qu'elle vient de ramasser.
Édouard en profite, s'adresse à Henri.

– C'est quoi sa coupe de cheveux, elle est
malade ?

– Non, Doudou, juste… amoureuse.

Édouard, en levant les yeux au ciel
semble dire « même pas grave ». La capitaine se penche sur la voiture, attrape le
visage d'Édouard et l'embrasse avant de lui
rendre les billets.

– Tu n'imagines même pas à quel point
tu viens de nous aider, Doudou. Bon
match ! On devrait y être aussi.

Henri regarde Lucie, étonné. Il ne comprend pas. Édouard est tout fier.

– T'es tellement belle. Si je peux t'être utile encore, t'hésites pas.

L'ambulance démarre, s'écarte d'eux. Édouard se penche par la fenêtre.

– Si tu changes d'avis, Lucie, tu sais où me trouver.

Henri est ailleurs. Tant de choses se bousculent dans sa tête, la bouille, le sourire et la gouaille de Doudou. Ces propos qui lui font ce drôle d'écho. Cette façon qu'il a de ne rien laisser paraître. D'être plus fort que la maladie, plus mature que les adultes, plus serein que l'avenir. Il regarde cette ambulance qui s'enfonce dans les entrailles de l'hôpital sous la lumière de son gyrophare et une autre qui sort, dans un mouvement perpétuel où la vie croise la mort.

– Henri, je crois que j'ai trouvé.

Saint-Donat essaye de comprendre ce que Lucie cherche à lui dire.

– Le code des légionnaires. Pour communiquer entre eux. Je crois que je l'ai déchiffré.

L'ambulance a disparu, avalée dans le parking souterrain. Seule sa barre lumineuse continue d'envoyer des reflets par intermittence. Ça fait bien longtemps qu'Henri a du mal à croire en Dieu, à tous ses descendants et prétendants. S'appeler « saint quelque chose » n'est pas gage de l'existence des messagers du Seigneur. Pourtant ce soir, il lève les yeux au ciel. Comme une envie, une nécessité de croire que les anges existent.

72

Marseille,
samedi 19 mai 2018.

La moto serpente entre La Ciotat et Marseille. La route est dégagée. Le soleil honore la Méditerranée de tous ses éclats. Le pilote prend un plaisir infini à travailler ses courbes, à la recherche de la perfection. Sous son casque, Saint-Donat murmure : « Là tout n'est qu'ordre et beauté, luxe, calme et volupté. » Une invitation au voyage. Une envie de fugue.

Le secret du motard réside dans ces courts instants de conduite. Ceux où la conscience du pilotage dépasse la simple habitude d'accélérer et de changer les vitesses. Où le pilote oublie tout le reste et se régale simplement d'être sur sa bécane. Seul. Sa Goldwing et lui. Avec comme guides la lumière blanche, la grande bleue et l'asphalte noir.

L'importance de la solitude pour mieux se laisser aller. Penser et rêver, mieux apprécier le silence, ne pas se laisser polluer le présent. C'est encore une thérapie. Son psy le lui a répété, il en aura besoin toute sa vie. Alors il se soigne, en roulant, juste avant d'arriver à l'Évêché.

Les heures qui l'attendent à l'hôtel de police vont être longues. Dans la fureur et la multitude. Le temps de l'action est venu. Il n'est pas inquiet, au contraire, il est soulagé. Presque serein. Si Lucie ne s'est pas trompée dans le déchiffrage du code, les braqueurs légionnaires dormiront ce soir sous les cloches de l'ancien palais épiscopal. Ils pourront leur expliquer qui a tué la Carlton et pourquoi. Alors il profite de ces derniers mètres au pied de la Gineste, avant de se glisser dans la circulation à hauteur du rond-point de Mazargues, où l'invasion automobile commence ses ravages.

Il prend la file des bus. Avec sa limousine à deux roues, c'est plus raisonnable que de slalomer entre les voitures. Quand il passe devant le Stade-Vélodrome, il sourit. Le match du soir de l'OM est le dernier du championnat, mais il est aussi capital pour la suite de leur affaire.

Huit jours de silence et d'attente. Huit jours que Lucie a percé le code sur le parking de la Timone grâce à Doudou et son billet pour le 38e match du championnat de France. Huit jours que le directeur trépignait, que Basile s'énervait et que Lucie doutait. Huit jours devant les écoutes des téléphones des képis blancs à attendre qu'ils resonnent.

Mais les portables des ténors restaient sans voix.

L'inaction ne faisait pas partie de leur mode d'emploi. L'apathie n'était pas leur choix, l'attente, pas leur volonté.

Quand, il y a deux jours, enfin, la Callas a contacté Pavarotti, Alagna et Caruso. Les écoutes ont fait mouche, leurs trois portables ont reçu le même message, indiquant : « 38MG08 ». Les ténors ont répondu par la même émoticône : un pouce dressé. Les trois chanteurs lyriques avaient bien compris le code de la diva et acquiesçaient. Ils seraient au rendez-vous proposé par la cantatrice. Il ne restait plus qu'à utiliser la méthode proposée par la capitaine pour déchiffrer leur message. Quand on connaît le code, le comprendre est un jeu d'enfant. Lucie a été la première à s'exclamer.

– Ils ont rendez-vous dans deux jours au Vélodrome. Le match OM-Lille. La 38e journée de championnat.

Elle a regardé Henri et Basile, fière d'elle, et dans un grand sourire leur a précisé :

– « 38 » comme la 38e journée du championnat de France de foot. « M », c'est l'OM qui reçoit, le match se joue à Marseille. « G », selon moi, cela signifie « Ganay », l'une des tribunes du Stade-Vélodrome, et « 08 », le numéro de porte… Merci Doudou.

L'excitation les a de nouveau saisis. Le directeur a pris une décision : les légionnaires seront interpellés au stade, avant tout commencement d'exécution d'un nouveau braquage. Il a été très clair.

– La question n'est pas de savoir quel coup ils préparent. Pour l'instant, on s'en fout. L'important est de les serrer, à la fois pour leur rôle dans l'affaire de la Carlton, mais aussi sur les autres braquages, la mort de la mamie à Melun et les actes de torture sur Dominguez. À ce stade, on a suffisamment de billes contre eux. N'oubliez pas d'aviser le juge d'instruction. Et de prévenir les Parisiens, qu'ils ne croient pas qu'on leur fait un bébé dans le dos.

Sur sa moto, Henri sourit encore plus. Il repense à Doudou et son billet pour le match, qui a tout déclenché chez Lucie. Il imagine la Carlton consultant le site de la Fédération française de foot pour s'aviser des stades où se déroulaient des matchs à proximité des objectifs qu'elle voulait braquer. Il y avait une raison à ce qu'on ne retrouve que des sites consacrés au foot sur sa tablette numérique. Et les policiers avaient vérifié : deux jours avant chaque braquage, la Carlton envoyait ce type de message à la Castafiore, alias Daniel Rabutin. Et à chaque fois, ils avaient trouvé un match de foot du championnat de France correspondant au jour, à la ville qui accueillait le match, et des indications concernant la porte où ils avaient rendez-vous. Henri avait quand même eu du mal à imaginer la Carlton faire la holà dans les tribunes du Groupama Stadium ou de l'Abbé-Deschamps.

Mais Lucie a forcément déchiffré le bon code.

La circulation est dense, Henri se décide à passer par le tunnel du Prado, même s'il est payant, il lui fera l'économie de trente minutes d'embouteillage et lui permettra de sortir place de la Major, à deux cents mètres de l'Évêché. Certaines dépenses sont utiles. Car il y a urgence. La dernière journée du championnat de France de foot débute ce soir, avec un match décisif au Vélodrome. Tous les joueurs doivent être prêts et connaître leur partition par cœur.

73

Francis Larrivée tourne en rond. Pourquoi a-t-il dit oui ? Il y a des obligations qu'un haut fonctionnaire ne peut refuser. Il est invité par le préfet à un cocktail avec des plénipotentiaires étrangers en visite marseillaise. Il aurait préféré accompagner ses hommes au Stade-Vélodrome, il avait des places dans le carré VIP et habituellement ne rate jamais un match de l'OM. Il tape du poing sur la table. Savoir ses subordonnés au combat quand il se la coule douce le rend malade. Pourquoi faut-il que ce pince-fesses tombe en même temps que le dernier match du championnat et que l'intervention de la police judiciaire ? Quelle heure est-il ? 19 h 30. Le coup d'envoi est dans une demi-heure, la réception dans une heure. Il a encore le temps. Il sort dans le couloir et prend la direction des bureaux de la Crim'.

60 000 supporters bleu et blanc se pressent aux abords du stade. Une foule bruyante et optimiste envahit les esplanades Ganay

et Jean-Bouin du Vélodrome. Les escaliers monumentaux devant l'entrée principale sont pris d'assaut par des aficionados à moitié dévêtus, écharpes sur le front, bouteilles de bière dans la main, clopes dans l'autre, ivres d'alcool et de certitudes : l'OM va gagner et eux aussi. Ils hurlent leur amour indéfectible aux Olympiens.

Lucie, Basile et quinze officiers de la Crim' et de la BRB sont déguisés en supporters locaux. Affublés de maillots de l'OM, d'écharpes, de casquettes bleu et blanc, tout est bon pour se mêler à la foule et se positionner à hauteur de la porte n° 8 de l'esplanade Ganay. Avec comme mission : repérer Rabutin et toute personne pouvant l'approcher, les filer à la sortie du stade, avant de les interpeller proprement. Des effectifs de la BRI couvrent les extérieurs.

Henri a pris la direction de l'opération. Il a obtenu du club un passe lui permettant de circuler dans tout le Vélodrome. Il tient à être au plus près de l'action. Il a placé un homme dans la salle de vidéosurveillance du stade, en lien avec les effectifs de la sécurité publique, pour assurer le visionnage des caméras. Il regarde sa montre, presque 20 heures, prend sa radio.

– Lucie d'Henri, alors ?

– Toujours rien. C'est pas normal. Et toi ?

– Pour l'instant, rien.

Depuis leur arrivée au stade, l'angoisse de la capitaine n'a fait qu'augmenter. Assise sur le haut des gradins, elle n'est même pas à côté de Basile, positionné au plus près du terrain. Sa main lui manque. Elle, par habitude si sûre, se ronge les ongles. Son inquiétude se mêle à la peur de l'échec. Et si elle s'était plantée sur le déchiffrage du code ?

– Henri, les collègues de la Crim', ils se sont pas fait détroncher ?

– Lucie ? Tu m'emmerdes !

La capitaine reprend son souffle, cherche de la sérénité. Henri transpire sa confiance.

– Tu ne t'es pas trompée, Lucie. On a quatre-vingt-dix minutes pour les trouver. Et on va les trouver.

Basile n'a jamais vu les joueurs de si près. Il ne peut pas s'empêcher de regarder le coup d'envoi. C'est quand même l'OM qui joue. Il se reprend vite. Il a suivi dans son oreillette l'échange radio. Il regarde le stade, lève les yeux, scrute les gradins, une vague bleue et blanche lui saute au visage. Pour détendre l'ambiance, il lance à la radio :

– En même temps, qu'est-ce qui ressemble plus à un supporter marseillais qu'un supporter de l'OM ?

Pas le genre de propos qui rassure Lucie.

Larrivée pousse la porte du bureau d'Henri Saint-Donat. Il ne lui faut pas longtemps pour trouver les trois tomes de l'enquête sur le meurtre de Nathalie Fournier. La procédure est rangée dans trois pochettes cartonnées, de 30 cm de haut et d'au moins trois kilos chacune. Dessus est inscrite la mention « LA CARLTON. Affaire C/X, homicide volontaire, actes de torture et barbarie, association de malfaiteurs… ». Larrivée ne regarde pas sa montre, il s'assoit dans le fauteuil du commandant, délie le tome I et commence sa lecture. Le tout premier procès-verbal, la saisine, les constatations sur le corps carbonisé de la Carlton, auxquelles est annexé l'album photographique établi sur les lieux. Malgré toutes ses années de carrière, il a un haut-le-cœur.

La première mi-temps a débuté depuis trente minutes. Le score n'a pas évolué, zéro partout. Comme l'OM et ses supporters, Lucie est en plein doute. Les ongles de ses mains sont ravagés. Elle est certaine de s'être trompée. Personne n'a signalé la présence de Rabutin. Elle jette des coups d'œil de tous les côtés.

– Merde, merde, merde !

Henri tourne dans toutes les coursives des tribunes Ganay. Chaque fois qu'il accède aux gradins, il scrute pour voir si une tête dépasse du rang. Lucie le contacte par radio. Persuadée qu'il faut laisser tomber.

– On a dit tout le match, Lucie, on fait tout le match !

Puis il s'inquiète :

– Henri de la vidéo, du nouveau ?

– Ça bouge de partout. Difficile d'avoir accès aux images.

Pour le dernier match de la saison, les incidents en tribune ou sur les coursives sont nombreux. Henri peste. Il aurait aimé pouvoir disposer d'un maximum de caméras, mais il faut aussi que la sécurité du stade soit assurée.

Larrivée quitte l'Évêché en urgence. Plongé dans la procédure, il s'est mis en retard. Mais un truc le chiffonne. Il ne sait pas quoi exactement, mais, après avoir relu le premier tome, il en est sûr, ils sont passés à côté. Quelque chose lui donne un goût amer et l'interroge. Et s'ils faisaient fausse route ? Quand il a vu l'heure, il a

lâché le procès-verbal de lien entre les procédures de la BRB de Paris et de la PJ de
Melun, où Lucie, en termes juridiques, a
synthétisé les informations échangées à
Cannes-Écluse, avant de se précipiter à la
préfecture.

À son arrivée, le représentant de l'État
se moque gentiment de lui. La PJ se fait
attendre, encore une grosse affaire sur les
bras, certainement. Le préfet ne croit pas si
bien dire. Parmi les invités, Francis Larrivée
reconnaît deux anciens secrétaires d'État,
ainsi que le consul du Maroc, étonnamment acoquiné avec celui de Russie. Après
les formules obligées de politesse, il écoute
les uns et les autres digresser. Il s'amuse du
consul marocain tentant d'échanger avec
son homologue russe, en arabe. Il lance
quelques vagues considérations sur la poli-
tique sécuritaire en France et sur l'augmen-
tation de la violence dans le monde, dans
les pays du Maghreb comme dans ceux
d'Europe de l'Est. Mais il n'y est pas, n'y
croit pas. Il regarde sa montre. La deuxième
mi-temps a dû commencer. Il s'étonne de
ne pas avoir de nouvelles de Saint-Donat,
maintenant les policiers auraient dû loca-
liser Rabutin. Il s'inquiète de savoir si
quelqu'un connaît le score. Le consul marocain lui répond : à la 70e minute, le score

est toujours vierge. Cela exaspère d'ailleurs le haut dignitaire étranger, qui a choisi son camp. Il est bleu et blanc.

À la 72ᵉ minute, l'énorme vacarme produit par les supporters faisant entendre leurs voix de l'Estaque aux Goudes s'éteint d'un coup. Chants et insultes restent coincés dans leurs gorges. Seuls quelque deux cents Lillois, supporters courageux mais inconscients, s'époumonent en rythme.

– Ici ! Ici ! C'est le Nord !

Lille a marqué, et avec panache. Un but d'anthologie, que les membres des Ultras ou des Fanatics rêveraient de voir marquer par leur équipe. Mais l'OM a-t-il encore les moyens de ses ambitions ? Cette équipe compte-t-elle des joueurs capables à eux seuls de faire la différence ? Mbappé est parisien, et il n'y a pas deux Mbappé dans le championnat de France. À part peut-être ce joueur de Lille, jusque-là inconnu, et qui vient par ce but remarquable de faire taire tout un stade, pleurer tout un peuple et s'effondrer toute une ville.

– *Abn awaa !* s'écrie le consul marocain.

Les invités se retournent vers lui, étonnés de cette interjection non maîtrisée. Le plénipotentiaire arabe se confond en excuses et se dirige vers Francis Larrivée, qui le regarde comme s'il venait d'avoir une révélation.

– Monsieur le directeur, Lille vient de marquer. Ils mènent 1 à 0. Il reste à peine huit minutes de jeu.

Francis Larrivée n'en a plus rien à faire du score de l'OM.

– Vous avez dit quoi, exactement, monsieur le consul ?

– Pardon ?

– Les propos que vous venez de dire en arabe, ça veut dire quoi ?

– C'est-à-dire, que... je n'ose pas...

Larrivée insiste. Le consul, après s'être assuré que personne ne les écoute, finit par lui répéter.

– *Abn awaa*... Le « chacal ». Ce joueur de Lille, qui a marqué ce but splendide.

– *Abn awaa* ?

– Oui...

– *Abn awaa*, ça signifie le « chacal », c'est bien ça ?

– Oui, monsieur le directeur, mais enfin...

– Merci, monsieur le consul, merci beaucoup.

Sans autre forme d'explication, Larrivée récupère ses affaires et sort en courant de la préfecture.

Le but distrait Henri deux secondes avant qu'il reprenne, encore plus déterminé, sa surveillance. Basile, en fan absolu de l'OM, gueule son désespoir à la radio. Il fait exploser le tympan de ses collègues. Depuis quelques minutes, Lucie est sortie des gradins pour arpenter les couloirs et les escaliers immenses du stade. Elle ne sourit pas à la désolation de son amoureux. Son angoisse s'est transformée en colère. Furieuse que Rabutin et ses complices n'aient pas été localisés. Ils sont plus de vingt flics dans le stade, ils auraient dû les remarquer. Quelques lascars aux cheveux très courts et aux bras tatoués ont bien attiré leur attention. Mais la mode des tatouages et des cheveux courts n'est plus l'apanage des légionnaires. Lucie n'a plus d'ongles à se mettre sous les dents, elle attaque les petites peaux au bout des doigts.

Larrivée stationne sa voiture en plein milieu de la cour d'honneur de l'Évêché. Lui d'habitude si posé, se met à courir. Les gardiens de la sécurité publique se regardent, étonnés. Ils n'ont jamais vu le DIPJ en petites foulées. Mais il y a urgence, il arrive dans le bureau du commandant Saint-Donat. La procédure est toujours ouverte sur la synthèse rédigée par Lucie à la suite des échanges avec les collègues de Paris et Melun. La fièvre l'envahit. Il relit ce PV. Il l'a vu, il le sait, il l'a déjà lu, et c'est dans ce procès-verbal, il en est certain, sa mémoire légendaire ne peut pas lui faire défaut, pas maintenant.

Après une première lecture, il se pose. Il est en nage. Il n'a pas trouvé, mais reste confiant. Il ôte sa veste, défait son nœud de cravate, remonte ses manches et décide de tout relire, de l'incipit au corps du texte, même les formules de droit obligatoires et indigestes.

Et il se calme, souriant. Il en était sûr. C'est là, devant lui, à la trentième ligne, la mention relative aux informations des Parisiens. Celle faisant état d'anciens légionnaires organisant des braquages millimétrés et qui auraient une dette envers un Marseillais surnommé le « Chacal ». Un ambitieux qui veut prendre la main sur tout Marseille.

Le chacal – *abn awaa* !

À la 85ᵉ minute, Lille souffre, Lille galère, mais Lille mène toujours 1 à 0. Le public est en ébullition. Insultes et quolibets pleuvent sur la pelouse. Des supporters lancent des fumigènes dont la fumée envahit le terrain. Le ballon est invisible. À grands coups de sifflet, l'arbitre suspend le match. Décidément, Henri ne comprend rien à ce sport. Au lieu de défendre leurs joueurs, les supporters les empêchent de revenir au score. Il lève les yeux au ciel et se décide.

Il se précipite à la salle de surveillance, au cœur du dispositif de sécurité du stade. Policiers et agents du club se disputent cette pièce, surplombant l'édifice au cinquième étage des tribunes Jean-Bouin, face aux tribunes Ganay. La surveillance vidéo, avec détours d'images sur une quarantaine d'écrans, leur permet de visionner ce qui se passe sur la pelouse, mais aussi dans les gradins. Rixes, banderoles douteuses, jets de bouteilles ou de fumigènes, rien n'échappe aux caméras. La qualité d'image est impressionnante et permet aux techniciens de zoomer au plus près des visages des supporters. Moustaches, rides, ou boutons d'acné, aucun détail ne leur échappe.

Larrivée se replonge dans la lecture des actes d'enquête. La transe ne le quitte plus. S'il a trouvé le « Chacal », il lui manque quelque chose. Les propos criés en arabe par le consul marocain résonnent en lui. « *Abn awaa* ». Il a vu ce mot écrit quelque part. Il feuillette avec fièvre toute la procédure. Est-ce dans les procès-verbaux ou dans un document les accompagnant ? Le plan des lieux de l'homicide ? Celui des braquages ? Une retranscription d'écoutes ?

Il pousse involontairement le sous-main du commandant et fait glisser la photo d'Octave tenant sa perfusion. Cette vision le calme instantanément. Il sait ce qui est arrivé au fils d'Henri. Il ne connaît pas cette souffrance d'avoir perdu un enfant, ose à peine l'imaginer. Par mimétisme, il se demande depuis combien de temps il n'a pas pris de nouvelles de son propre fils, âgé de 32 ans, devenu avocat autant par réaction familiale que par talent. Il faudra qu'il le fasse. Quand cette enquête sera terminée. Puis il percute. Une photo, c'est sur une photo anthropométrique qu'il a vu l'inscription « *abn awaa* ».

La commissaire divisionnaire Sandrine Desroches assure d'une main de maître la direction du service d'ordre pendant toute la durée du match. Son mètre soixante-deux et ses 44 ans assumés, ses yeux bleus et ses cheveux blonds, qu'elle garde toujours magnifiquement coiffés, même sous son casque de maintien de l'ordre, en disent long sur sa personnalité. Les 150 officiers, gradés et gardiens qui travaillent sous ses ordres l'apprécient pour ça. Depuis quatre ans qu'elle est à la tête de ce service, elle est devenue une légende urbaine. Au Vélodrome comme à l'Évêché, où Henri l'a déjà croisée, casque sous le bras, brushing impeccable, gilet tactique aux multiples poches, dont l'une contient des cigarillos qu'elle ne s'interdit jamais de fumer après un jeté de grenades lacrymogènes pour disperser une foule hostile. Selon elle, l'odeur du tabac de La Havane annihile complètement celle de la « lacry ».

Quand elle voit débarquer Henri dans la salle, en lieu et place de son subordonné, elle comprend l'urgence de la situation. Malgré l'effervescence dans le stade, elle met à sa disposition un manipulateur vidéo, qui sur ses instructions positionne les caméras sur les spectateurs de la zone « 8 » de la tribune Ganay. Et commence à balayer les gradins, rang après rang.

Tant pis si ce soir des jeteurs de pétards ne seront pas localisés, elle l'assumera.

Larrivée reprend les fiches anthropométriques des personnes impliquées dans le dossier. Nathalie Fournier et Daniel Rabutin en font partie. Celle d'Ernesto

Dominguez, casquette à l'envers, le fait sourire, celles des frères Hosni l'inquiètent. Bilal, le benjamin, interpellé par Lucie pour trafic de stupéfiants, en détention provisoire aux Baumettes. Yassine, le cadet, retrouvé nu et enroulé dans une bâche au fond de l'Yonne, et enfin Khaled, le frère aîné, détenu également à la maison d'arrêt des Baumettes pour une affaire de trafic international de stupéfiants.

Dans les tribunes, un mouvement insolite attire l'œil du manipulateur. La caméra zoome. Des supporters se lèvent pour en laisser passer un autre. Certains pestent, cette sortie intempestive les empêche de suivre la fin du match, mais, devant la taille et la corpulence de l'insolent, ils se ravisent et le laissent passer. Henri souffle, enfin ! Il peut l'annoncer à Lucie, elle ne s'est pas trompée. Elle a déchiffré le bon code. Il demande au manipulateur vidéo de suivre cet individu. Dans le même temps, il annonce à la radio.

– À tous d'Henri, objectif repéré. Rang 16, porte 8A. Je répète, rang 16, porte 8A.

Dans le couloir médian de la tribune Ganay, Lucie se fait mal à la gorge en hurlant : « Yes ! » Elle se met à courir comme une folle. Bouscule deux-trois personnes plus ivrognes que fans de l'OM. Quand elle arrive à la porte 8A, emportée dans son élan, elle est sur le point de heurter l'immense supporter qui sort des gradins. Elle s'excuse à peine, monte son bras à hauteur de sa bouche et déclenche sa radio.

– Je l'ai, Henri. Putain, je l'ai. Je le lâche plus.

Rabutin n'a qu'à bien se tenir. La sangsue de la PJ vient d'accrocher sa cible.

Sur les fiches anthropométriques, la ressemblance entre les frères Hosni est frappante. Même air antipathique, même faciès de tueur, mêmes yeux mauvais jusque dans les tatouages dont leur corps est tapissé. Bras, ventre, dos, aucune partie de peau ne semble épargnée. Mais si Yassine et Bilal ont eu le bon goût de ne pas toucher à leur visage, ce n'est pas le cas de Khaled, qui porte au niveau du cou, en lettres gothiques noires, formant un demi-cercle, comme un slogan affichant sa détermination : *awaa*.

Larrivée murmure pour lui-même :

– *Awaa* : le chacal ! Khaled Hosni, l'aîné des frangins.

Et tout s'éclaire.

74

Francis Larrivée est en pleine réflexion quand son téléphone sonne. Saint-Donat se veut rassurant.

– C'est bon, monsieur le directeur. On l'a. Lucie est au cul de Rabutin.

– Saint-Donat !

– Elle le suit à distance dans la foule. Avec sa taille, il est facile à filocher, le légionnaire.

– Saint-Donat !

– On attend qu'il soit dehors, je fais déplacer deux équipages de la BRI.

Le directeur est presque obligé de hurler :

– SAINT-DONAT, ON ARRÊTE TOUT !

Lucie sort du Vélodrome par l'esplanade Ganay, rejointe par Basile. Elle peut de nouveau lui donner la main et se réjouit de jouer les amoureux. Rabutin est devant eux, à quinze mètres. Il vient d'être accosté par deux individus. Pas de doute, leur tenue vestimentaire, leur démarche, il s'agit d'anciens légionnaires. L'excitation est à son comble. Lucie annonce la progression de leurs objectifs par radio. Les mercenaires empruntent l'allée Ray-Grassi, la remontent en direction du boulevard Michelet.

– De Lucie aux équipes BRI, positionnez-vous sur Michelet, une à hauteur du rond-point du Prado, l'autre en dessous, vers la maison du fada.

Une voix lui répond.

– La maison du fada, c'est quoi ?

Ce genre de questions rendent dingue Lucie. Elle se tourne vers Basile pour partager sa colère et son étonnement, mais lui-même semble perdu. Tous les flics de Marseille n'ont pas le manuel du parfait petit minot en poche et ne connaissent pas les expressions locales. Lucie revoit son jugement hâtif.

– La Cité radieuse... suivez les gars, merde.

– C'est quoi, la Cité radieuse ?

– Vous vous foutez de ma gueule ?

Lucie se tourne vers Basile, cherche de la compréhension pour sa réponse vive. Les yeux de son amoureux lui font surtout savoir qu'elle s'est encore emportée.

– L'immeuble Le Corbusier, quoi ! Sur Michelet, en direction de Mazargues, sur la droite, l'immense bâtiment sur pilotis en béton avec des balcons en couleurs.

Les deux amoureux poursuivent leur filature, entourés par des collègues de la Crim' et de la BRB mêlés à la foule, silencieuse et amère, assommée par la défaite de son club préféré.

Le ton du directeur est sans appel.

– On arrête tout, commandant.

– Quoi ?

Même Sandrine Desroches a entendu. Saint-Donat semble abattu. Comme lui, elle ne comprend pas cette décision du directeur. Qu'est-ce qu'il lui prend ? Le commandant insiste.

– Mais... Lucie vient de me contacter, Monsieur. Rabutin a été rejoint par deux mecs. L'équipe est presque au complet.

Le directeur tente de lui expliquer.

– Rabutin et ses danseuses, s'ils sont à Marseille, ce n'est pas pour faire un braquage. Ils préparent autre chose.

– Quoi monsieur ?

– J'en sais rien encore, mais c'est en lien avec les Hosni. Hosni, la réponse de Dominguez à l'hôpital. Vous cherchiez qui l'avait torturé, mais il fallait savoir aussi pourquoi.

– Et pourquoi, monsieur ?

– La question est dans la réponse, Saint-Donat. La réponse étant Hosni, Dominguez étant le seul lien entre la Carlton et ses affaires marseillaises, la question des légionnaires était donc de savoir avec qui la Carlton traitait à Marseille. Hosni ! La douleur lui a fait répéter ce nom *ad libitum*.

Saint-Donat se demande comment le directeur est capable, à ce moment-là, d'employer une expression latine.

Plus ils avancent, plus la foule autour d'eux diminue. Conséquence de la défaite, les supporters se dispersent comme une volée de moineaux. Les policiers vont devoir passer à l'acte. Mais Saint-Donat ne répond plus. Lucie tente encore de le joindre par radio. En vain. Elle s'inquiète, et si Acropol* avait un problème technique inattendu : un décrochement de réseau ? Une perte relais ? Rabutin et sa clique ont atteint le boulevard Michelet et s'apprêtent à le traverser. Elle regarde Basile, aussi embarrassé qu'elle. Il hausse les épaules, ils n'ont pas d'autre choix que de suivre les légionnaires.

Saint-Donat baisse le son de sa radio, qui n'arrête pas de crépiter. Il réfléchit à ce que

---

* Acropol : réseau et poste radio utilisés par les policiers.

le directeur vient de lui dire. Bilal Hosni est au trou, Yassine est mort. Lequel des deux a tué la Carlton ? Et pourquoi ?

– C'est là où on s'est fait avoir, commandant. Il fallait tout remettre en perspective. L'information du tonton parisien était bonne. Un voyou marseillais, surnommé le Chacal, veut mettre Marseille en coupe réglée. Dans la famille Hosni, il fallait demander le frère aîné : Khaled. Surnommé « *Awaa* », le « Chacal » en arabe. On avait la solution sous le nez, Saint-Donat, ou plutôt sur le cou. Celui de Khaled Hosni. Il a fait tatouer ces lettres au niveau de sa gorge.

Le commandant digère l'information. Cette assertion n'explique pas tout. Des questions restent sans réponse. Pourquoi Yassine Hosni est retrouvé mort dans une écluse de l'Yonne ? Pourquoi Lucie retrouve de la came dans un sac ayant appartenu à la Carlton dans les mains de Bilal Hosni ? Surtout, il ne voit pas en quoi ça change la stratégie décidée. Ils ont besoin de Rabutin et de ses hommes de main. Pourquoi retarder leur interpellation ?

Sandrine Desroches lui fait signe que sa radio continue d'émettre. Henri augmente le son et répond à Lucie. L'excitation de la capitaine est montée d'un ton.

– Henri enfin. Tu foutais quoi ? Rabutin vient d'être rejoint par un troisième homme. Ils sont au complet. Faut taper.

Les quatre hommes ont fini de traverser le boulevard Michelet et empruntent la rue Negresko.

– Henri, il faut y aller maintenant. Après ce sera trop compliqué. C'est le moment.

– Attente...

– Quoi ?

Lucie a failli s'étrangler.

– Attente. Pour l'instant, vous les lâchez pas.

– Henri, qu'est-ce que ça veut dire ?

– En ligne avec le patron, je t'explique après.

Lucie est folle de rage. Les quatre légionnaires sont à vue. Elle pourrait presque les toucher. Avec les collègues de la BRI, de la Crim' et de la BRB, ils sont plus d'une trentaine. Le rapport de force est en leur faveur et ils ont l'effet de surprise. Pas certain qu'une occasion comme celle-ci se reproduise. C'est quoi, ce changement de programme ? Elle n'hésite plus, le terrain décide ! Elle monte son micro à sa bouche, prête à donner le « top interpel' ».

Perdu au milieu des écrans de télévision, filmant maintenant des gradins vides,

Saint-Donat ne sait plus quoi penser. Il n'a qu'un mot à dire et les légionnaires sont interpellés. Sur le terrain, l'adrénaline monte. Certains se rassurent en touchant leur arme. Tous ont hâte d'en découdre. D'autant qu'ils ont été prévenus, les quatre individus sont des mercenaires, habitués au combat. Il va falloir agir vite, de façon simultanée. Et déterminée.

Ils ne comprennent pas ce qui se passe. Il y a encore deux minutes, ils devaient intervenir, avant d'être dans le flou. Le pire. Au moment de l'action, être dans l'indécision. Signe de doute et d'incompréhension, qui peut conduire au drame. Certains profitent de l'anonymat de la radio pour exprimer leur mécontentement. Henri rappelle tout le monde à l'ordre.

– Silence sur les ondes !

Sandrine Desroches le regarde, les yeux interrogateurs. Mais l'attitude de Saint-Donat est significative. Il est désabusé. Il hoche la tête. Pas totalement convaincu. Mais Francis Larrivée lui a donné des instructions claires, il abdique.

– On ne serre plus. Le directeur a une meilleure idée.

La commissaire divisionnaire n'y comprend rien, pas mécontente d'avoir quitté la PJ pour la sécurité publique.

Lucie monte le bouton-poussoir de sa radio à hauteur de son visage et regarde Basile. Il a compris sa décision et se colle à elle. Il écarte délicatement sa main de sa bouche et l'embrasse. Lucie cherche à le repousser.

– C'est pas le moment.

Mais Urteguy sait être convaincant. Il repousse une nouvelle fois sa main de sa bouche.

– Henri a dit de patienter, on patiente. On les a toujours à vue, rien ne presse.

Une vague d'émotion la submerge devant ce jeune homme si souriant, si gentil, si élégant. Et qui est raide dingue d'elle.

– Comment tu fais pour rester aussi calme ?

– Premier prix de piano au conservatoire Maurice-Ravel de Bayonne.

– Je vois pas le rapport ?

– Si tu savais le nombre d'auditions en public que je me suis tapées. Bien obligé d'apprendre à gérer mon stress.

Devant eux, Rabutin et les trois hommes se sont arrêtés. Hésitation ou vérification. Ils se retournent. Basile en profite. Il serre de nouveau Lucie contre lui et l'embrasse encore plus langoureusement. Il n'a pas besoin de faire semblant. Lucie le regarde droit dans les yeux, lui murmure.

– Henri attend quoi, putain ?

– Que j'aie fini de t'embrasser.

Il pose de nouveau ses lèvres sur les siennes et fait durer le plaisir. L'oreillette de Lucie crépite enfin.

– À tous d'Henri. On lève le dispo. Je répète, on lève.

Lucie ne comprend pas. La colère monte en elle. À vingt mètres d'eux, les légionnaires, rassurés d'avoir derrière eux des amoureux qui se chamaillent, poursuivent leur chemin. Lucie est prête à les rejoindre. Elle n'a pas pour habitude d'abandonner devant l'obstacle. Malgré les baisers de Basile, elle est folle de rage.

– Il a intérêt à avoir une bonne explication.

Puis elle se tourne vers Basile et dans un excès de colère lui lâche :

– Toi, tu ne recommences plus jamais ça !

Basile espère qu'il n'aura pas à le regretter. Et Henri aussi. Lucie ne lâchera rien.

La capitaine Clert a oublié ses bonnes résolutions du cap Canaille. Être amoureuse ne l'empêche pas de tomber dans ses vieux travers. Elle entre avec furie dans le bureau du commandant.

– C'est quoi, ce souk, Henri ? On les avait tous les quatre, on pouvait les taper sans problème.

Basile, qui l'accompagne, se fige. Il a remarqué la présence du directeur. Lucie, aveuglée par sa colère, continue :

– Et pourquoi t'as rien dit sur les ondes ? On monte un dispo de dingues. Et au dernier moment t'annules tout ! C'est quoi, le blème ?

– C'est moi, le blème, mademoiselle Clert.

Il n'y en a qu'un qui peut l'appeler par son nom sur ce ton : le directeur. Pourtant Lucie n'est pas prête à s'excuser. Quand elle est dans cet état, rien ne la retient. Elle se tient droite devant lui, ses deux mains sur ses hanches. Effrontée et décidée.

– Je vous écoute.

L'attitude de Lucie irrite Francis Larrivée, autant qu'elle suscite son admiration. Cette petite a du tempérament, presque plus que son père, et il aime ça. Mais il reste le patron et tient à le faire savoir.

– Je comprends votre légitime interrogation, Lucie. Mais si ça ne vous dérange pas, je ferai un débrief à toute l'équipe. Suivez-moi...

Il sort avec dans son sillage Urteguy suivi de Lucie dont les yeux jettent des éclairs à Henri.

75

Le décor est somptueux, certainement une ancienne chapelle de l'Évêché, boisée et toute en longueur, qui se termine en arc de cercle, lieu où l'évêque célébrait les offices. Deux vitraux rouge, jaune et vert trient la lumière pénétrant dans ce vestige de l'histoire. Avec les ans, c'est devenu la salle de réunion officielle de la DIPJ, tout au bout du couloir central de l'état-major. Elle n'est utilisée que pour les grandes occasions.

Peu habitués à cet endroit solennel, les policiers de la BRI, de la BRB et de la Crim' sont intimidés. Installés derrière les chaises, autour de la table, ils se redressent quand le DIPJ rentre enfin, suivi par Henri, Lucie et Basile. Leurs visages fermés reflètent incompréhension et colère. Le directeur invite tout le monde à s'asseoir et reste debout à l'endroit où l'évêque officiait. Il laisse quelques secondes de silence, en scrutant du regard, comme il aime le faire, les participants, avant de prendre la parole.

– Du bon boulot, mesdames et messieurs. Je connais votre investissement et je sais que vous étiez sur le point d'interpeller nos amis les légionnaires. Mais j'ai changé d'avis. C'est moi, et moi seul, qui ai pris la décision de ne pas le faire.

Ce disant, il se tourne ostensiblement vers Lucie, qui ne se laisse pas intimider. Elle ne le lâche pas des yeux, sa colère est encore prégnante, la flatter ne sera pas suffisant.

– On a failli faire fausse route, messieurs. En serrant Rabutin et sa clique, on aurait eu les auteurs de différents vols à main armée d'importance et du meurtre d'un témoin gênant. Très bien. Mais pas celui ou ceux qui ont tué la Carlton. Dont le principal suspect : Khaled Hosni, le frère aîné de Yassine et Bilal.

Brouhaha dans la salle, personne ne comprend comment Khaled Hosni apparaît dans ce dossier. Larrivée leur expose les éléments qu'il a mis en perspective au cours de sa soirée. La découverte du tatouage « *awaa* » que porte Khaled Hosni au cou, visible sur sa fiche anthropométrique, le chacal qui voulait avoir la mainmise sur tout Marseille.

– Dans les expertises psychiatriques des procédures où il est mis en cause, il est décrit avec un ego surdimensionné et un énorme besoin d'affirmation de sa supériorité.

Tous suivent avec attention son discours. Khaled Hosni était le voyou « montant » de Marseille, avec qui la Carlton était en contact. Intelligemment, elle cloisonnait. Discrétion, élégance et prudence d'une sacrée dame. D'un côté le chef des légionnaires Daniel Rabutin, de l'autre le Chacal. Elle ne traitait jamais en direct avec lui, mais toujours par l'intermédiaire de son homme à tout faire, Ernesto Dominguez, tchatcheur, hâbleur, à l'aise aussi bien à la Cayolle qu'à l'Intercontinental.

– Quand la Carlton est retrouvée assassinée à Marseille, Rabutin et ses sbires sont comme des dingues. On a tué le chef de leur bande, mais aussi celle qui, peut-être, était beaucoup plus pour eux. Et ils ne savent pas avec qui elle traitait.

Sourires dans les rangs. Les caïds aussi tombent amoureux. Ça arrange les policiers : parfois, pour chercher le voyou, il suffit de trouver la femme. Quelques-uns ont du mal à imaginer les légionnaires avec un cœur de midinette. Le directeur fait signe de se calmer.

– Résultat, les légionnaires veulent comprendre ce qu'il s'est passé à Marseille.

À cause de la discrétion de la Carlton, ils n'ont pas beaucoup d'éléments, ils savent juste qu'elle est en lien avec un voyou marseillais, dont ils ignorent tout. Pour le découvrir, une seule solution, passer par son messager : Ernesto Dominguez. C'est pour ça qu'ils l'enlèvent, le torturent et obtiennent leur réponse : Hosni.

Il marque une pause avant de rajouter :

– Mais, dans la famille Hosni, il fallait chercher Khaled, le grand frère, alias le Chacal.

Comme les autres, Lucie est suspendue aux lèvres du directeur. Elle n'est pas complètement calmée, mais écoute avec attention. Elle cherche de nouveau la main de Basile, qui n'attendait que ça pour la lui serrer. Comment ont-ils fait pour ne pas penser au grand frère Hosni ? Être détenu l'empêchait-il de figurer sur la liste des suspects ? Comme s'il suivait leur raisonnement, Larrivée poursuit.

– C'est le principe de la lettre volée d'Edgar Poe. C'est parce qu'on a la solution sous les yeux qu'on ne la trouve pas.

Si Lucie a bien suivi la démonstration du directeur, des questions la chiffonnent encore. Tout ceci n'explique pas pourquoi ils n'ont pas interpellé Rabutin et sa clique ? Le directeur prend son temps, pose ses deux mains sur la table et la regarde droit dans les yeux.

– Parce qu'au lieu de résoudre une seule affaire, Lucie, nous allons les résoudre toutes d'un coup.

Grâce aux légionnaires et à leur rendez-vous au stade, ils ont enfin un coup d'avance sur eux.

76

C'est un matin du mois de mai où Marseille se croit au cœur de l'été. Tout brille et semble joyeux. La Méditerranée inonde les plages de son bleu limpide, le soleil arrose la ville de sa chaleur vive, et le mistral distribue avec entrain ses rafales gagnantes. Aux terrasses des cafés, le sourire est sur les lèvres, les femmes portent des jupes courtes, les hommes plaisantent, un « pastaga » à la main, tous profitent de ce moment où la ville a sorti ses atours pour séduire jusqu'aux plus récalcitrants. Aznavour avait raison, la misère est moins pénible au soleil.

Au pied du parc national, juste avant la calanque de Morgiou, se trouve une construction qui n'est pas touchée par cette grâce méditerranéenne. Une bâtisse sans âme, dont la fonction même ne donne pas envie de s'y rendre. Si certains s'y pressent et y retournent, ce n'est jamais pour le plaisir. Le centre pénitentiaire des Baumettes étend sa monstruosité sur plus de 30 000 m², insuffisants pourtant pour accueillir dans ses quatre bâtiments sa surpopulation carcérale.

Aujourd'hui, un seul prisonnier intéresse les policiers. Le juge d'application des peines a signé sa levée d'écrou il y a cinq jours. Sa sortie est prévue à 10 heures. Le temps d'assurer toutes les formalités administratives, Lucie et Basile en planque devant l'immuable porte verte de la prison le savent : avant midi, Khaled Hosni devrait être sorti. À compter de ce moment, ils ne le lâcheront plus. Le dispositif mis en place avec la BRI, la Crim', la BRB et les policiers parisiens descendus pour l'occasion devrait permettre d'assurer sa filature jusqu'à ce que les légionnaires aillent au contact.

– … c'est là que nous interviendrons, avait prévenu Larrivée.

Pendant le match de l'OM, il n'avait pas seulement consulté la procédure, il avait aussi vérifié le fichier des personnes détenues. La libération de Khaled Hosni était imminente. C'était la raison pour laquelle Rabutin avait réuni ses inféodés au match, selon lui. Non pas pour préparer leur prochain braquage, mais bien pour décider du sort qu'ils réserveraient au Chacal. Urteguy avait bien tenté de lui objecter :

– Rabutin n'a pas accès au fichier des prisons, comment il a pu savoir que Khaled Hosni sortait ?

– C'est un ancien taulard. Il doit avoir ses contacts aux Baumettes. Tout se sait dans une prison, mon petit Basile, surtout quand un mec de l'envergure de Khaled Hosni est libérable.

Avisés de ces avancées, les flics parisiens étaient descendus à Marseille et un dispositif de surveillance conséquent, jalonnant tout le 8e et le 9e arrondissement, de Morgiou au rond-point du Prado, avait été mis en place. Le soleil était de la partie. Ça allait être une belle journée. Il ne restait plus qu'à attendre la vedette principale.

77

Tous les taulards doivent faire ça. Après des mois d'enfermement, quand la porte de la prison s'ouvre, ils sortent, avancent de quelques mètres, posent leurs rares affaires, avant de se frotter les yeux, éblouis par le soleil, étonnés par l'absence de contrainte, étourdis par la liberté. Tous, sauf Khaled Hosni. Quand enfin le portail des Baumettes s'ouvre, il ne s'attendrit pas sur ce qu'il découvre, il n'a qu'une hâte, se tirer le plus loin possible. Avec une sale manie : pester et insulter tout ce qui se trouve sur son passage.

Il descend le chemin de Morgiou à pied, l'air excédé. Dès sa sortie, Lucie et Basile l'ont reconnu. À force de regarder sa fiche anthropométrique, son visage s'est imprimé dans leur cerveau. Même de loin, les cinq lettres tatouées sur son cou sont visibles. Leur rythme cardiaque accélère immédiatement. Malgré la légèreté de l'air, les deux policiers ne sont pas d'humeur à plaisanter. Ils n'ont qu'un souci : ne pas perdre la surveillance qui commence.

– À tous de Lucie, il vient de sortir. Jean noir, tee-shirt blanc, cheveux rasés, sac beige sur le dos. Il est à pied, seul, il descend Morgiou, direction Marseille centre.

Depuis leur « soum », ils ne peuvent pas l'entendre, mais ils sont sûrs que, depuis sa sortie, Hosni répète en boucle, sans trop d'originalité, le même mot :

– Enculé.

Une BMW X6, noire, vitres teintées, remonte le chemin de Sormiou et à hauteur du libéré fait demi-tour. La portière avant droite s'ouvre. Hosni ne regarde même pas à l'intérieur. Il lance son sac dans l'habitacle avant de monter dans le véhicule. Les policiers cette fois-ci l'entendent bien.

– Enculé, c'est à cette heure-ci que t'arrives ? Fils de pute, le *time*, c'est le *time*. Tu le sais. La prochaine fois, je te fume. OK ?

Lucie réagit au quart de tour, relève le numéro d'immatriculation et identifie le propriétaire de la voiture au fichier des automobiles.

– À tous de Lucie. Cible chargée dans une BMW X 6 noire, vitres teintées, LG971SA. Oualid Melhouri. Un p'tit con de la Cayolle.

La voiture démarre dans un grand bruit de moteur et une épaisse fumée blanche. Basile n'essaye même pas de la suivre.

– À tous de Lucie, ça descend Morgiou à fond. Ça devrait arriver devant l'église de Mazargues. Henri, c'est pour toi.

– Lucie d'Henri, on l'a en visuel, on prend.

Henri est accompagné de son ex-adjoint, le commandant Laval. Reconstitution de ligue dissoute, mais ils n'ont pas le temps d'échanger leurs vieux souvenirs, la BMW vient de leur passer devant à toute allure. Feux rouges et panneaux stop ne signifient rien pour elle.

– À tous d'Henri. Ça prend la traverse Magnan, direction le rond-point de Mazargues. Ça roule très fort.

– BRI 12 d'Henri. Rond-point de Mazargues, on prend.

– Reçu.

Henri souffle. Heureusement, le directeur n'a pas lésiné sur les moyens et a engagé un dispositif important. Seul, avec sa fidèle Mondeo, il n'assurerait pas la filature.

– À tous de BRI 12, on est trois écrans derrière eux, stoppés par la circulation.

Dans le « soum », Lucie se tourne vers Basile, son regard en dit long. Si la BMW est bloquée par la circulation, la filature devrait être plus facile. Elle s'autorise un sourire. De courte durée.

– Putain, c'est quoi, ça ?

Le silence tombe sur le dispositif. Dans les voitures, les regards ont changé d'intensité. Souffle coupé, palpitant à 12 000, radio collée à l'oreille, tous sont dans la même attente : que BRI 12 leur explique ce qui se passe. La radio de nouveau crépite, un bruit de sirène de police se fait entendre.

– L'équipage qui vient sur eux, annoncez-vous !

Personne ne répond. Lucie regarde Basile, elle n'ose comprendre. Saint-Donat jette des yeux incrédules à Laval. C'est quoi, cette histoire ?

– BRI 12, des précisions ?

Quelques crépitements de radio. Dans le fond sonore, la sirène de police cesse, mais des cris résonnent.

– J'y crois pas, la BAC* les tape au contrôle.

Lucie ne respecte plus le protocole radio, elle hurle.

– La BAC ? C'est quoi, ces conneries ?

– Dispo de BRI 12, une Renault Talisman marron, immatriculée CJ123DV. Plaque police, gyro et deux-tons. Quatre collègues à l'intérieur.

---

* BAC : brigade anticriminalité, travaillant au sein de la direction de la sécurité publique, ayant pour objectif d'interpeller des malfaisants en flagrant délit.

Lucie et Basile percutent en même temps, devancés par Henri.

– La BAC n'a pas de Talisman en dotation. Ça pue.

Lucie a déjà pianoté sur son NEO et a rentré l'immatriculation relevée par BRI 12. Le fichier des automobiles est formel. Elle hurle.

– Plaque bidon. C'est nos lascars, top interpel' !

– À tous de BRI 12, on peut pas intervenir, on n'est que deux.

– Les lâchez pas !

Lucie fait signe à Basile d'accélérer, mais le sous-marin que le jeune lieutenant conduit n'est pas une Lamborghini. Ils passent à peine l'église de Mazargues. Malgré tout, Basile arrive à se faufiler dans la circulation.

– BRI 12, priorité. Ils braquent la BMW avec des Uzzi. C'est du lourd. Le chauffeur ne bouge plus. Ils arrachent le passager, je répète, ils chargent la cible dans la Talisman, et ça part, direction Prado. Ils enquillent la voie des bus. Gyro et deux-tons actionnés.

Dans la Ford, Laval regarde Henri, incrédule. Saint-Donat garde son calme, reprend les ondes.

– À tout le dispositif, les individus ont chargé la cible dans une Renault Talisman marron CJ123DV, faussement plaquée, direction de fuite rond-point du Prado. On les colle au plus près. Pas d'intervention pour le moment.

Les messages tombent les uns derrière les autres.

– BRI 10, rond-point du Prado, ils viennent de passer devant nous, ils remontent Prado, direction centre-ville.

– BRI 8, Perier, ils continuent tout droit, direction Castellane.

– BRI 6, rond-point Castellane, ils prennent Baille, direction la Timone.

Basile se démène derrière une vieille 2 CV qui l'empêche de progresser. Il se tourne vers Lucie. Ivre d'excitation, elle tape la carrosserie à grands coups de poing. Basile à coups de klaxon et d'appels de phares parvient à se dégager, accélère.

– BRI 6, ils refont le tour du rond-point Castellane. Les enfoirés, c'était un coup de sécurité. Ils descendent de nouveau Prado... Non, non, ils enquillent Cantini, direction parc du 26e Centenaire.

Lucie bondit. Cantini, parc du 26e Centenaire, elle connaît par cœur, il a été construit sur l'emplacement de l'ancienne gare du Prado, où, gamine, l'été, elle passait le plus clair de son temps. Elle les tient.

78

Les équipages BRI, Crim' et BRB suivent comme ils peuvent la progression de la Talisman, essayant d'anticiper son parcours. Équipée d'un gyrophare et d'une sirène, elle est imprévisible. BRI 6 est au plus près et annonce les rues qui se succèdent. Dans le sous-marin, Lucie conseille Basile sur l'itinéraire à suivre. Le jeune lieutenant n'hésite pas. Trottoirs, lignes blanches, feux tricolores, ils ne reculent devant aucune infraction pour aller plus vite. Le soleil en prend ombrage. Lui, encore si bienveillant il y a quelques minutes, se cache derrière un cumulus inattendu. Un roulement de tonnerre se fait entendre. La météo n'influence pas les décisions de Lucie.

– Au rond-point du Prado, tu remontes Rabateau. Au bout, on peut les choper à contresens à hauteur de Schlœsing.

Les premières gouttes de pluie commencent à tomber. Basile, plus concentré que jamais, actionne les essuie-glaces.

– BRI 6, priorité. Ils viennent de calibrer, on est détronchés. Coups de feu dans notre direction, on est repérés.

Nouveau silence sur les ondes. La filature vient de prendre une nouvelle dimension et tous le savent. Pluie, coups de feu, tout peut dégénérer en moins d'une seconde. Lucie hausse les épaules. Sa détermination est sans limite.

– Détronchés ! Les baltringues.

Dans la Ford, Martin regarde Henri. Il n'a pas besoin de lui parler, il connaît d'avance sa décision. Elle est immédiate : la sécurité des citoyens et de ses coéquipiers avant tout. Même si c'est la deuxième fois qu'il est obligé d'annoncer ce type de message.

– À tous d'autorité, pas de risques inutiles. On est en ville, on laisse tomber. Je répète, on laisse tomber.

Les équipages, sonnés, un peu désabusés, annoncent au fur et à mesure l'arrêt de la poursuite. Lucie ne répond rien. Poings et dents serrés, elle demande à Basile d'accélérer. Dans 200 mètres, ils sont à Schlœsing. Elle n'abandonnera pas encore.

– Au bout de Rabateau, à gauche et tu coupes la chaussée sur Cantini.

– Mais Lucie...

– Tu passes sous l'autopont. Maintenant, j'te dis.

– Lucie, t'as entendu Henri ?

– Sous l'autopont, j'te dis, coupe, coupe, maintenant… barre la route.

Basile, presque malgré lui, obéit à Lucie, il positionne le sous-marin, perpendiculaire à l'avenue Jules-Cantini, warnings allumés, il bouche la circulation sur les deux voies. Derrière lui, le mécontentement est immédiat. Le Marseillais n'est pas patient, encore moins sous la pluie. L'embouteillage qu'il provoque prend vite de l'ampleur. Des klaxons résonnent, des insultes fusent. Le jeune lieutenant se retourne, mais Lucie a déjà quitté l'habitacle. Brassard « police » enfilé, elle a bondi hors du véhicule et s'est positionnée devant, jambes légèrement écartées, bras tendus, flingue au bout. Elle met en joue la Renault Talisman qui arrive droit sur elle, sirène hurlante, plaque police abaissée, gyrophare tournant.

Pour Basile, le temps est suspendu. Un ralenti de cinéma. Cette femme flic, qu'il aime, seule au milieu de la chaussée, en position de cow-boy, armée, avec en ligne de mire, une Renault Talisman forçant le passage dans la circulation, obligeant les autres voitures à s'écarter, qui fonce droit sur elle.

Un duel inévitable. Improbable. Déséquilibré.

Basile sait qui se trouve dans cette voiture, il connaît leur détermination, leur expérience, il devine leur armement. La Talisman est à cent mètres. Son chauffeur fait hurler le moteur. Le bruit est assourdissant. Insupportable. En plus de la sirène, il se met à klaxonner. Mais Lucie ne s'écarte pas, un étrange sourire aux lèvres.

Basile est étourdi par tant de vacarme. Il arrête machinalement les essuie-glaces. Ne plus entendre le son rassurant des balais en caoutchouc sur le pare-brise le fait réagir. Il s'éjecte du sous-marin. La Talisman est à 50 mètres. Il se jette en direction de Lucie. La voiture est à 30 mètres. La capitaine arme calmement son flingue, assure sa visée. 20 mètres. Le jeune lieutenant saute sur la capitaine. 10 mètres. La plaque au sol. 5 mètres. L'empêche d'appuyer sur la queue de détente. 2 mètres.

La voiture les frôle, mais ne peut éviter le sous-marin. Le choc qui suit est sans effet sur la Talisman, qui poursuit sa route à toute vitesse. Le véhicule de surveillance tourne sur lui-même et termine sa toupie sur les deux policiers. Basile protège de tout son corps Lucie, qui lui tape du poing sur le buste.

– Pourquoi t'as fait ça, je les avais, putain. Je les avais.

Fatigue, colère, trop-plein d'émotions, la réaction de Basile n'est pas contrôlée, sa main s'abat sur la joue de Lucie. Il va le regretter toute sa vie. Il le regrette déjà. Mais c'est trop tard. L'effet est instantané, Lucie peut supporter beaucoup de choses, mais jamais un homme qui lève la main sur elle. Elle regarde Basile droit dans les yeux, médusée, en se frottant la joue. Se demande si c'est bien l'homme avec qui elle a fait l'amour il y a à peine quelques heures. Basile est paralysé à côté d'elle, ne se rend même pas compte de la pluie qui tombe, le transformant en éponge vivante.

Depuis l'habitacle du sous-marin, le son de la radio se fait entendre. Saint-Donat répète en boucle.

– Lucie de Henri, tout va bien ?

Basile se relève, hébété, ramasse le flingue de Lucie qui avait glissé sous l'impact, le lui tend sans rien dire. Ses yeux parlent pour lui, mais pourquoi avec son caractère de merde a-t-il fallu qu'elle gâche tout ? Il l'aimait tellement. Se rend compte qu'il parle d'elle déjà à l'imparfait. Secoue sa tête. La pluie se mélange à ses larmes. Il se rend à la voiture, récupère la radio et annonce :

– Rien ne va plus. Je ne joue plus. Elle a gagné... Je... je...

– Quoi ? Qu'est-ce que tu racontes, Basile ? Qu'est-ce qui se passe ?

– Je... je démissionne.

Et sans un regard pour Lucie, il s'en va. Sans savoir où. Il s'en va en pleurant, sous la pluie. Mais il s'en fout. Ça devait être une si belle journée. Demain sera encore meilleur. Demain est un autre jour. Alors il s'en va, en chantant. Le seul air qui lui passe par la tête. Loin de Bob Dylan et de Téléphone. Un air d'opéra. Ironie ou provocation ? Il ne se rend même pas compte. Mais un air que chantait si bien la Callas.

« L'amour est enfant de bohème, qui n'a jamais, jamais connu de loi. Si tu ne m'aimes pas, je t'aime. Et si je t'aime, prends garde à toi. »

79

La voix de Larrivée résonne des cellules de garde à vue jusque sous les toits de l'Évêché. Debout devant lui, dans un garde-à-vous mal assuré, Lucie prend la soufflante de sa vie. Plus que de ne pas obéir au chef de dispositif, elle a mis sa vie en danger et celle de son jeune collègue. C'est irresponsable. Même si leur stratégie n'a pas abouti, elle n'a pas respecté les ordres. C'est inadmissible.

Henri est à ses côtés. Les propos du directeur ne le concernent pas, pourtant il baisse la tête, inquiet pour Basile. Depuis maintenant plus de deux heures, il est sans nouvelles. Le lieutenant ne répond plus au portable. Ne s'est pas présenté au service, n'est pas chez lui. Si, dans un premier temps, la sonnerie retentissait avant de basculer sur sa messagerie, maintenant cette dernière se déclenche immédiatement. Comme s'il avait volontairement coupé son téléphone, pour ne pas permettre à ses collègues de le géolocaliser.

Ça l'emmerde. Il est en train de s'attacher à ce jeune flic. Pourvu qu'il ne fasse pas de connerie. Ce gamin qui pourrait être son fils. Il n'arrive pas à le dire. Il y a des mots qu'il fuit depuis des années. Ils ont perdu de leur sens. Ne surtout pas les dire pour ne pas leur donner d'existence et s'éviter la souffrance.

Il se tourne vers Lucie, silencieuse. Toujours droite, le visage penché en avant. Et il comprend. Lucie n'écoute pas le directeur, détachée de ce qu'elle entend. Des larmes perlent, elle est perdue dans le vide. Elle ne sait qu'une chose : son jusqu'au-boutisme lui a fait perdre Basile.

Basile qui la fait rire, qui l'aime pour ce qu'elle est. Basile qui lui sourit, qui joue de la guitare, qui chante Dylan, Téléphone et Anne Sylvestre. Basile qui se moque d'elle et de lui surtout. Basile, si tendre, si fort, si joyeux. Basile qui lui manque. Déjà. Elle refuse de parler à l'imparfait. Ne peut pas imaginer qu'un jour elle utilisera un autre temps que le présent pour parler de lui. Cette blessure lui tord le bide. Elle a tellement merdé. Si elle était le directeur, elle s'engueulerait encore plus fort. Ne se le pardonnerait pas. Basile pourra-t-il le faire ?

Plus personne ne bouge. Lucie met quelques secondes avant de comprendre que le directeur s'est tu. Elle est étonnée que l'engueulade soit déjà finie. Elle regarde, interrogatrice, le DIPJ, se tourne

vers Henri, qui se tait également, scotché
à sa chaise, le visage ravagé. Elle s'en veut
aussi de le mettre dans cet état. Elle s'apprête à prendre la parole, mais Larrivée ne
lui en laisse pas le temps.

– J'ai baisé avec un chameau.

Les propos décalés du directeur font réagir Henri. Lucie reste de marbre. Larrivée
n'est pas déçu, son test a marché au-delà
de ses espérances. La capitaine ne se rend
même pas compte de l'incongruité de cette
assertion, soulagée que le directeur reprenne
la parole. Pour l'instant, elle veut seulement
penser à Basile. Rester dans cette position
de garde-à-vous et attendre que ça passe.
Elle se laisse porter par la voix grave et
mélodieuse du directeur, qui la ramène à
son amoureux. Elle ne cherche pas à comprendre les propos de Larrivée, elle est d'accord avec toute sa morale hiérarchique. Elle
veut juste l'entendre sans l'écouter, comme
un mouton se laisse tondre, avec indiffé-
rence mais certitude. Et retrouver Basile,
dans ses pensées d'abord, en réalité ensuite.

Son regard se perd derrière les fenêtres
du bureau de Larrivée, il ne lui faut pas
beaucoup d'imagination pour qu'il la trans-
porte de l'autre côté du Vieux-Port, en dessous de la Bonne Mère, à quelques mètres
du Pharo, au fort Ganteaume. Tout n'est

pas perdu. Elle a peut-être encore une chance de le récupérer. À cette idée, elle frémit. Le directeur explose.

– Foutez-moi le camp, Clert. Je veux plus vous voir.

Encore une fois, Lucie ne se rend pas compte du ton du directeur, elle le salue et sort du bureau. L'air ahuri, mais toujours aussi décidée. Henri se lève à son tour, en tentant d'excuser le comportement de Lucie. Le directeur hausse les épaules.

– Je l'envie presque… être amoureux comme ça, c'est tellement beau.

Henri n'imaginait pas le directeur sentimental. Larrivée n'a pas fini.

– Et retrouvez-moi Urteguy. Lucie a besoin de lui… Et vous aussi, non ?

La réflexion du directeur le surprend. Laisserait-il transpirer ses émotions plus qu'il ne le pensait ?

– Tout ne s'est pas déroulé comme on le voulait aujourd'hui, hein, Saint-Donat ? La vie nous réserve parfois de sérieuses surprises. On en prend plein la gueule. Notre job à nous, flics, c'est d'apprendre à encaisser. Et d'accepter qu'on ne puisse pas toujours tout prévoir.

Un léger pincement de lèvres s'amorce sur son visage. Il s'arrête de pianoter sur son bureau.

– Même si c'est dur d'accepter qu'on s'est planté. Mais la pluie, la X6, la Talisman équipée police, les Uzzi en plein centre-ville, on ne pouvait pas tout imaginer. Vous avez pris la meilleure des décisions, tout à l'heure, Saint-Donat. La seule qui s'imposait.

Il lui serre la main, longuement, en le regardant droit dans les yeux.

– Et je ne suis pas inquiet, on va les retrouver, la diva, les ténors et leur maître-chanteur. Dans quel état, je ne sais pas. C'est juste une question de temps. Faites fonctionner votre imagination, Saint-Donat, et vous allez voir, on va leur tomber dessus plus vite que prévu.

Henri aimerait que les propos du directeur soient prémonitoires. Mais Basile disparu et Lucie ravagée ne sont pas les meilleures conditions pour loger les légionnaires. L'imagination trouve souvent sa limite dans la réalité des états d'âme. L'inquiétude prend le dessus sur sa réflexion. Pourtant, depuis qu'il est sorti du bureau du DIPJ, il entend une petite voix intérieure, qui en mode répétitif lui murmure : ose… ose encore, ose toujours. « Oser est encore le meilleur moyen de réussir. » La réflexion préférée de son père.

80

Pourquoi faut-il qu'à cet instant il pense à lui ? Il a toujours trouvé son père trop exigeant. C'est peut-être pour ça que, ces derniers temps, il n'a pas pris beaucoup de ses nouvelles. Son père, 1,80 m d'élégance et de dérision, 110 kilos de gouaille et de certitudes. Charles Saint-Donat, instituteur bougon, toujours une citation au coin de la bouche, une certitude à asséner, une vérité à professer, a fait trembler des générations de gamins. À l'époque où son père avait toute sa tête, il n'hésitait pas à se moquer de lui.

– Papa, dix minutes de présence, une heure de conseils... record à battre.

Charles Saint-Donat avait arrêté de battre des records après son AVC. Peu de temps après le départ d'Octave. Henri avait toujours refusé de faire le lien entre ces deux événements. Depuis, Charles végétait dans un Ehpad, aussi désespérant qu'éloigné de Marseille, situé dans une ville sans âme de l'agglomération parisienne. Il avait perdu kilos et gouaille et ne faisait plus peur aux aides-soignants, qu'il bassinait de ses poncifs dépolis. Henri n'est pas dupe, quitter Paris pour Marseille avait été aussi un moyen de fuir les visites dominicales. Et de cultiver sa souffrance liée à la perte d'Octave, pour ne pas avoir à traiter celle de son père vieillissant.

Il secoue la tête. Pas tout à fait lui.

Il regarde sa limousine sur deux roues. Son père lui a donné son sens de la dérision, de l'aventure, et des bécanes. Il enfile casque et gants et enfourche sa Goldwing. Elle ne le trahit pas. Malgré la pluie qui s'est abattue, elle démarre au quart de tour. Ça n'a pas été le cas de toutes ses motos. Il se souvient de la première, une Suzuki. Et des propos de son hérésiarque de père qui lui avait déconseillé ce choix.

– Si tu pars en Suzuki, n'oublie pas ta trousse à outils.

Il démarre et se laisse porter par son instinct, la partie cachée de l'imagination. C'est pour ça qu'il pensait à son père. Parce que celui-ci lui avait transmis ce don et lui avait toujours conseillé de le développer. Pour mieux armer ses rêves et défendre son présent. Ces dernières années, avec les épreuves qu'il avait traversées, il l'avait oublié. Pourtant, il s'en rend compte, c'est bien ce don qui lui avait évité de sombrer.

Quand tout est mort et noir, seule l'imagination donne de la couleur à la vie.

Les propos du directeur ont réveillé ses souvenirs. Son père n'a pas que des défauts. Et ses conseils, comme certaines de ses formules définitives, sont encore de bons outils dans sa trousse de secours.

Avant d'enfourcher sa moto, il a laissé les consignes. Vingt voitures de la police judiciaire sillonnent Marseille et ses environs, de la plus petite traverse à la plus grande avenue, des cités nord aux calanques du sud, de La Ciotat à Martigues, avec les signalements des légionnaires et de leur prisonnier. Son imagination lui a rappelé qu'il fallait aussi savoir compter sur la chance. Et que la chance se provoque. Les services de sécurité publique ont été également destinataires d'une fiche de diffusion, avec les mêmes renseignements. Sur l'ensemble du département, plus d'un millier de flics sont à la recherche de Rabutin et de sa clique.

81

Ses premiers tours de roue le conduisent place de Lenche. Basile n'est toujours pas rentré. Il tente de joindre Lucie, qui ne donne pas non plus de nouvelles. La légèreté des amoureux l'agace. Comme s'ils oubliaient que les légionnaires avaient le Chacal entre leurs mains. Il ne préfère pas imaginer ce qu'ils seraient capables de lui faire. Il en a déjà eu un aperçu avec Ernesto.

Il redémarre et se met lui aussi à fureter partout. Même imposante, sa moto lui permet d'accéder à des endroits où la voiture ne peut pas aller. Il en profite. Tourne dans les rues de Marseille, des ruelles serrées du Panier aux avenues immenses du 8e arrondissement. À chaque Renault Talisman qu'il croise, son cœur palpite. Il n'hésite pas, fait demi-tour quand il a un doute, prend des sens interdits, vérifie. Jamais il n'aurait imaginé que cette voiture était aussi répandue dans la cité phocéenne.

Il tente de raisonner comme pourraient le faire les légionnaires. Ils ont les flics aux fesses, ne sont pas originaires de Marseille

et ont enlevé Khaled Hosni pour lui demander des comptes sur la mort de la Carlton.
Ils ont déjà secoué Dominguez, qu'ils ont
abandonné route des Crêtes. Il y a urgence
pour eux à agir. Où conduire le Chacal
pour le faire parler en toute discrétion ?

Il freine brusquement. Comment n'y a-t-il
pas pensé plus tôt ? Lieu éloigné de la ville,
possibilité d'échappatoires. Lieu propice à
la réflexion solitaire, pour les rendez-vous
amoureux ou pour ceux qui veulent en
finir tout seuls.

Lieu idéal pour les règlements de comptes.

Il n'a pas besoin de rentrer dans son
GPS les coordonnées, il connaît cet endroit
par cœur. Il fonce, grille les feux, dépasse
les lignes blanches, glisse sur la voie des
bus. La circulation se fait plus fluide, il
emprunte les ronds-points de Mazargues,
du Redon et celui menant au campus universitaire de Luminy. Il peut encore accélérer, il est tout seul sur la route des Crêtes.

Son casque étant relié à son portable, il
reçoit un appel de Lucie. Au son de sa voix,
il comprend qu'elle a retrouvé Basile.

Au fort Ganteaume. L'endroit où leur
histoire a commencé. Il avait besoin de respirer les odeurs de ses souvenirs récents.
Depuis la fenêtre du bureau du directeur,
quand elle se faisait engueuler, ses yeux

erraient de la cathédrale de la Major aux bateaux sur la Méditerranée, rejoignant leur ponton ; elle a ressenti le même appel. Elle s'y est précipitée et a retrouvé Basile, les yeux bouffis. Lucie a posé son doigt sur sa bouche, lui murmurant de ne rien dire. Elle lui a juste demandé avec une douceur dans la voix qu'il ne lui connaissait pas s'il voulait bien la suivre sur son bateau et prendre l'avenir ensemble. Il a souri, en dégoulinant de larmes. Il avait eu si peur de ne plus traverser de tempête avec elle.

Les minauderies terminées, les affaires peuvent reprendre. Henri lui explique ce qu'il compte faire. Lucie hésite.

– T'es sûr que c'est très procédural ?

– Si on met la main sur nos lascars, personne ne nous le reprochera.

Henri lui précise sa pensée et lui laisse une demi-heure. Rendez-vous au cap Canaille.

82

Drôle d'endroit pour une rencontre. Perdu au milieu de nulle part, suspendu entre terre et mer. La route monte et serpente entre Cassis et La Ciotat, il ne faut avoir ni le mal de voiture ni le vertige pour s'y aventurer. L'endroit est aussi magnifique qu'improbable. Zone préservée des promoteurs, jusqu'ici les élus locaux ont résisté à leurs sirènes. Aucune habitation ne vient polluer la virginité de la nature. La terre est ocre et rocheuse, la végétation dense. Et la vue sur la Méditerranée, exceptionnelle, à 300 mètres de hauteur. Aucune lumière artificielle ne vient souligner les lieux. Seule la lune, presque pleine, sert d'éclairage naturel. À cette heure de la nuit, peu de véhicules empruntent cette route.

C'est ce qui inquiète Saint-Donat. Il a assuré un aller-retour Cassis-La Ciotat et n'a pas repéré la moindre voiture stationnée sur les parkings improvisés jalonnant la route. Pour autant, il en est sûr, son imagination ne peut pas le trahir ainsi, les légionnaires ont conduit Hosni par ici.

Il a fini par stationner sa moto au même endroit qu'il y a quelques nuits. Maux de ventre et sourire amer, il se souvient de ce qui l'avait guidé jusque-là. Il s'efforce de ne pas y penser et se concentre sur l'instant. Il en est sûr, après avoir coupé le moteur de sa cylindrée et s'être plongé dans le silence, il a entendu des sons qui ne sont pas naturels.

En attendant Lucie, il vérifie son arme, bien accrochée à sa ceinture. Il fait jouer la culasse. La cartouche est dans la chambre. Il est prêt, étonnamment serein. Il a suivi les conseils du directeur, s'est rappelé les vieux principes de son père, il a imaginé une solution pour trouver les malfaiteurs et a osé la mettre en pratique. Il ne pourra rien se reprocher.

83

Drôle d'endroit pour mourir.

La beauté des lieux l'a saisi. Il ne peut s'empêcher de s'émerveiller. Malgré les quatre hommes qui l'entourent, les flingues qui le menacent et cette putain de peur qui lui troue le bide.

La lune est de sortie pour l'accompagner. Il voit les falaises comme en plein jour. Elles dominent la Méditerranée. Drôle de sensation, comme si la mer l'attendait. Il n'a pas pour habitude d'être philosophe, pourtant il se demande, depuis vingt-sept ans qu'il vit à Marseille, pourquoi il n'est jamais venu admirer ce point de vue. S'il était poète, il le regretterait. Mais il n'en a rien à foutre de la poésie. Pourquoi il n'est pas en train de baiser plutôt ? Une bonne partie de cul avec trois ou quatre gonzesses, plein de came et d'alcool. Il crache par terre.

Jamais en se levant ce matin Khaled Hosni n'aurait pensé que cette journée plombée de soleil allait être sa dernière. Elle devait être une journée de liberté, elle est devenue une putain de journée de

merde. À peine libéré, de nouveau prisonnier. Et par des mecs ayant moins le sens
de l'humour que les matons des Baumettes.
Il balance encore un mollard au sol.

Si les connards qui le menacent arrivent
à leurs fins, il ne pourra jamais marquer
de son empreinte le milieu marseillais ; ne
sera jamais aussi cruel que Farid Berrahma.
Même s'il risque de finir comme lui : des
cartouches plein le buffet. Mais, contrairement au « rôtisseur », il risque bien d'être
donné à bouffer à la poiscaille. Cette image
lui donne envie de vomir. Et l'emmerde.
Son corps ne sera jamais retrouvé, comment vont faire ses admirateurs pour hono-
rer sa mémoire ?

En sortant de l'A50, ils coupent gyrophare
et sirène et traversent Cassis endormi avant
d'emprunter la route des Crêtes menant au
cap Canaille. Le rythme est doux. Basile
ouvre le convoi, il conduit comme il joue
de la musique, avec légèreté et finesse. Les
quatre voitures roulent en file indienne
dans le même ronronnement, qui estompe
presque le bruit des moteurs. Dès qu'ils
arrivent, Saint-Donat leur fait signe de
couper le contact. Il est heureux de revoir
Basile, qui a retrouvé Lucie et son sourire.
Derrière eux un véhicule break conduit par

un policier en tenue, suivi de deux véhicules de la BRI, avec six agents en combinaison d'intervention. Henri leur demande
de se préparer en silence. Puis s'approche
de la capitaine, qui tient dans ses mains un
bocal, placé sous scellé.

– On a du bol, les bocaux d'odeur pré-
levés par Malmaison dans la bagnole gare
Saint-Charles partaient demain au labo. Il
a un peu hésité, mais il ne me refuse rien.
Il m'a remis le numéro deux.

– Pourquoi le deux ?

– Celui prélevé sur le siège passager
avant droit. On a affaire à des légionnaires,
ils ont aussi leurs règles. Si on ne s'est
pas trompés, c'est celui du chef de bord :
Rabutin.

Henri acquiesce. Peu importe le numéro,
ils ne pouvaient pas prendre tous les
bocaux. Il fallait surtout éviter celui correspondant à l'emplacement qu'occupait
Ernesto Dominguez. Les légionnaires n'ont
pas dû le transporter à l'avant de la voiture.
Alors le bocal numéro deux, contenant les
bandelettes prélevées sur le siège passager
avant, est une excellente idée, forcément
l'odeur d'un légionnaire.

Henri le récupère, en brise le scellé et
dévisse le couvercle. Le policier en tenue
sort du break, une laisse à la main. Il

ouvre le hayon arrière, protégeant un coffre fermé par une grille. À l'intérieur se trouve un chien, qui s'agite et tourne en rond. Le maître-chien ouvre le cadenas, accroche le canidé à la longue lanière en cuir et lui parle à l'oreille. Lucie assure les présentations.

– Inox, berger belge malinois de 4 ans. Chien pisteur et d'intervention de la police marseillaise, le meilleur. Et le seul.

Elle désigne le bocal.

– On le fait, Henri, t'es sûr ? On n'est pas dans les clous, là !

Henri sait qu'il n'est pas en train de respecter la procédure d'odorologie. Elle sert normalement à confirmer l'identification d'un malfaiteur, pas à permettre de le suivre à la trace. Mais être imaginatif et oser, c'est savoir prendre des risques. L'heure n'est plus aux interrogations, place à l'action. Quatre malfaiteurs en ont enlevé un autre, dans le but de le tuer. La vie d'un homme, même d'un voyou comme Hosni, vaut bien une entorse procédurale.

Khaled se retourne, voit les quatre hommes en face de lui. La Carlton l'avait pourtant prévenu que les mecs avec qui elle travaillait n'étaient pas des tendres. Des anciens légionnaires, habitués à tous les combats, entraînés à tuer, prêts à exécuter. Ernesto Dominguez lui avait confirmé ces messages de prudence. C'est une des raisons pour lesquelles elle n'avait jamais voulu qu'il les rencontre.

Mais voilà, Yassine était entré dans la danse. Il s'était pris d'ambition, ce con, et voulait aussi marquer la délinquance marseillaise, à sa façon. Pour se différencier de son frangin, qui faisait dans le trafic de stups, Yassine s'était mis dans la tête de devenir un braqueur de fourgons. Mais il n'y connaissait rien. Ni sur la méthode, ni sur l'armement ou la préparation de ces coups. Avoir vu *Heat* en boucle ne lui permettait pas d'être un braqueur de renom comme De Niro et ne lui donnait pas non plus toutes les ficelles du métier.

C'est là où il avait eu cette idée. Une idée de merde, une idée de mort, même. Puisque la Carlton voulait diversifier ses activités, en prenant des parts dans son trafic de stups, de son côté, il lui demandait de former son frangin aux bonnes pratiques du braquage. Le marché était simple. Une formation accélérée, dispensée par les meilleurs dans leur genre. Pas des acteurs de cinoche, des vrais. Échange de bons procédés.

Au départ, la Carlton avait refusé. Il y a des milieux qui ne se mélangent pas, qui doivent même ne jamais se croiser. Mais Yassine avait insisté, il avait entendu parler du surnom et des exploits de sa nouvelle associée. Alors Khaled s'était obstiné, même si son frère lui cassait les pieds, il n'allait quand même pas baisser son froc devant une gonzesse. La Carlton avait cédé. Après tout, le contrat n'était pas compliqué. Une sorte de stage de quinze jours, ponctué par un braquage de fourgon, et l'affaire était conclue. Dans la foulée, elle investissait une partie du butin dans son trafic de stups, de quoi multiplier ses gains par dix. Par l'intermédiaire d'Ernesto, ils s'étaient mis d'accord sur les modalités. Et Yassine était parti à Paris, pris en main par Rabutin et ses hommes.

Fidèle à ses principes, la Carlton avait cloisonné. Elle avait juste prévenu les légionnaires que c'était un de ses vieux amis qui cherchait pour son fils une préparation militaire spécialisée. Très particulière. Ils n'avaient pas posé d'autres questions et avaient obéi. En s'offusquant, quand même, de l'attitude, des propos et de l'accent de leur jeune stagiaire.

Inox plaît instantanément au commandant. Ses yeux sont immenses, ses oreilles dressées, sa langue tendue. Le berger belge malinois est réputé pour être un chien puissant, athlétique et doté d'une intelligence remarquable. Henri relève tout de suite l'osmose entre le chien et son maître. Ce dernier lui glisse quelques mots en désignant Henri. Le canidé va avoir envie de lui démontrer tout ce qu'il sait faire. Saint-Donat se dirige vers lui, ouvre le bocal. Inox attend l'approbation de l'homme qui le tient en laisse avant de plonger son museau dans les bandelettes d'odeur, son guide lui chuchote :

– Vas-y, Inox, cherche… cherche, Inox.

Saint-Donat va savoir si son pari est gagnant. Sa sérénité s'est envolée, son rythme cardiaque augmente. Le chien sort sa truffe du bocal. Hume l'air autour de lui. Hésite. Les palpitations d'Henri doublent. Inox pose son museau au sol, renifle à droite, à gauche. Pour l'instant, il ne repère rien et donne même l'impression d'être perdu. Il se dresse sur ses pattes, avant de replonger son museau dans les végétations, mais ne fixe rien. Même son maître semble douter. Henri peste. Se dit qu'il a perdu et enrage.

Quand soudain Inox tire sur sa laisse. Il se redresse, son museau droit, la patte en l'air, il ne bouge plus pendant quelques secondes. Une éternité pour le commandant.

Le berger malinois fixe une direction, ne la lâche pas du flair. Henri regarde Lucie, son cœur bat à tout rompre. Inox a bien repéré quelque chose, sa queue remue de plus en plus vite. Il cherche à avancer. Son maître a du mal à le retenir. L'homme se tourne vers Saint-Donat, dresse son pouce. Et donne du mou à la laisse. Inox se lance, suit sa piste.

Henri souffle, referme son poignet sur son arme et s'élance derrière le malinois. Il est talonné, en silence, par Lucie, Basile et la colonne des flics de la BRI. Tous se préparent au combat. Il n'est plus très loin, au bout du flair d'Inox.

Pourtant il ne fait pas froid, mais Khaled Hosni sent un vent glacial souffler dans son dos. La beauté du décor qui l'entoure le glace d'effroi. Il l'a compris, sa vie va s'arrêter là. Il essaye de marquer sa mémoire de tout ce qu'il voit. Sa dernière demeure sera cette falaise impressionnante, que la lune éclaire, en jetant des ombres fantasmagoriques sur ce qui l'entoure. Il veut s'en souvenir jusqu'à son dernier souffle. Et même après. La peur l'a saisi, les hommes derrière lui le forcent à avancer de quelques mètres, au plus près de la falaise. Il frissonne en voyant le spectacle majestueux qui s'ouvre devant lui.

La lune comme une cible se reflète dans la Méditerranée. Amoureuse et mortelle, elle lui tend les bras. Il repense à ses parents, qui se sont saignés pour ses frères et lui. Se dit qu'il aurait mieux fait d'écouter sa mère, quand elle lui répétait qu'il ne suffisait pas d'avoir une belle intelligence, encore fallait-il en faire un bon usage. Il a dû merder sur l'utilisation de ses neurones, et dans quelques secondes il va rejoindre son frère Yassine.

D'un geste de révolte, il se retourne. Maintenant qu'il remet tout en perspectives, il comprend.

– C'est vous... c'est vous qui avez buté Yassine ?

La réponse de Rabutin tombe, sèche comme un couperet. Ironique, compte tenu de la situation.

– On ne bute jamais, nous. Sauf quand c'est nécessaire. Tu parles de qui, là ?

– Mon frère, Yassine. Le deal avec la Carlton, lui apprendre à braquer.

Les quatre anciens képis blancs se regardent. Pour eux aussi, tout s'éclaire.

– C'était ton frangin, l'autre excité de la rafale ? Je comprends mieux.

– Tu comprends quoi ?

– Pourquoi t'as buté la Carlton.

– J'ai pas buté la Carlton.

– C'est pas ce que nous a dit Ernesto…

– J'étais à la rate.

Rabutin s'avance vers Hosni, arme la culasse de son flingue. Le dirige vers sa tête. La lune devient plus pâle et fait trembler son ombre. Khaled a un mouvement de recul. Les légionnaires se foutent de lui. Ça l'énerve. Il n'a pas dit son dernier mot. Il se redresse, avale son orgueil. Il va leur montrer qui il est vraiment. Les hommes devant lui ont déjà buté son frangin, ils ont leur certitude. Quoi qu'il dise, il ne s'en sortira pas. Quitte à mourir, autant le faire comme il a vécu, en maître des saloperies. En Chacal.

– Je l'ai pas butée. Mais je l'ai fait buter… j'aime pas me salir les mains.

La provocation est trop évidente pour inquiéter les légionnaires. Ils ont entendu tellement pire. Pour l'empêcher de continuer à déblatérer ses saloperies, Rabutin colle le canon de son arme sur son visage. Le Chacal ne recule plus, un sourire narquois aux lèvres, un regard de défi dans les yeux, et se frotte avec jubilation sur le flingue de Rabutin.

Un pas trop lourd fait craquer une branche. Lucie se tourne vers la colonne de flics encagoulés qui la suit. Son regard en dit long sur ce qu'elle pense. Henri, d'habitude si calme, sent lui aussi son cœur battre à mille à l'heure. Il fait signe à tous d'être encore plus discrets. Ce n'est pas le moment de se faire repérer. Le malinois n'a pas arrêté de suivre sa piste. Il s'est redressé une fois ou deux, à peine, le temps de retrouver les bons effluves, de replonger son museau au ras du sol et de continuer sa course.

À chaque mètre, ils se rapprochent. Le moindre craquement pourrait les faire repérer. Les policiers de la BRI, avec leur matériel d'intervention, marchent lentement. Ils font attention à chaque endroit où ils posent leurs rangers. Ne faire aucun bruit avec tout ce qu'ils transportent sur eux est une gageure. Jamais on ne pourrait imaginer qu'ils sont six à avancer lourdement armés.

Des éclats de voix. Henri s'arrête. Il en est sûr, il a entendu des éclats de voix. Il fait signe de stopper et de se baisser. Le maître-chien enserre la gueule d'Inox et l'empêche d'aboyer. Tous ont les sens aux aguets. Saint-Donat ne s'est pas trompé, des bribes de conversation leur parviennent.

Les flingues sont sortis de leurs étuis. Le chef de la colonne de la BRI donne ses instructions par gestes. Des hochements de tête lui répondent. Il se tourne vers Henri, ses hommes sont prêts à intervenir. Saint-Donat lui demande de patienter, il va s'avancer encore un peu, seul. Au plus près, visionner la disposition des lieux et compter les individus présents. Il commence sa progression.

Lucie ne laisse pas le choix à Henri et l'accompagne. Basile veut faire de même, mais la main puissante du chef de la BRI l'en empêche. S'approcher à un, c'est risqué. À deux, c'est dangereux. À trois, ce serait débile. Urteguy ronge son frein.

Le canon du flingue laisse une trace rouge sur le front de Khaled. Mais Rabutin ne tire pas tout de suite, il a encore besoin d'explications.

– Pourquoi t'as fait ça ?

Hosni s'énerve.

– Pourquoi ? Mais tu crois quoi, connard ? Que je ferais pas payer la mort de Yassine ? Quand Dominguez m'a fait passer le message de la Carlton, que mon frère s'était fait flinguer sur le braquage, j'ai décidé de me venger. Un mot, un seul, et je fais buter qui je veux dans cette ville.

Il montre son cou.

– *Awaa*, tu sais ce que ça veut dire ? Le « chacal ». Et quand le Chacal ordonne, on obéit. Quand elle est venue à la Cayolle filer la part de Yassine sur le braquage où il s'est fait fumer, avec sa jolie moto et son petit sac Vuitton, elle a été reçue par Bilal, mon autre frangin. Il avait des ordres. Il a pas eu de mal à la suivre et à la choper sur le parking de l'Interco. Une bastos dans le crâne et un barbecue. Je me suis vengé. Je l'ai fait cramer, votre légende des braquages. Réduite en cendres, la Carlton.

Il prend son temps, avant de leur dire droit dans les yeux, encore provocateur :

– Fallait pas buter Yassine.

Et il balance au sol un glaviot encore plus gros que les autres. Le seuil de tolérance de Rabutin est atteint, il n'en peut plus de son cinéma. Il lui balance une énorme gifle, de toute la puissance de sa main. Hosni s'attendait à mourir, pas à souffrir. Il tombe à genoux, visage amoché, saignant. Jamais il n'aurait pensé qu'une telle douleur au nez soit possible. Rabutin le regarde gémir au sol. Il secoue la tête.

Leur cœur bat à tout rompre. Un nuage bienfaiteur a dissimulé la lune, pendant quelques secondes la nuit était presque noire. Henri et Lucie ont pu s'approcher au plus près des légionnaires menaçant Khaled Hosni. Étendus dans la végétation, ils ne perdent rien de la scène qui se joue devant eux. Les pulsations de leurs artères font trembler la terre sous eux.

Allongée à son côté, Lucie fait comprendre à Henri qu'ils en ont assez. Ils ont tout entendu, presque tout vu. Ils ne peuvent pas laisser les ravisseurs frapper leur otage. Quand bien même il s'agirait d'une ordure. À ce rythme, ils vont le buter avant qu'ils n'aient eu le temps d'intervenir. Un sentiment étrange retient Henri. Il la fait patienter. Presque rien, quelques secondes. Pour la Carlton d'abord. Et pour toutes les personnes qu'Hosni a flinguées et transformées en barbecue. Attendre aussi pour Octave, le fils de Nathalie Fournier. Pour qu'il sache que certains ont défendu l'honneur de sa mère jusqu'au bout. Qu'ils ont demandé à son meurtrier des comptes que personne ne lui demandera plus. Attendre aussi pour la dame âgée morte par la connerie de son frère Yassine et attendre enfin pour son fils, pour Doudou et pour tous les enfants qui ne trouvent pas à temps de donneur compatible.

Peut-être aussi parce qu'eux n'auront jamais le droit ni la possibilité de donner une telle correction au Chacal.

Dédaigneux, Rabutin se recule de quelques pas, respire un grand coup, avant d'envoyer une nouvelle claque monumentale à Hosni, qui s'allonge de tout son long, la tête au sol. Son nez plein de sang se mêle à la terre. Il a du mal à respirer. Rabutin l'attrape par le col.

– Pauvre connard, ton frangin s'est flingué tout seul.

– Quoi ?

– J'sais pas ce qu'ils t'ont raconté, Dominguez et ton frangin. Mais si t'avais pris le temps d'écouter la Carlton, t'aurais su ce qui était arrivé à Yassine. On l'a pas buté, il n'a pas eu besoin de nous. S'il avait été moins camé, il serait encore en vie.

À genoux, Hosni se frotte le nez avec la main. Elle est pleine de sang. Les poissons le repéreront encore plus vite pour le bouffer. Il tente malgré tout d'écouter Rabutin.

– Au moment de partir taper le fourgon, ton frangin s'est enfilé la merde que tu vends. Après, il maîtrisait plus grand-chose. On l'a tenu le temps du braquage, mais quand on a changé de bagnole, il s'est refait une ligne. Plein les narines. Ça débordait. Quel crétin. Et là, il a pété une durite. Il est devenu ingérable. Il a pris la mémé qui passait pour des flics, et il l'a allumée.

Elle est morte pour rien, à cause de ton frangin. Et par la même action, il a fait une mauvaise manip. J'arrive toujours pas à comprendre comment, mais il s'est pas raté, ce con. Incapable de gérer sa kalach. Il s'est envoyé deux pruneaux dans le bide.

Hosni se redresse avec difficulté. Avec la manche de sa chemise, il essuie ses narines, qui dégoulinent de sang. Il refuse de croire les propos de Rabutin.

– Ton frère s'est flingué tout seul, Hosni.

– Tu mens.

– Pourquoi je te mentirais, face de merde. Quel intérêt on avait à le flinguer ?

Hosni regarde les autres légionnaires, calmes et posés. Ils acquiescent aux propos de Rabutin.

– On a même essayé de le soigner. C'est notre mental' à nous. On laisse pas un équipier à terre, même le pire des connards. Mais il s'était pas raté, ce baltringue.

– Pourquoi vous l'avez jeté dans le fleuve, alors ?

Rabutin regarde encore Hosni, il se moque.

– Je croyais que tu fonctionnais bien du ciboulot, Khaled. À ton avis, pourquoi ?

Même à l'instant de mourir, Hosni n'aime pas qu'on remette en cause son intelligence.

– Pour ne pas laisser de trace.

– Eh bien tu vois, t'es pas si con. Y'en a qui crament les corps, d'autres qui s'en débarrassent au fond de l'eau. Question de culture.

Un sourire ironique affleure les lèvres de Rabutin.

– Somme toute, tu finiras au fond de l'eau, comme ton frangin. Tu le retrouveras plus vite. Tu vois, à la Légion, on a le sens de la famille.

Il s'avance vers lui, actionne sa culasse.

Ils en ont assez entendu. Attendre, c'est conduire Hosni à une mort assurée. Henri et Lucie essuient la poignée de leur flingue. À force de transpirer, elle est glissante. Saint-Donat respire un grand bol d'air, hoche la tête. C'est le signal. Le bon moment. Lucie porte sa main au micro de sa radio et lance le top interpellation.

D'un côté le flingue, de l'autre trois cent quatre-vingt-dix mètres de hauteur et la mer comme tapis de réception. Trop tard pour se rappeler le premier adage du voyou. Pour survivre, reste à ta place.

Il y a toujours plus fort, plus grand, plus intelligent que toi.

La présence des hommes armés devant lui en est la démonstration. Il s'est vu trop beau, trop puissant, trop vite. Sa vanité a obstrué sa lucidité. Il ne sera jamais le plus grand parrain de Marseille.

Comme tant d'autres avant lui, il finira en bas du cap Canaille.

Il se retourne, il est le Chacal quand même, il ne va pas mourir comme ça, en silence. Il ne peut pas dire mieux que de les traiter d'enculés. Se rend compte de l'arrogance vile de ses propos. Regarde la mer, où personne ne retrouvera ses restes.

Il crache par terre. Sale endroit pour mourir.

84

– Police, personne ne bouge…

En écho, des voix d'hommes répondent aux injonctions de Lucie.

– Jetez vos armes !

Hosni n'en croit pas ses oreilles. Jamais il n'aurait pensé que l'arrivée des flics lui ferait autant plaisir. Les légionnaires sont tout aussi étonnés, les flics les ont retrouvés. En combattants professionnels, ils cherchent immédiatement à leur échapper. Les falaises éclairées par la lune deviennent une zone de combat où règne un grand foutoir. Des ordres fusent, des chargements de culasse résonnent, des cavalcades se font entendre.

Les sommations n'impressionnent pas Rabutin, il tire. Au même moment, une douleur fulgurante le saisit à son poignet. Les crocs d'un chien viennent de le happer et ne le lâchent pas. Contre toute attente, Inox a échappé à la surveillance de son maître et a décidé de s'en mêler. Plus Hosni se débat, plus l'animal serre. La brûlure est insupportable. La morsure l'oblige à lâcher son arme, son tir détourné ne touche pas le Chacal en pleine tête, comme il le souhaitait, mais il en est certain, il l'a atteint. Emporté par Inox, il se roule au sol dans un combat au corps à corps. Coups de poing, coups de pied, il tente de se défaire de l'étau de la mâchoire puissante de l'animal.

Khaled profite du cafouillage pour se jeter à terre. Ça ne l'épargne pas. Rabutin l'a bien atteint, plein ventre. Son sang coule à gros bouillons, la souffrance le plie en deux. Mais passer pour mort est la meilleure solution pour s'assurer de rester vivant. À condition qu'il arrive à ne pas brailler tellement il a mal. En face de lui, dans un nuage de poussière, Inox continue de se rouler par terre avec le légionnaire.

Hosni cherche à éviter le lieu du combat, trop dangereux, trop près du bord de la falaise. Malgré son mal de ventre, il rampe, quand un rayon de lune transperce la nuit et lui renvoie l'éclat d'un objet métallique au sol. C'est un signe, un appel, un désir insoutenable. Il est là, à cinquante centimètres à peine de sa position. Il n'a qu'à tendre son bras pour s'en saisir. Le flingue de Rabutin. Prêt à servir.

La surprise passée, les trois autres légionnaires comprennent qu'ils sont pris au piège. Mer et falaise d'un côté, les flics de l'autre, ils n'ont pas d'échappatoire. Les six policiers en face d'eux, encagoulés, armés et équipés comme des porte-avions, sont déterminés. Ils ont l'avantage du nombre et de la surprise. Ils affichent fièrement leur logo « BRI » sur leurs combinaisons. Les légionnaires n'ignorent pas quelle est cette unité de la police. L'adversaire est plus fort, ils préfèrent cesser le combat et appliquer à la lettre la devise de la Légion : pas vu, pas pris, et son exact corollaire : vu, pris.

– Au pied, Inox, au pied.

L'ordre suffit, le malinois lâche sa proie et rejoint son maître en remuant la queue. Bien que le comportement de l'animal l'ait pris de court, le gardien le caresse en le félicitant. Rabutin est sonné, mais peut enfin souffler. Il se tient le poignet, les crocs du chien ont traversé l'épaisseur de ses vêtements. La manche de son treillis part en lambeaux. Devant lui, trois flics en civil, arme à la main, brassard police ajusté, arrivent. Lucie en tête, suivie par Henri et Basile. Faire bonne figure, toujours : il a perdu, mais est un soldat avant tout. Prêt à s'incliner devant ses vainqueurs.

À côté de lui, une ombre se redresse. Rabutin est surpris, presque abasourdi. Il craint de comprendre : il n'a pas abattu Hosni. Vêtements déchirés, des traces de raisiné du visage au ventre, des yeux de fou, clopin-clopant, le Chacal est vivant, un flingue dans la main. Son propre pistolet. Un Uzzi.

Et ce con se met à hurler en visant les flics.

Les policiers ont peine à reconnaître Khaled Hosni, qui, bras tendu, fait feu. Henri se jette sur Lucie et roule avec elle au sol, pendant que Basile riposte et ne rate pas sa cible. Hosni titube, laisse tomber son pistolet. Mais continue d'avancer sur les policiers. Basile lui ordonne de stopper, hésite à tirer. Ses propos sont sans effet, Hosni, sonné et désorienté, marche vers lui.

Basile hurle encore plus fort, mais le Chacal progresse, sourire narquois aux lèvres. Le lieutenant n'a pas d'autre choix, il tend son flingue. C'est alors qu'il lui semble avoir une hallucination. Pourtant la lune éclaire bien cette scène surréaliste. Désarticulé comme un pantin, à l'horizontale, bras et jambes pendantes, sans réagir, Hosni vole, s'envole, en lévitation à deux mètres au-dessus du sol. Son ombre se reflète sur la terre, comme une croix sans crucifié.

Urteguy lève les yeux et comprend. Rabutin porte Hosni au-dessus de lui, comme un haltérophile soulèverait ses poids à l'arraché. Interloqué, le jeune lieutenant est incapable d'intervenir. Il fige la scène dans sa mémoire.

Le légionnaire basketteur vient de s'arrêter au bord de la falaise. Jambes écartées, bras tendus, il porte toujours Hosni au-dessus de lui. Le corps du Chacal tangue. Rabutin tremble, mais ne fléchit pas. Il redresse les épaules, assure son fardeau au-dessus de lui. Pour se donner plus d'élan, il abaisse ses coudes, avant de tendre ses bras d'un coup sec. Et de jeter Hosni dans le vide.

Basile ferme les yeux. Il s'attend à entendre crier, mais le Chacal s'est déjà tu. Aucun hurlement n'accompagne sa chute. Ce silence, à peine troublé par le fracas du corps qui s'écrase, le surprend. Quand il ouvre les paupières, Rabutin lui fait face, le regard vide. Du sang d'Hosni sur le visage.

– On ne tire pas sur une femme. Jamais.

Sa silhouette massive s'incruste dans le paysage. Au fond, derrière lui, la mer a déjà avalé Hosni, rien ne semble pouvoir la perturber. Son mouvement perpétuel de va-et-vient marque le temps. Rabutin la regarde, belle et infinie, désirable jusque dans ses ondulations. Il paraît hagard et en même temps déterminé. Basile, en face de lui, est interdit. Sa courte carrière de policier ne l'a jamais conduit à vivre une telle expérience. Rabutin, habitué aux situations les plus improbables, semble comprendre son désarroi. Il lui désigne Lucie et Henri à quelques mètres d'eux, enlacés et ensanglantés au sol.

— Tu devrais y aller, gamin. Ils ont besoin de toi.

Et comme si sa décision était prise depuis longtemps, il se retourne, s'avance d'un pas déterminé. Un pas martial, un pas de mort. Et se laisse aspirer par le vide infini des falaises du cap Canaille. Sans un cri.

85

Ce tunnel n'en finit pas. Il ne ressemble à rien de ce qu'il a déjà connu. Long, noir, avec juste cette lumière au bout. Éblouissante. Et ces échos de fête de l'autre côté. Il marche, mais ne progresse pas. S'il le pouvait, il se mettrait à courir. Il a tellement envie d'arriver au bout. Découvrir ce qu'il y a après. Mais une force le retient. Il ne comprend pas pourquoi. Là-bas, il a reconnu quelqu'un qu'il aime par-dessus tout. Quelqu'un qui lui manque plus que tout. Cette voix, ce visage, ses yeux, ce sourire : son fils, Octave. Henri n'est que sourire. Tellement longtemps qu'il attendait ce moment. Retrouver Octave. Il veut le rejoindre. Force encore plus pour se dégager, mais la pression se fait violente. On l'empêche de bouger. Il veut hurler.

– Laissez-moi le rejoindre. Encore une heure, dix minutes, une seconde, laissez-moi encore le voir, le toucher, le sentir. Laissez-moi le serrer contre moi.

Depuis qu'il avait été touché par les balles d'Hosni, il n'avait pas mal. Au contraire. Il se sentait bien. En apesanteur. Il ne comprenait pas ce qui lui arrivait, mais il ne souffrait pas. Il se voyait allongé par terre, Lucie et Basile à ses côtés. Tous deux s'acharnaient sur son corps et lui pratiquaient un massage cardiaque. Lui hurlant de ne pas partir, de rester avec eux. Lucie hargneuse, Basile combattant, les larmes aux yeux, refusaient l'inéluctable. À tour de rôle sur sa poitrine, ils maintenaient la pression, avec toute la force de leur désespoir.

Mais, s'ils savaient, ils arrêteraient de suite. Il va voir grandir son petit bonhomme, son seul rêve depuis dix ans, qui va enfin devenir réalité. Il sourit encore plus. Pourquoi s'en prendre à son corps ? Son esprit, son âme, son cœur sont déjà ailleurs. Tournés vers cet amour qu'il ne veut plus perdre. Tournés vers Octave, son fils, là-bas dans la lumière, au bout du tunnel. Il ferme les yeux. Ça y est, il avance, plus rien ne le retient. Il n'a jamais été aussi près. Il va le toucher, de nouveau.

– OCTAVE.

Il a hurlé. La violence du coup l'a fait bondir. Et Octave a disparu. Il n'est que souffrance. La lumière du tunnel s'est éteinte, la lune éclaire le visage d'un pompier au-dessus de lui. Ils l'ont ramené, il était moins une. Mais qu'est-ce qu'il a mal. Une larme coule de ses yeux. Il était si près. Il est de nouveau si loin. Il tourne légèrement la tête, voit Lucie tomber en sanglots dans les bras de Basile et rire en même temps.

– Sauvé, on l'a sauvé, j'ai eu si peur.

Les pompiers s'affairent, il est revenu à lui, mais il n'y a pas une seconde à perdre. Avec précaution, il est installé sur un brancard, branché sous perfusion et transporté en direction de l'ambulance, qui s'apprête à partir, sirène hurlante, en direction de la Timone.

Juste avant, la porte arrière du véhicule de secours s'ouvre. Dès qu'il a su, Francis Larrivée a foncé les rejoindre. Il n'a pas mis longtemps pour accéder au cap Canaille. Il regarde Henri, allongé sur la civière, du sang se mêle à la terre sur son visage. Des perfusions sortent de ses bras, des câbles sont reliés à des écrans au-dessus de lui, reflétant des chiffres incompréhensibles dans une lumière blafarde. Il cherche ses mots, ne les trouve pas. Attrape la main d'Henri, la serre. Il hoche la tête, regarde la beauté des lieux l'entourant. Un peu maladroit, se contente de sourire.

– Ce n'est pas un endroit pour mourir, commandant.

Épilogue

La Suisse,
cinq mois plus tard.

La grosse cylindrée remonte la rue de Suisse. La pluie a abandonné l'idée de tomber sur la rive droite du Léman. Même si elle avait décidé le contraire, elle n'aurait pas dérangé le conducteur ni le passager, confortablement installés sur leur deux-roues. Élégants et protégés dans leur combinaison. Ils affichent la même tenue et portent un casque similaire. Rien ne semble les perturber. Pas même les nombreuses voitures de luxe circulant en cette fin d'après-midi dans les rues de Versoix.

À hauteur de la résidence Bon-Séjour, ils se penchent à droite et tournent dans la rue de Sauverny. Ils se faufilent avec aisance dans la circulation qui grossit. Le conducteur maîtrise parfaitement les 1 500 cm^3 et presque 400 kilos de sa Goldwing. Même si elle est un peu plus basse et moins puissante que celle qu'il pilote habituellement, elle est tout aussi agréable. Les 470 kilomètres de route et les cinq heures de trajet depuis Marseille ont été un réel plaisir. Presque un pur bonheur, n'étaient ses cicatrices au ventre, encore très douloureuses.

Le pilote remonte la rue de Sauverny jusqu'au numéro 74 et s'arrête enfin devant le portail monumental du collège du Léman. Henri enlève son casque, juste avant sa femme. Assommés par le voyage, ils sont aussi abasourdis par l'institution qu'ils découvrent. Le collège du Léman est à la hauteur de sa réputation. Tant par la formation qu'il dispense que par l'origine variée des élèves qui le fréquentent. Plus de cent nationalités sont réunies. Mais également par les infrastructures anciennes, riches en histoire, qui se mêlent aux nouvelles, dans un écrin de verdure surplombant le lac Léman. Ici, apprendre est un luxe, et tous les moyens sont mis œuvre pour le confort et le bonheur des étudiants. Avec un seul objectif : leur réussite par l'excellence.

Merveilleux endroit pour étudier.

Henri regarde une dernière fois la moto. S'assure que le voyage n'a pas laissé de traces sur sa belle robe. Il prend un chiffon et nettoie quelques impuretés imaginaires sur la calandre. Isabelle le sait, son mari est nerveux et cherche à gagner du temps, reculer l'échéance de la rencontre. D'une douce autorité, elle lui enlève le chiffon, prend sa main dans la sienne et l'oblige à avancer. Ils franchissent le portail et se dirigent vers le bâtiment d'accueil, vieux manoir tout en pierres apparentes.

Les époux Saint-Donat s'encouragent et se comprennent du regard. Même s'ils lui reconnaissent un charme désuet et une élégance rare, ce n'est pas le type d'établissement qu'ils aiment fréquenter. Tout est trop lisse, trop propre, trop éloigné de Marseille pour être vrai.

Le plus compliqué pour Henri avait été de convaincre sa femme de l'accompagner. Dès qu'il avait eu cette idée, Francis Larrivée l'avait trouvée judicieuse et intelligente. Sentimentale aussi, mais un peu de romantisme dans ce monde de flics ne faisait pas de mal. Et puis sa nomination comme nouveau directeur central de la police judiciaire, en lieu et place de son ancien subordonné, qui avait décliné le poste, lui permettait de jouer de tout son poids auprès du juge d'instruction en charge de l'information judiciaire concernant le meurtre de Nathalie Fournier. En définitive, le magistrat aussi avait trouvé cette idée pertinente et donné son accord.

Isabelle, pendant la convalescence d'Henri, avait localisé l'institution privée où était scolarisé depuis plusieurs années Octave de Gounod. Bien dans les plans de la Carlton, de tout prévoir pour son fils. À défaut de le voir régulièrement, elle assurait ses études dans une des meilleures écoles internationales du monde. Henri avait décidé de lui rendre la moto de sa mère. Elle avait eu l'intelligence de faire établir la carte grise à son nom. Il en était donc le propriétaire. Il ne restait plus qu'à trouver le moyen de la lui restituer.

Isabelle ne se trouvait pas légitime à accompagner son mari. Il avait fallu qu'Henri joue de diplomatie et d'amour pour lui faire comprendre l'importance de sa présence à son côté.

À l'accueil, pour ne pas jeter le trouble dans cet établissement de sérénité et de culture, ils se sont présentés comme parents éloignés du jeune de Gounod. Ils patientent dans la salle d'attente, en feuilletant brochures et magazines mettant en valeur les activités pratiquées au sein du collège. L'établissement propose même des cours de musique classique. Le téléphone d'Henri sonne. La voix de Basile, joyeuse et entraînante, résonne.

– Ça va, commandant ?

– On vient d'arriver.

– Alors ?

– *Ici tout n'est qu'ordre et beauté, luxe, calme et volupté.*

– Et le môme, vous l'avez vu ?

– Pas encore. On a été annoncés, il devrait arriver.

– Nous aussi.

Henri n'est pas sûr de comprendre.

– Quoi ?

– On a suivi tes conseils, Henri. Les Antilles, c'est top pour un voyage d'amoureux. Ti-punch, sable fin et soleil éclatant, ça porte ses fruits, crois-moi. Et le bébé a été annoncé, il devrait arriver.

– Non ?

– Si... bon, y'a peut-être encore du boulot pour bien le réussir, alors, je vais m'y remettre tout de suite. Lucie s'impatiente. Et tu la connais ? Vaut mieux pas la faire attendre.

– Basile ?

– Oui.

– Félicitations.

– Merci, commandant. Henri ?

– Oui ?

– Bon courage.

Une douce mélancolie remplit les yeux d'Henri. Il n'a même pas eu le temps de dire à Basile qu'ici ils formaient des mélomanes. Un ancien élève du collège est devenu un virtuose du violon et se produit bientôt en concert au Grand Théâtre de Genève, revisitant sur son instrument des grands airs d'opéra.

La porte du manoir grince, des pas résonnent. Isabelle et Henri se regardent, se comprennent. Il arrive. C'est le moment, celui des explications, des réponses aux questions. Qui était sa mère, comment elle a vécu, comment et pourquoi elle est morte. De lui apprendre aussi d'où vient son nom. Et son prénom.

Ils se mettent debout, un peu gauches, se tiennent côte à côte, se frôlant les mains. La porte s'ouvre. Il est là. Vingt ans, beau, sportif et souriant.

Octave.

En harmonie, ils fondent en larmes.

Remerciements

Merci,

Aux membres du jury. Vous m'avez choisi anonyme. Je vous avais en modèle. Vous ne m'offrez pas un prix, vous m'offrez un cadeau.

Aux flics, d'ici et de là-bas, d'hier et de demain. Hués et admirés. Toujours debout même sous la critique. Cœurs brûlants.

À mes parents. Je vous aime.

À mes sœurs et frères, nombreux et variés. Richesse incontournable d'une saga familiale. Avec Toi, Bruno.

À mes enfants. Source inépuisable d'impertinence, d'inspiration et d'enchantement.

À mes belles filles, jamais très loin de l'héroïne de ce roman.

À Serge. Beau-père et premier lecteur. Intraitable défenseur de la langue française et des dates des matchs de l'OM.

À Kevin. Son enthousiasme. Ses connaissances encyclopédiques, littéraires et musicales. « Pétanque et tarot sont œnologie-compatibles… »

À Éric, l'incroyable « Schmoll » (de la police). Son accueil, ses petits plats, ses conseils. Merci d'avoir fait la carrière de tant de « patrons », il était temps qu'un directeur le reconnaisse...

À Emmanuel et César. Aux conseils judiciaires et savoureux. La robe ne fait pas l'avocat, mais la défense fait l'ami.

À Alexandre. « La Freluque » lui doit beaucoup. Talentueux auteur et ami.

À Olivier et Bruno. Monstres sacrés de talent, de sincérité et d'amitié. Sans vous, rien ne serait arrivé.

Merci enfin à Christelle. L'intelligence de ses conseils, l'élégance de son humour, la présence de son amour. Parce que : Elle.

Cet ouvrage a été imprimé en France par
CPI Brodard & Taupin
Avenue Rhin et Danube
72200 La Flèche (France)

pour le compte des Éditions Fayard
en octobre 2020

Photocomposition Nord Compo à Villeneuve-d'Ascq

Fayard s'engage pour
l'environnement en réduisant
l'empreinte carbone de ses livres.
Celle de cet exemplaire est de :
0,300 g éq. CO_2
PAPIER À BASE DE   Rendez-vous sur
FIBRES CERTIFIÉES   www.fayard-durable.fr

85-5040-3/1 - N° d'impression : 3040076